ARMOURED FORCES

ARMOURED FORCES

FORCES

*A History of Armoured Forces
and their Vehicles*

by

R. M. OGORKIEWICZ

ARMS AND ARMOUR PRESS

Published by
Arms and Armour Press
Lionel Leventhal Limited
677 Finchley Road, London N.W.2
© R. M. Ogorkiewicz, 1960
This edition first published 1970
Introduction, illustrations and bibliography
© R. M. Ogorkiewicz, 1970
© Lionel Leventhal Limited, 1970

SBN 85368 049 3

Armoured Forces: A History of Armoured Forces and their Vehicles
was first published 1960, in Great Britain as *Armour: The Development
of Mechanised Forces and their Equipment;* in the United States as
Armor: a History of Mechanised Forces; and subsequently in Italy
as *I Corazzati: l'Evoluzione delle Forze e dei Mezzi Corazzati.*

The Publishers are pleased to acknowledge the co-operation of
The Central Library, Bedford, in making possible the production
of this edition.

Reproduced and Printed by
Redwood Press Limited
Trowbridge & London

Contents

List of Illustrations

viii

Introduction

THIS book was originally written to meet the need for a comprehensive treatment of the subject of armour in its collective sense, embracing mechanised forces as well as their armoured vehicles. As such it was well received and the continued demand for it after the original British and United States editions went out of print has prompted its reprinting in what is essentially its original form.

Armour has developed further, of course, since the book was written in the mid-fifties but the broad picture which it presented has remained substantially unchanged. This is particularly true of the first part of the book which provides an introduction to the more detailed discussions of armour. It is made up of three chapters which present, in turn, a broad survey of the background to the evolution of armour, a general pattern of its development and an examination of its position in relation to nuclear weapons. The military implications of nuclear weapons have been the subject of much further study since the third chapter was first written but so far as the general issues are concerned one need only add that the reservations expressed at the time, particularly about tactical nuclear weapons, have become more widely shared.

The second part of the book deals with armour in its more specific sense, confined to mechanised, or armoured, forces. In particular, it deals with their organisation in the five leading countries, as well as the evolution of their tactics and some aspects of their logistics.

The organisation of the armoured forces has changed considerably, but mainly in detail and not to the extent which would invalidate the general thesis that it has tended towards progressively closer integration of the different components of armoured formations. The process of integration has not, however, advanced as far, or as fast, as was expected. Thus, in most cases, battalions or battalion-size units called regiments have remained homogeneous, that is composed of tanks, or of mechanised infantry, or of self-propelled artillery, and the permanent combination of these different components of armour has not advanced beyond the level of the brigade. In fact, there have been some retrograde developments; for instance, the French Army abandoned its *Régiments Inter-armes*, battalion-size units composed of a mixture of tanks, infantry and other elements. On the other hand, the Swedish Army has successfully adopted as its basic armoured unit a mixed armoured battalion consisting, in essence, of two companies each of tanks and armoured infantry supported by a company of howitzers.

Considerable progress has been made during the past decade in the development of tanks and it is to this that the third part of the book is devoted. It consists of nine chapters, each dealing with the development of tanks and, to a lesser extent, of armoured forces in a different country. Of these nine countries, seven have continued or resumed the development of battle tanks. One of the other two, Italy, has continued to rely on United States-designed tanks while Poland has produced Soviet designs, and so has Czechoslovakia. Soviet T-54-type tanks have also been produced in China which joined the ranks of the tank producing countries in the late fifties. During the sixties India also became a tank producer, its first tank being the Vijayanta, a battle tank designed and originally produced in Britain by Vickers Ltd.

Switzerland is another country which during the sixties produced its first battle tank, the Pz.61. At about the same time France resumed the production of battle tanks with the AMX-30 and so did Germany with the Leopard. Both the AMX-30 and the Leopard were originally designed as alternative models to a joint 1957 Franco-German-Italian specification for a single European battle tank, but Italy dropped out of its development and each of the other two countries eventually adopted its own design. However, since it began to be produced in 1965, the Leopard has been adopted not only by the German forces but also by the Belgian, Netherlands and Norwegian armies, and has become Western Europe's second most numerous battle tank—the most numerous being the United States M60 battle tank.

Sweden has also resumed the production of tanks with its highly controversial, turretless S-tank and so has Japan with the Type 61 medium tank. As before, the Soviet Union has been producing tanks on a large scale, introducing the T-62 as a successor to the earlier T-54 and T-55 medium tanks and also to the heavier JS-3 and T-10 tanks which have gradually been withdrawn from service. Britain has produced the Chieftain as the successor to both the Centurion and the Conqueror which was, in fact, withdrawn from service before the arrival of the first Chieftains. The United States, on the other hand, has tried to develop its M60A1 into the M60A1E1 and M60A1E2 while working with Germany on a much more advanced battle tank, the MBT-70.

Detailed features of these new battle tanks follow, in general, the trends indicated in the fourth part of the book which deals with the armament and the automotive components of tanks, as well as other types of armoured vehicles and a number of more general questions concerning armoured equipment. In particular, battle tanks have continued to be armed with long-barrelled, high-velocity guns. However, the average calibre of these guns has risen still further, as a result of most new tanks being armed with 105mm guns and some with even larger guns. Thus, the Vijayanta, Pz.61, AMX-30, Leopard and the S-tank are all armed with 105mm guns and a number of American M48 tanks have also been rearmed with guns of this calibre in place of their original 90mm guns, while the Soviet T-62 is armed with an even larger 115mm gun and the British Chieftain with one of 120mm.

The one exception to the prevailing pattern is provided by

the United States' M60A1E1 and M60A1E2 which are armed with a short-barrelled 152mm gun/launcher and which rely for their ability to fight other tanks not on armour-piercing projectiles but on Shillelagh guided missiles. The same type of 152mm gun/launcher was mounted even earlier in the American M551 Sheridan air-transportable light tank which was first produced in 1966 and which has become the world's first tank with guided missiles as its primary anti-tank armament. A development of the 152mm gun/Shillelagh missile launcher is also mounted in the MBT-70. But in this case the gun/launcher has a long barrel and is capable of firing high-velocity armour-piercing projectiles in addition to firing missiles with their shaped-charge warheads, which means that it can pose a two-fold threat to enemy armour.

In several other instances guided missiles have been mounted as supplementary armament on gun-armed vehicles or as the primary armament of limited-purpose anti-tank vehicles. The original example of the first kind of missile application is represented by the French AMX-13 light tank with four externally mounted SS-11 missiles; a good example of the second application is provided by the German *Jagdpanzer* (*Rakete*), a specialised tank-destroyer armed with SS-11 or more recently the more advanced HOT missiles with semi-automatic guidance. Anti-tank guided missiles remain, however, to be fully proved on the battlefield even though some have now been tried in action, first during the fighting between India and Pakistan in 1965 and then during the Six-day War between Israel and the Arab countries in 1967. Contrary to contemporary reports, reflected in Chapter 24, anti-tank guided missiles were not used during the Sinai campaign eleven years earlier even though SS-10 missiles were already in the Israeli Army inventory in 1956.

For protection battle tanks have continued to rely on steel armour but aluminium alloy armour has been increasingly adopted for light armoured vehicles where a lower degree of protection is generally involved. In fact, the aluminium-armoured M113 personnel carrier built in the United States has become the most numerous armoured vehicle outside the Soviet bloc. In all cases the amount of armour which vehicles can have is restricted by their weight which needs to be kept to a minimum for the sake of their mobility. In the particular case of battle tanks the aim of their designers has generally been to keep the weight down to 40 tons, or less, but the actual weight of recently produced tanks ranges from 34 to 36 tons, for tanks such as the AMX-30, T-54, Pz.61 and the Japanese Type 61, to 51 tons in the case of the Chieftain.

While possible increases in the thickness of armour have remained restricted by the permissible weight of tanks, there has been considerable scope for improving tanks' chances of survival on the battlefield by lowering their silhouette and thereby reducing the size of the target which they offer to enemy weapons. Within the constraints of conventional designs, this has been done with particular success in the design of the Leopard. Further progress towards lowering the silhouette of battle tanks has been achieved with the Chieftain where the driver adopts a supine position and the height of the hull can be consequently reduced. Still further progress in the same direction has been made with the MBT-70 and the S-tank, both of which have departed from the conventional 'two-tier' arrangement of the main armament above the driver's compartment. In the case of the MBT-70 this has been done by placing the driver in the turret, albeit in a complicated counter-rotating cupola; in the case of the S-tank the main armament has been placed in the hull, alongside the driver, the gun being elevated by altering the pitch of the hull by means of an adjustable suspension and traversed by turning the whole vehicle.

Relatively little progress has been made in improving the cross-country mobility of tanks, even though some, such as the S-tank and MBT-70, have been fitted with hydropneumatic suspensions. Maximum road speeds have, however, generally increased owing to the use of more powerful engines giving higher power-to-weight ratios. In the case of the AMX-30 and the Leopard the power-to-weight ratio has, in fact, risen to 20 b.h.p. per ton and in the MBT-70 it is almost 30.

So far as engines themselves are concerned, no more battle tanks have been built with spark-ignition gasoline engines although these continue to be used in light armoured vehicles. Further experiments have been made with gas turbines but so far this type of engine has only been adopted in the S-tank and even then only in combination with a diesel in a twin-engine power plant. All other recently produced battle tanks are powered by diesels and so is an increasing number of light armoured vehicles.

Next to battle tanks, the type of armoured vehicle which has received most attention is the armoured personnel carrier. Following the lead set by the United States' M59 and M113 carriers, armies throughout the world have been equipping their infantry with tracked armoured carriers and developing them further into mechanised infantry combat vehicles— developing them, in other words, into vehicles from which infantrymen could fight, on the move, and not merely for use as a 'battle taxi' carrying them to fight on foot, which is all that carriers of the M113 type are really suitable for.

In contrast, very little progress has been made in the field of anti-aircraft tanks. One of the few recent exceptions to the general neglect of this type of armoured equipment is provided by the Soviet ZSU-23-4, an anti-aircraft vehicle with four turret-mounted, radar-controlled 23mm automatic guns. As a result, most armoured units remain without effective, organic protection against ground attack aircraft or helicopters.

More understandably, there has been little further development of the turretless assault gun of which only two further examples have been produced, the Soviet ASU-85 and the German *Jagdpanzer* (*Kanone*). Other types of self-propelled guns have continued to be developed on some scale, tending either in the direction of tracked mountings with very little protection or of fully armoured vehicles with the guns mounted in turrets with all-round traverse.

The development of sea-going amphibious vehicles of the 'Landing Vehicle, Tracked' type has been confined to those built in the United States for the Marine Corps. The latest example is the aluminium-armoured LVTPX12 which, in contrast to all its predecessors but like other recently built amphibious vehicles, propels itself in water not by means of its tracks but by means of water jet propulsion units.

Wheeled armoured vehicles have continued to be used and developed further on a considerable scale but not in all countries. The United States Army, for instance, has continued virtually to ignore them. The Soviet Army, on the other hand, has developed more sophisticated vehicles to replace its earlier models. In particular, it has developed and produced in large numbers the eight-wheeled BTR-60P amphibious armoured personnel carrier, as well as the four-wheeled amphibious BRDM. Britain and France have also produced new armoured cars, the aluminium-armoured Daimler Fox and the Panhard AML.

This brief summary of recent developments cannot, of course, cover them all but it should be sufficient to indicate the principal ones and to supplement the original text which though wide in its scope, has had nevertheless to be confined to the more important issues.

London, 1970   R.M.O.

Part 1

A Broad Survey

1

Weapons and Mobility

THE tank made its first appearance in the midst of the First World War of 1914 to 1918. The event has become a landmark in the history of land warfare and from it dates the large-scale development of armoured vehicles and mechanised forces. The appearance of the tank and its subsequent development were, however, also related to earlier happenings. Its true measure must, therefore, be assessed against the broad background of military trends and developments which preceded it, as well as those which accompanied it.

The background to the evolution of the tank extends into the dim and distant past of ancient methods and devices. In fact, the origins of the tank are commonly traced to chariots and other ancient vehicles, which show that for centuries man has tried to evolve a means akin to the modern fighting vehicle and which add a certain depth to the picture of the modern tank.

The perspective in which the tank and other armoured vehicles are to be viewed can be brought out even more clearly by setting them out on a broader scene. That is, by looking at them against the general development of weapons and mobility and of mobile land forces, of which armoured or mechanised forces are the present embodiment.

The first of these, the development of weapons, is essentially a search after a weapon which would dominate the enemy. Were it successful and the dominance complete there would hardly be any further military problem. In the absence of an absolute superiority in weapons, as is generally the case however, the military problem becomes that of finding the most effective way of using such weapons as are available.

One, and probably the most important, approach to this has been through mobility. In all contests the more agile and

3

mobile of the opponents always has the advantage of being able
to seize and keep the initiative.   Thus, when some 2,000 years
before our era the light horse-drawn war chariot was introduced it gave its users a marked degree of superiority over the
slower foot troops who had hitherto prevailed.   Its use spread
and in the hands of the Egyptians and the Hittites, in the latter
part of the second millennium, chariotry became the dominant
arm of the Ancient Near East.

After a time the chariot gave way to the more adaptable
horseman but this altered the form of mobile troops and not
their importance.   Thus, under Persian domination and then
under Alexander the Great it was cavalry which took over the
decisive role and which, by its swift and violent intervention,
came to decide battles in a way with which the slower foot
troops could not compete.   This and their greater overall
mobility gave the mounted troops a permanent and decisive
superiority, even though their weapons were not materially
different from those of the foot soldiers.

The evolution of mobile troops was not, of course, uniform.
In ancient times, as at present, it was governed by geographical,
economical and social conditions as much as purely military
considerations.   Often, as in the case of the Roman armies,
the existing methods and mobility below the contemporary
optimum gave a sufficient margin of superiority over the enemies.
Clearly, as long as battles such as Carrhae, in 53 B.C., where
the legionary infantry was routed by Parthian horse-archers,
were the exception rather than the rule the necessity for troops
more mobile than the legions was not very urgent.

Another reason why mobile troops frequently could not
displace all others was the difficulty of using them with even
a degree of control and order.   While it was comparatively
simple to array men on foot in a solid body—which accounts
for the infantry phalanx being the primeval tactical formation
—it was a different matter with men on horseback.   In fact,
in the absence of suitable methods, mounted actions were no
more than wild melées followed by headlong flight or equally
chaotic chase.   It required a discipline and organisation of the

highest order before a comprehensive set of tactics could be evolved for mounted troops. But when this was achieved, as in the heyday of the Eastern Roman Empire or by the Mongols of Jenghis Khan, the infantry could be entirely dispensed with and the mobile mounted troops ruled the field by themselves.

In Western Europe too mounted troops eventually achieved predominance. In the fourth century the legionary infantry of the Roman Empire was already being displaced by cavalry and in the next two centuries, under the impact of the barbarian horsemen with whom the best foot troops could not cope for long, cavalry became the principal arm. The ascendancy of the horsemen was further strengthened by the political and social conditions which followed the disruption of the Roman Empire and, later, by the feudal system of the Middle Ages.

To the medieval knight, however, the horse was not so much a means of achieving optimum tactical mobility as of personal transport and carrying his heavy equipment. With the decline of military organisation warfare had already relapsed into pitched mob-battles, in which valour and brute force held sway and generalship and skill in tactical manoeuvres were usually conspicuous by their absence. In such circumstances, as long as he met nothing more dangerous than his like, the mailed knight ruled supreme. What mattered most under the contemporary conditions was individual prowess and equipment, including armour, which accounted for his dominance over the poorly provided peasantry or his superiority over more primitive enemies. It is not surprising, therefore, that he strove to improve it as much as possible and was quite willing to sacrifice his mobility for greater protection, with the result that his movements became progressively slower and more ponderous.

Formidable as he was in individual combat, when confronted by superior tactics the armour of the medieval knight did not save him from defeat at the hands of his better organised enemies. For instance, the more mobile Turks and the Mongols were frequently able to fight it out and win on their own terms. The latter, under Jenghis Khan, evolved what was probably the most successful expression of that age of muscle power by combining the traditional mobility of the nomadic horseman with a highly developed military organisation and, as shown by the battlefields of the thirteenth century, proved greatly superior to all their opponents.

In Europe too the knights met more than a match once the infantry organised itself. As they themselves refused to change their old ways, and did nothing to exploit their potential mobility, they spent themselves in vain charges and hence forfeited their leadership. The position of the infantry, restored by Swiss pikemen and English archers, was further strengthened by the introduction of firearms, which slowly but steadily displaced the earlier muscle-powered weapons. As a result, even in the sixteenth century, battles began to assume the form of fire fights.

As the use of firearms increased attempts were also made, in the sixteenth and seventeenth centuries, to combine them with the mobility of the cavalryman. But the combination, exemplified by the caracoling, pistol-firing cuirassiers, did not prove successful. Under Gustavus Adolphus, Cromwell, Condé and others, cavalry reverted to the methods of an earlier era and charged home, sword or lance in hand, relying on speed to offset the effect of the slowly developing firearms. The return to these methods was temporarily highly successful but it demonstrated that the more effective new weapons and the highest order of battlefield mobility then available were incompatible. And from this moment mobility and weapon power inevitably began to diverge.

By the eighteenth century a pattern clearly established itself with the infantry, combining the mechanical power of the musket and the muscular methods of the bayonet, as the main component of every army. At one end of the scale its efforts were supported by the cavalry which, relying almost entirely on the *arme blanche* and speed, compensated for the infantry's lack of mobility. At the other end of the scale was the artillery, which based its action entirely on the fire power of its weapons and which completed the trinity—an order of things which came to be regarded down to this day as " fundamental."

However, as firearms improved, the importance of the physical struggle declined and the muscle-based tactics of the cavalry had to give way. In spite of many gallant, but fore-doomed, attempts to uphold traditional methods the cavalry had to fight more and more like the infantry—rifle in hand—and use its horses only as a means of transportation off the battlefield. Similarly, in the case of the infantry, the importance of the bayonet charge gradually dwindled away while the power and importance of the artillery increased by leaps and bounds. None other than Napoleon pointed out this process when he spoke on St. Helena that " the artillery decides the fate of armies and nations."

But, while the evolution of firearms slowly displaced all earlier muscle-powered weapons by mechanical ones, there was for a long time no corresponding development in the field of locomotion. As before, movement continued to depend on the muscles of men and horses. Under such circumstances a slow estrangement between striking power and mobility became inevitable. The advantage consequently shifted to static defence which, once established in strength, was not concerned with movement while an attacker could only with great difficulty combine the two essentials of offensive action : striking power and movement.

The infantry, for instance, could still advance when suitable methods, such as the infiltration tactics of the German infantry in 1918, were evolved. But the rifle was no longer the principal source of fire power, its place having been taken by the field gun whose movement was restricted and which, in its horse-drawn form, could not move up sufficiently closely with an attacking force. Thus, in general, the latter lacked weapon power.

It was not until the advent of the automotive vehicle that effective weapon power and mobility could again be combined. Attempts at combining the two in the form of automotive fighting vehicles began at the turn of the century with wheeled vehicles and they came to fruition for the first time with the British and French tanks of 1916 and 1917.

However, the first tanks did not appear on the scene as a general means of making weapons more mobile but rather as special siege vehicles, introduced under the particular conditions of trench warfare, into which the Western Front of the First World War settled. Their wider possibilities were recognised by a few but in general for many years there was little understanding of the full potentialities of armoured vehicles and mechanised forces. Therefore, any move to develop them and to extend their application had to contend not only with the technical limitations of the contemporary equipment but also the inertia of the established military systems, deeply rooted in the practices of the previous hundred years or so. All this, together with the original method of employment, weighed heavily upon the early development of the tank.

The original method of employment and, even more, the initial success of the tank were mainly based upon its relative immunity to machine-gun fire. The latter had been one of the principal causes of failure of earlier offensive actions in the First World War and the obvious value of the tank's armour protection made a strong impression. In fact, there grew an idea that armour protection was the principal characteristic of the tank. From this, later, came the many erroneous conclusions that the tank was finished whenever a new armour-piercing weapon appeared and the inevitable will-o'-the-wisp chase after the invulnerable armoured colossus, to the detriment of the tank's far more important characteristics of weapon power and mobility.

Reinforcing this emphasis on armour protection, and as important in its own right, was the influence of the infantry which the tanks were called upon to assist, as barbed wire crushers and machine-gun destroyers. The infantry found in tanks a useful auxiliary and as the established principal arm managed to subordinate them to itself, as happened in France and many other countries after the First World War. This might not have mattered much had the infantry been willing to make full use of the potentialities of the tank and tried to bring its other units up to the standards of mobility which the tank and other armoured vehicles made possible. Unfortunately, infantry remained rooted in the past and looked upon tanks solely from the point of view of its own traditional methods. What it saw in them were not their broad characteristics but only an auxiliary to the riflemen and it tied tanks down to its own slow pace, with the corollary emphasis on armour protection.

Together the two—the emphasis on armour protection and the use of tanks as an adjunct to the traditional infantry methods—obscured the full potentialities of the tank and conspired against the full use of the combination of weapon power and mobility which the tank made possible.

On the other hand, attempts to exploit the mobility of armoured vehicles were apt to lead to another extreme : to an over emphasis on mobility, to the detriment of its combination with weapon power. This tendency manifested itself in mobile but under-gunned tanks and in the concept of mechanised forces confined to a very limited mobile role.

The reason for this again largely lay in traditional practices —in the role to which horse cavalry was reduced towards the end of its existence. The mobile tanks, that is tanks which were not already an adjunct to the infantry, came to be regarded as successors to the cavalry and were automatically restricted to the limited roles of exploitation and raiding of their immediate predecessor. It was commonly overlooked that the successful mobile forces of earlier days, before cavalry was reduced to near-impotence, were versatile and effective fighting forces capable of winning a decision in battle, as well as exploiting it. The Mongols of Jenghis Khan were but one example. Had they lacked the ability to strike, their drives would have been like the raids of so many other nomadic tribes—of considerable nuisance value but generally lacking in decisiveness, for no degree of mobility could compensate for lack of adequate striking power.

There was no reason, other than the weight of established practices, why mobile tanks and the mechanised forces of which they formed the basis should remain confined to the limited role of the later-day cavalry, just as there was no real reason why other tanks should be confined to the role of a slow moving auxiliary to the infantry. Either method failed to make full use of the combination of effective fire power and mobility which the tank made possible, the one by over emphasising mobility at the expense of striking power and the other by not exploiting the mobility and concentrating instead on the passive attribute of armour protection.

The same traditional outlook which confined tanks either to a limited mobile role or to close infantry support also obstructed the development of new-style mechanised forces. Mechanised forces based not on the particular conditions of the immediate past, with its division into infantry and cavalry, but on the general capabilities of the existing weapons and automotive equipment.

Looked at in this light, that is within a framework of new mechanised forces based on automotive vehicles, the tank is essentially a mobile gun carrier, a means of increasing the effectiveness of heavy crew-operated weapons through the mobility of the armoured vehicle. It made possible a far more effective, mobile use of these weapons, which had become so important, and consequently revived the long-lost combination of effective weapon power and mobility. Thus, combined with complementary weapons—ranging from light portable ones of the mechanised infantry to the heavy guns of self-propelled artillery—the tank made possible a new type of force which was both mobile and powerful. This was a type of force and a combination which had become progressively more difficult to effect during the previous three hundred years. And in this combination of effective weapon power and mobility lies the principal value of the tank and its real significance.

2

The First Thirty Years

THE routes by which tanks and armoured forces have advanced are many and varied. But, considered in broad outline, the first thirty years of the evolution of the tank, from its inception in 1915 to the end of the Second World War in 1945, can be represented by relatively few dominant themes and tendencies. In turn, the themes and tendencies can be identified with a number of chronological periods and the thirty years' progress conveniently divided into a few main phases, which are neither rigid nor mutually exclusive but which epitomise the whole process.

Common to it all is the background of the gradual development of automotive vehicles and the steadily growing importance of heavy crew-operated weapons. Both are particularly significant in connection with the origin of the tank, although its invention, or synthesis, was more immediately concerned with the particular conditions of the First World War.

It was as a direct outcome of the trench warfare conditions, into which the Western Front settled after the initial moves of 1914, that the processes which led to the development of the tank started. The problem which these conditions posed was how to attack in face of dug-in machine-guns and barbed wire. And the answer was an armoured vehicle, built on the caterpillar tractor chassis, which could move across the bullet-swept no-man's-land and over the barbed wire and which could destroy the machine-guns with its weapons.

It was in this role of a machine-gun destroyer and barbed wire crusher that the first British tanks went into action on September 15, 1916, on the Somme in France, and similar methods were employed in many later actions, usually of a local character, by both British and French tanks.

11

Such success as was achieved was due mainly to the effectiveness of armour protection which enabled tanks to disregard machine-gun fire. Thus, from the original ideas right through the first phase of the development runs the theme of mobile protection as the principal characteristic of the tank—although the early tanks were by no means invulnerable. From this too sprang the dictionary definition of the tank as a " perambulating fortress " and much of the later emphasis on its armour protection.

The other legacy of this period has been a tendency to regard the tank as some specialised piece of equipment and not as a general means of increasing the mobility of ground units. At first, of course, it was associated in many minds with the peculiar conditions of trench warfare. After the First World War, when a return to more mobile warfare was visualised, there were even some who proclaimed that the usefulness of the tank was over.

There were, however, others, both among the originators such as General Swinton in Britain and General Estienne in France and among those who joined the first tank units such as Colonel (later General) Fuller, who saw the wider possibilities of tanks. What they saw in particular was the capacity of tanks for surprise mass assaults with little or no preliminary artillery bombardment, which had hitherto precluded all chances of tactical surprise. Proposals on those lines were in marked contrast to the early tendencies among Allied commanders to use tanks in driblets in local actions. They also necessitated the grouping of tanks in larger units, of regiment or brigade size, and careful planning by staffs familiar with the characteristics of tanks.

The British Tank Corps was the first to put such ideas to test. At Cambrai, in November, 1917, no less that 474 were used and for the first time they became the principal factor in battle. A spectacular break-through was achieved but, through lack of suitable means and technique, it was not exploited. Much the same thing happened later at Amiens, where some 600 British tanks were concentrated, and in the French tank assault at Soissons.

The three battles demonstrated the potentialities of the tank as a means of breaking through strong hostile fronts and the saturation technique of surprise mass assaults. The tank attacks were still executed in close contact with the infantry but tank units now operated chiefly for the benefit of higher formations and their scope was wider. The main problem which remained after that of the initial break-through proved capable of solution was how to extend the action. It had been hoped that horse cavalry would be able to exploit a tank break-through but in all three battles cavalry proved quite unable to do it. The existing tanks, with maximum speeds of only 4 or 5 m.p.h., and limited endurance, were equally incapable if for different reasons.

Faster vehicles were being developed, however, and Colonel Fuller, who was then Chief of Staff of the Tank Corps, conceived the idea of deep tactical penetration by fleets of the new mobile tanks. This was embodied in his " Plan 1919," which was subsequently elaborated into an operation involving 10,000 tanks.

Before any of this could be put into effect the First World War came to an end and the Plan was never put to test. But the idea of wider-ranging and more independent employment of tanks remained. So did the record of the efficacy of large tank units in the role of an operational battering ram. Both were resumed later but in the meantime other ideas prevailed.

In the immediate post-First World War period it was France which had the strongest army and the largest tank force with a stock of some 3,000 tanks. This, together with various political and economic circumstances, added considerable weight to French ideas on tanks which were adopted by most countries during the twenties.

The first French tank units were regarded as mobile assault artillery and were, in fact, originally designated as *artillerie d'assaut*. But, as the original 75 mm. gun tanks were followed by smaller vehicles armed with lighter weapons, they became closely linked with the infantry. After the war this connection was made official and permanent and in 1920 tanks became an integral part of the infantry. At about the same time their role was defined as that of accompanying the infantry and silencing enemy automatic weapons.

In many ways, the Renault light tanks which formed practically the whole of the French tank force were only suitable for an accompanying role and there is little doubt that the existence of a large stock of them had a deadening influence on further development. But even when the Renault F.T., and similar tanks elsewhere, were replaced by more advanced designs there was little change in ideas on their employment. They were organised into light tank battalions which were meant to be allotted to infantry formations, when required, in the ratio of one tank battalion to one infantry regiment, to form a *groupement mixte*. Tanks were further distributed by companies to infantry battalions and, as laid down in the French " Instructions on the employment of tanks " of 1930, they were to be regarded as no more than supplementary means placed at the disposal of the infantry, entirely subordinate to the infantry units to which they were attached.

Similar ideas prevailed in the United States where the wartime Tank Corps was abolished in 1920 by Act of Congress and tanks became a part of the infantry. The role of the tank was defined as that of " facilitating the uninterrupted advance of the riflemen in the attack " and the majority of tanks were distributed among divisional light tank companies.

The Russians also subscribed to such ideas when they began to build their tank forces in the late twenties and early thirties. Their counterpart of the accompanying tanks were the *N.P.P.*, or close infantry support, light tank battalions, one of which was incorporated in each regular infantry division. Similar ideas also held sway in Italy, Japan, Poland and many other countries. In the late thirties even the British Army partially subscribed to them.

It was in this role of an auxiliary to the infantry that tanks were used in the fighting between the two world wars. The

French operations in Morocco in the twenties, the Gran Chaco war between Bolivia and Paraguay, the Italian conquest of Abyssinia, the Japanese invasion of China and the Spanish Civil War all saw them in this role. So did the early stages of the Second World War, on the part of most French and Soviet tank units, when these methods were swept away by others.

In many ways the third, or infantry-accompanying, phase was a continuation of the first one : tanks were regarded as auxiliary and specialised equipment and acted mainly by virtue of their immunity to machine-gun fire. Their usefulness to the infantry was acknowledged but it was simultaneously denied outside the accompanying role. With this and closely related to the importance attached to armour protection went the belief that tanks met more than a match in contemporary anti-tank guns and, therefore, could only be used in close liaison with the infantry and the slow artillery barrages.

In fact, of course, such methods were best designed to expose tanks to the full effectiveness of anti-tank fire. As the German *Truppenführung* manual of the thirties put it, " if tanks are held in too close liaison with the infantry, they lose the advantage of their mobility and are liable to be destroyed by the defence." This was not meant to preclude co-operation between tanks and riflemen but it rightly condemned the contemporary tendencies to subordinate tanks entirely to the infantry.

The narrow and usually pessimistic views on tanks can generally be ascribed to a tendency to approach their problem with rigid, preconceived ideas of how tanks should fit in with the older arms—particularly the infantry—instead of a rational analysis of their relative potentialities and limitations. To some extent they can also be ascribed to the over emphasis on armour protection, which has led to hasty conclusions that the tank was doomed every time some new armour-piercing weapon was introduced.

A notable exception to the views which prevailed after the First World War existed in Britain in the Royal Tank Corps. Although reduced to only 4 tank battalions, the latter was saved from the post-war fate of the French and American tank units and its independence, combined with the possession of new, mechanically much more advanced tanks, created conditions favourable to further progress.

The independence and the progress in mechanised warfare were only achieved as a result of a hard struggle by a small band of enthusiasts against an abysmal lack of understanding and prejudice. The most prominent in this group of pioneers was General Fuller but it included others like Captain Liddell Hart and Generals Lindsay, Broad and Martel. Fuller's own ideas evolved from his " Plan 1919 " and were on the lines of armoured formations composed almost entirely of tanks. Their operations were to resemble those of fleets at sea, the " land-ship " influence being quite marked in all the early British tank philosophy, and other arms were at best regarded as subsidiary.

Such "all-tank" views, which corresponded to the natural proclivities of the Royal Tank Corps, exerted a strong influence on the experiments carried out in Britain during the late twenties and early thirties. As a result, although the first Experimental Mechanised Force, assembled in 1927 on Salisbury Plain, was made up of several elements apart from tanks, most of the later Tank Brigade experiments were carried out solely with tanks, which were regarded as virtually or potentially self-sufficient.

The experiments themselves demonstrated for the first time many of the potentialities of mechanised forces. They also pioneered the operational technique of tank units freed from the slow-motion infantry methods. Unfortunately, the development tended to be one sided or, at least, unbalanced.

For one thing, while great stress was placed on developing the advantages of mobility of tank units, the importance of their weapon power tended to be overlooked. Also, while the strategic potentialities of mechanised forces were rightly emphasised, the tactical limitations of tanks were apt to be glossed over. In consequence, the type of armoured formation which was developed was of limited use. It was suitable, perhaps, for the limited role formerly performed by the cavalry but incapable, on its own, of effective participation in many phases of fighting.

This was not, however, entirely due to the over-enthusiasm of the " all-tank " ideas and the concentration on the sweeping employment of mobile tanks on their own. Whatever the exponents of mechanised warfare may have believed, there was the rest of the Army which was very sceptical about mechanised forces, if not actually hostile to them. When eventually and reluctantly the majority of the Army accepted the idea of mechanisation it could conceive—or admit—of nothing further than the concept of mechanised forces as a substitute for horse cavalry.

In this context, the limited cavalry-role concept of mech-anised forces initially served a useful purpose. It helped to make the new ideas of more mobile employment of tanks more palatable to the tradition-bound majority and without it, perhaps, little progress would have been possible. To a large extent, however, the " cavalry " concept represented the price exacted by traditional thinking for the existence of a tank branch untied to the infantry. It reflected the influence of this thinking and it confined the development of mechanised forces to the limited roles of the cavalry of the late 19th and 20th centuries.

Thus, both sides contributed something to the diversion of tank units to a limited mobile role. In turn, this hampered the evolution of a new type of versatile mechanised forces in which tanks and other arms would jointly play their part.

Nevertheless, in spite of their shortcomings, the British experiments provided a lead which was followed in other countries. In fact, they set off a kind of chain reaction in experiments with mechanised forces. In the United States, for instance, a force similar to the British Experimental Mechanised Force was assembled in 1928 at Fort Meade and in 1930 this was followed by another at Fort Eustis. In France the *exercises combinés* of 1932, in which infantry and cavalry mechanised units took part, and the mechanised cavalry experiments at Reims in 1933 were also influenced by British developments. So were the contemporary experiments in Russia and Germany.

Of all these, the Russian results most closely approached the British pattern : Soviet mechanised brigades were composed almost entirely of tanks and although they were mobile their capabilities were limited.

Somewhat different results were arrived at in France. There a gradual mechanisation of the cavalry began soon after the First World War, when motor-vehicles began to replace horses—a little surreptitiously at first since emotional prejudices were strong. However, by 1930 French cavalry divisions were almost half-motorised and in 1934 the first fully motorised cavalry division was placed on a permanent footing.

In its organisation, with a tank brigade and a brigade of motorised riflemen, this first *Division Légère Mécanique* had many of the characteristics of the later armoured divisions. But its role and method of employment were still very much on the lines of the cavalry of the previous hundred years or so. Its main role was, in fact, that of strategic reconnaissance and security for the benefit of the infantry formations ; or, in other words, only that of an auxiliary mobile arm.

Elsewhere a similar process of gradual and at first only partial mechanisation of the cavalry was taking place. At the same time the idea of mobile mechanised forces taking over the duties previously entrusted to horse cavalry gained wider recognition and was put into effect not only by the gradual mechanisation of the cavalry but also by developing the mobility of tank units. This was the case with the British Tank Brigade which was combined with mechanised cavalry units into the Mobile Division of 1938.

But, if some tanks were considered suitable for the cavalry role, other tanks were still wanted to help the main body of the armies which continued to be represented by the infantry.

In other words, tanks were also wanted for the harder task of fighting in conjunction with the infantry. Put in this way, that is as separate requirements, these demands gave rise to two separate specialised categories of " cavalry " and " infantry " tanks, which became a characteristic feature of the thirties. Even in Britain, where close infantry support was given little attention by the tank pioneers of the twenties, special " infantry " tank units were formed after 1934.

In fact, right up to 1940 the majority of tank units in practically all armies was represented by " infantry " tanks, used by platoons or companies to support small infantry units. Such were the French *bataillons de chars légers*, Soviet divisional light tank battalions, American divisional tank companies, Japanese tank regiments, Italian *reggimento fanteria carrista* and tank units of many smaller countries.

But, as tanks improved and increased in number and as their potentialities were slowly recognised, some and usually the more powerful infantry tanks were withheld for use at higher formation levels. Instead of acting for the benefit of infantry battalions or companies they were used at the level of infantry divisions or corps, especially in break-through operations, where they paved the way for the infantry and its accompanying tanks by destroying hostile anti-tank guns and tanks. This could be observed most clearly in France where, in keeping with their role, units of such tanks were called *chars de manoeuvre d'ensemble*.

Grouping of such tanks, even if only for administrative convenience, led to the formation of larger units of infantry tanks. Two good examples of this are provided by the British Army Tank Brigades and the Soviet Tank Brigades, each of which had three battalions of heavy tanks. With the addition of other elements, such as motorised infantry and artillery, some of these large infantry tank units grew into divisions, as shown by the French *Division Cuirassée* of 1939 and the contemporary Italian *Divisione Corazzata*.

In many ways the infantry armoured formations occupied an intermediate position between the tank units intended for close infantry support and the mechanised cavalry. On the other hand, their employment approximated to that of the tanks used in the first massed assaults of the First World War. As time went on, however, ideas about them began to move away from the narrow concept of an operational battering ram and their wider possibilities began to be recognised. Thus, not only tactical striking power but operational mobility were beginning to be taken into account.

At the same time, in the case of the cavalry armoured formations, striking power was beginning to be considered in addition to mobility and there is little doubt that in time both types of armoured formations would have merged into a single versatile type of mechanised division.

However, by and large, the division into the two separate categories of tanks and tank units stood firm right up to the early stages of the Second World War. It then largely disappeared except, oddly enough, in Britain where it was adhered to until 1945 with deplorable consequences in the shape of the two narrowly specialised categories of " cruiser " and " infantry " tanks. Nevertheless, it still finds supporters who arbitrarily divide tanks into two separate categories on the traditional lines of the division into infantry and cavalry rather than accept the truism that a tank is a tank, whether it is used with the infantry or any other troops, and consider objectively its general characteristics.

The Germans were the first to do away with the division of tanks into two separate categories, to show, in practice, the way between the extremes of the " all-tank " views and the complete subordination to the infantry and, also, the ultimate form of the cavalry light mechanised divisions and infantry tank formations. In short, they were the first to create a single versatile armoured force.

The idea of such an armoured force was neither unique nor entirely original. Soon after the First World War Captain Liddell Hart in Britain and General Estienne in France had advocated versatile mechanised forces made up of tanks, armoured infantry and self-propelled artillery. So, in the mid-thirties, did General de Gaulle in France and General von Eimannsberger in Austria. But it was only with the creation of the German panzer divisions, on which, incidentally, neither de Gaulle's nor von Eimannsberger's books had any influence, that the ideas began to be translated into practice.

As in other armies, older arms tried to subordinate tanks to their own particular ways but the German armoured force managed to emerge untied to any of them, to the everlasting credit of the architects of the *Panzerwaffe* and General Guderian in particular. The panzer divisions represented a new-style fighting force of both greater mobility and greater striking power than the rest of the Army and they were based not on any preconceived ideas about the superiority of any one arm but on the potentialities and limitations of several elements. Thus, each panzer division contained several types of units, including motorised infantry, artillery and engineers, as well as tanks. This showed that the panzer pioneers were as conscious of the tactical limitations of the tank as they were of the potentialities of mechanised forces and it made panzer divisions effective, versatile fighting formations.

In spite of this, panzer divisions have been equated sometimes with the contemporary cavalry-type mechanised formations of other armies. But what similarities there were were largely superficial and did not extend to the all-important question of operational doctrine. In particular, while panzer divisions achieved some of the most striking results in brilliant strategic exploitation they were by no means confined to this role. In general, not only did they exploit the successful outcome of battles but they also fought out the necessary successes and were as capable of smashing opposition as of rapidly outflanking it. As a 1940 German armoured force manual put it, panzer divisions were especially suited for " rapid concentration of considerable fighting power, obtaining quick decisions by breaks-through, deep penetration on wide fronts and the destruction of the enemy." This was quite a different concept from that expressed, a little later, in a

British manual that armoured divisions were " designed for exploitation after the enemy's position has been broken."

In practice panzer divisions formed the mobile spearhead of the German Army in all of its early *Blitzkrieg* campaigns. Concentrated in panzer corps and later panzer armies, they delivered the main and decisive blows in Poland in September 1939, in France in May and June 1940, in the Balkans in April 1941 and then in Russia in the summer of 1941. In the process they also defeated various tank units which opposed them piecemeal, each going about its own limited task. In France 10 panzer divisions accounted for, one by one, 3 *divisions légères mécaniques*, 4 *divisions cuirassées*, 1 British armoured division and many infantry tank battalions. In Russia 17 panzer divisions routed numerically greatly superior Soviet armoured forces to the tune of some 17,000 tanks destroyed or captured.

The German successes in the first two years of the Second World War had a profound influence on the development of armoured forces everywhere. To begin with, they swept away many of the older concepts which disappeared with the destruction of the French and of the bulk of the old Soviet armoured forces. At the same time the German successes showed clearly how tanks and mechanised forces ought to be used and forced others to adopt similar methods.

Thus, in July 1940, the United States Army abolished its previous division into infantry and cavalry tank units and created an armoured force whose main element were to be armoured divisions on the model of the panzer divisions. The Italian *divisioni corazzate* had already approached their German partners and in Russia tank divisions on the pattern of the panzer divisions were being hurriedly created when the Germans attacked. In contrast to some of the official theories, British armoured divisions also acted as effective and versatile fighting formations, like the German divisions.

With these developments and the rapid numerical expansion armoured forces became the truly dominant arm on the battlefields of 1941 and 1942. They were used extensively on all sides and whether the operations were carried out on the Russian plains or in the African deserts their outcome depended largely upon the success or failure of the armoured formations. Infantry, on its own, was hard put to it to defend itself against armour and had to seek refuge in built up areas or behind vast natural or artificial obstacles in the form of extensive minefields. There it could defend itself but usually no more.

The growing importance of tanks and other armoured vehicles was reflected in the soaring production figures. Tanks themselves were better armed, a feature of this period being a general move from smaller calibres to guns of 75 mm. or 76 mm. on the basic medium tanks. This made up for much of the neglect of armament of the earlier periods, caused by overconcentration on armour protection or on mobility, and transformed the average tank into a really effective combination of fire power and mobility. Operationally the period saw the great armoured offensives and deep penetrations on the Russian front, the rapid thrusts of Rommel's *Afrika Korps*, British desert offensives and numerous lesser actions in which armoured forces played a leading and decisive role.

To some extent, of course, the conditions in the main theatres of operations were particularly favourable to the employment of armoured forces. Whatever the difficulties of operating in the extremes of temperature and of logistical support, there is little doubt that both the Russian plains and the African deserts offered exceptional opportunities for highly mobile mechanised forces. When action shifted to other theatres many of these opportunities disappeared.

In Sicily, in 1943, and then in Italy, British and American armoured units found their movements severely restricted by the nature of the country which favoured static defence. In consequence they had to operate more cautiously, in small bodies and in closer liaison with infantry. In this way they were able to render valuable service and operated over many types of terrain hitherto considered impassable for tanks. But it was all a far cry from the dashing and spectacular employment of the previous two years. And it is always one of the unfortunate consequences of a series of successes that any subsequent failure, real or imaginary, is apt to be greatly magnified. This is precisely what happened with tanks. Many political and military leaders and, after them, the general public, having come to expect nothing but spectacular successes, jumped to the other extreme, that " tanks are finished " when these successes were no longer forthcoming. More soberly the usefulness of armoured forces was again thought to be confined to special occasions, when they could be used in the cavalry role, and tanks were either held back or else employed in small units in close support of the infantry.

The employment of tanks in close support of the infantry was particularly true of the war in the Pacific. There, in the island-hopping operations, only small bodies of tanks were generally used; in the Philippines, in 1944, the Japanese produced an armoured division but this too was used up in small-scale actions. Similarly, the initial employment of Anglo-American armour in the first phase of the Normandy operations in 1944 was circumscribed, both by the difficulties of such an assault landing and the conditions of the bridgehead build up.

Yet, in spite of all the difficulties and pessimistic opinions, not all was regression. True, the methods used did not exploit fully the advantages of mechanised mobility. But tanks were able to demonstrate, even under some of the most adverse conditions, their capabilities as a means of increasing the effectiveness of the armament with which they were armed and which they carried forward with the infantry. In fact, tanks and self-propelled guns very often formed the main source of striking power and the core of various mixed battle groups, combat teams and task forces which, at their best, exemplified the ideal close tactical teamwork between heavy weapons and riflemen.

The apparent eclipse—for it was only apparent—of armour on the Russian front was brought about by different conditions. After the costly failure of their offensive against the Kursk salient in July 1943 the Germans never possessed sufficient resources to mount another really large-scale offensive. Their armoured forces continued to render very valuable service but in local counter-offensives or in blocking Soviet armoured thrusts; they were never strong enough again to resume large-scale offensive operations in which armoured forces demonstrate their full capabilities.

The Russians, on the other hand, had the numbers—the Germans identified no less than 258 different Soviet armoured brigades during the fighting on the Eastern Front. But they were slow to make full use of them and for a long time confined themselves to the bludgeon tactics of massed assaults.

The absence of sweeping armoured drives and the loss of some of the associated glamour did not mean, however, that the importance of armoured forces diminished. They maintained their position as the most effective combination of striking power and mobility and were used both to deliver massive blows and swift counter-blows and, when the necessity arose, proved very effective on the defensive. In consequence, the issues of major operations were still largely decided by the fortunes of tank and mechanised corps on the Soviet side and panzer divisions on the German.

Striking power, combined with mobility, being the most important characteristic, attention concentrated on increasing it further and making armoured formations more powerful still, especially to master enemy armour which represented the greatest single threat. The outcome of this were the heavily armed tanks, such as the German Tigers and Soviet Stalins, and the armoured battles when the German forces were being pushed back across Eastern Europe in 1943 and 1944.

In the West, in the meantime, after the process of attrition wore out the German forces in Normandy, Allied armour was able to break out of the bridgehead and then exploit this by a spectacular advance across France and Belgium. Operating among shattered enemy formations, the Allied armoured divisions were able to take full advantage of their mobility and were only stopped when they outran their logistical support.

After the crossing of the Rhine, in the final stages of the war, Allied armour was able to repeat its exploitation performance and its total exceeded 20 divisions, American, British and French.

As a result there was a revival of interest in armour and it even seemed restored to something like the position it held during the 1940–42 period. However, being associated with the particular conditions of exploiting a major enemy defeat, the revival was somewhat one sided. It applied to only one of several roles which armoured forces could perform and under the circumstances mobility was accorded greater, and striking power less, attention than they would otherwise have been. Nor, in any case, did all this last long enough to make a sufficient impression on the many sceptics.

What happened was, in consequence, less of a revival of the 1940–42 position than a return to the pre-war conditions where armour was generally regarded as a complementary mobile arm and the principal strength of the armies still lay in their infantry formations. The position in the West was considerably different, therefore, from that of the German and Soviet armoured forces which were looked upon as being more powerful as well as more mobile than the rest of the German and Soviet armies and their principal striking force. They represented, in fact, a continuation of the ideas and methods put into effect by the panzer divisions in 1939 and 1940. At times they appeared less mobile than the latter or the armoured formations of the Western Allies but they did not lack in weapon power and if they were not as mobile as they might have been they certainly avoided the far worse policy of under-gunned mobility which characterised the tanks of the American and British armoured divisions.

On this divergent note ended the employment of tanks during the Second World War and the first thirty years of their development. The thirty-year period brought the tank from small-scale beginnings under conditions of trench warfare, through the first massed assaults and the many years of humble service as an auxiliary to the infantry. It saw armoured forces replace horse cavalry as the mobile arm and, in the early part of the Second World War, assume the role of a versatile and decisive arm which swept away the earlier division into cavalry and infantry tanks. The resounding armoured victories were followed by disappointments and regression in the latter part of the Second World War, a period when, to many, offensive power and mobility again seemed incompatible and when armoured forces had to struggle once more for full recognition of their capabilities.

3

Nuclear Age

THE explosion of the two atomic bombs over Japan in August 1945 marked the end of the Second World War in which armoured forces played such a prominent part. It also marked the beginning of the new era of nuclear power which has come to exert an increasingly important influence on all military developments, including that of armour.

In the immediate post-war period, however, the potential employment and influence of nuclear weapons were limited to strategic air warfare—a euphemism for the aerial bombing of centres of industry and urban population initiated during the Second World War. Moreover, for several years, until the first explosion of a Soviet nuclear device in 1949, the actual possession of nuclear weapons was thought to be confined to the United States Strategic Air Force.

Thus, for a time, the development of ground forces was influenced by other considerations far more than by nuclear weapons. So far as armour was concerned, the principal factors were compounded of the earlier theories on the employment of armoured forces and of the more recent developments in the field of anti-tank weapons.

The existing theories consisted of two which were compatible and complementary and one which was largely opposed to them. Of the first two, one maintained that the principal role of tanks was still that of an auxiliary to the infantry ; the other continued to regard armoured forces as a mobile arm with a limited role. Between them they divided armoured units into two specialised categories, one intended for close infantry support and the other for mobile operations of limited scope. The third theory, which was largely opposed to the other two, advanced the use of tanks within versatile

28

mechanised formations made up of several arms and such formations as the principal element in ground warfare.

When the armies emerged from the post-war period of reorganisation it became clear that the first two theories found continued favour in the United States and that the third had won in the Soviet Union. Britain and France, the only two countries left with modern armoured forces of any size, occupied something of an intermediate position. Both attached greater importance to their tanks than the United States were inclined to do at the time but neither accorded to its armoured formations anything like the importance their counterparts enjoyed in the Soviet Army.

In practice, the post-war American policy amounted to a dispersion of the majority of tanks among infantry formations, in regimental tank companies and divisional tank battalions. Only one (under strength) armoured division was retained and there were serious doubts about the future of tanks in general, generated by the appearance of rocket firing planes and new infantry anti-tank weapons, such as rocket launchers and recoilless rifles.

In contrast, the Soviet Army continued to attach great importance to its armoured forces, which had played a decisive part in the Soviet advance into the heart of Europe. Not only were they maintained in strength but, in marked contrast to the contemporary American policy, the proportion of armoured formations was greatly increased in relation to the rest of the Soviet Army. Within five years of the end of the Second World War the total of the reorganised armoured formations exceeded 50, which amounted to about one third of the Soviet Army and its principal striking force. For a time this force formed the chief military asset of the Soviet *bloc* and an effective counterbalance to the American monopoly of the atomic bombs by its threat to the bordering countries.

The Soviet emphasis on armour and the realisation of the need for an alternative to the undue reliance on American atomic bombs for the defence of Western Europe led to a reappraisal of armoured forces outside the Soviet *bloc*. The reassessment of armoured forces in the West was greatly assisted by the invasion of South Korea, in June 1950, when a few battalions of North Korean manned Soviet tanks disproved the exaggerated claims about the obsolescence of armour and, in a broader sense, demonstrated the futility of excessive reliance on the atomic bombs of the strategic air forces.

As a result, in the late forties and early fifties, armoured forces of the countries which formed the North Atlantic Treaty Organisation, as well as those of the uncommitted nations, began to revive. Within NATO and other allied countries the process was greatly assisted by the mutual security programme, under which considerable quantities of American and some British-built armoured equipment were supplied by the United States, and the Soviet *bloc* was no longer alone in emphasising the value of armoured formations. The value of tanks used within versatile mechanised forces was again recognised by the Western armies and particular attention was attached to them as an antidote to the Soviet armoured forces, in keeping with the old maxim that the best defence against a tank is another tank.

The revival of the Western armoured forces had barely begun when two new factors appeared upon the scene. One was the development of the hydrogen bomb of fearful power, heralded by the first American thermonuclear explosion in November 1952 and, within 10 months, by a similar Soviet explosion. The other factor was the development of nuclear weapons smaller than the original atomic bombs and, therefore, adaptable to a wider range of uses, particularly in the tactical field.

The tremendous power of the hydrogen bomb opened the possibility of inflicting damage on a vast territorial scale and radically altered previous theories about the strategic use of nuclear weapons. No longer could a full-scale conflict between two powers armed with nuclear weapons be visualised in terms of " broken-back " warfare, where after an initial exchange of atomic bombs the war would be carried on, in the traditional manner, by the forces which survived the initial bombardment.

Instead, the probability emerged that an all-out war with nuclear weapons would lead to mutual suicide on a national scale.

In such a context the role of the ground forces, armoured or otherwise, shrank to negligible proportions. Some thereupon jumped to the conclusion that ground forces should be restricted to a light frontier cordon, or " trip-wire " as it was called, which could set off the nuclear weapons of mass destruction. This implied basing all defence to aggression on the threat of fearful reprisals with nuclear weapons, a policy epitomised by the concept of " massive retaliation " first announced in the United States in 1954 but logically derived from the earlier American concentration on strategic atomic bombing. The only role which would have remained to armour in this extreme situation was that of a mechanised constabulary.

A more valid conclusion from the devastating power of the thermonuclear weapons would have been that in face of an enemy armed with similar means they were useless as an instrument of national policy, except in the supreme role of a deterrent to the use of their like. Since the ability to retaliate in kind is the only defence against an attempt to exploit the tremendous power of nuclear weapons this, in itself, justifies all the effort devoted to the development of nuclear weapon systems by each of the opposing *blocs*. Otherwise, outside their proper role of a mutual deterrent, the value of nuclear weapons of mass destruction became highly questionable for, short of an all-out war of annihilation, their use would have far worse consequences than whatever it was trying to counter.

In contrast to the suicidal implications of the more powerful nuclear weapons, the smaller ones, developed at about the same time as the thermonuclear devices, opened the possibility of tactical employment of nuclear power which would not, perhaps, incur the same frightful consequences. The successful development of small nuclear weapons was demonstrated by a long series of American tests started in January 1951 at Las Vegas in Nevada and particularly clearly by the firing of a nuclear shell from a long-range 280 mm. gun in May 1953. In 1951 also, Exercise Southern Pine in the United States included for the first time the simulated use of nuclear weapons against ground troops, and from then on this became a regular feature of American and then NATO manoeuvres.

The development of the smaller tactical nuclear weapons was particularly welcome to the NATO Powers in view of their continued weakness in other ground armaments and the advantage which they enjoyed due to an initial American lead in this field. In the United States, and later Britain, tactical nuclear weapons found favour all the more readily because neither expected to use them on its own territory and all NATO countries were forced to rely on them increasingly because of their common failure to develop other, safer but more arduous, ways of opposing aggression.

The twin hope that the American introduction of tactical nuclear weapons would counterbalance superior Soviet ground forces and make possible nuclear warfare limited in scope and magnitude was largely unfounded. For one thing, the initial American superiority in this field could not be relied upon in view of the Soviet technological capabilities, amply demonstrated by the lead in long-range ballistic missiles and earth satellites. Secondly, the possibility of restricting the employment of nuclear weapons to a particular set of targets and some arbitrary yield range remained very doubtful. To keep nuclear weapons restricted to local tactical employment and to prevent them setting off a disastrous full-scale nuclear war would require not only a remarkable degree of self-restraint on both sides but, also, an unprecedented degree of precision in the political control and military execution. Such conditions are not inconceivable but their practical realisation difficult to visualise outside some short sharp local military demonstrations.

In the meantime, while the wider issues remained in doubt, the implications of tactical nuclear weapons were clear in relation to armoured and other ground forces. To start with, and in contrast to the strategic nuclear weapons, the smaller tactical types implied the continuation of effective ground forces. At the same time they called for a radical transformation. Previously, the development of the strategic nuclear weapons was either assumed to mean the virtual end of all other forms of military power or else it produced little more than concern about logistics and large troop concentrations. But the appearance of the more adaptable nuclear weapons, suitable for tactical employment, called for ground forces of a new type which could be used with and against such weapons.

The principal impact of tactical nuclear weapons has been on the mode of tactical deployment. In their presence the time-honoured massing of troops became an invitation to wholesale destruction, and to escape this fate dispersion became a necessity. In consequence, a more resilient disposition in depth had to replace untenable static defence lines while the offensive counterpart of the latter, the outmoded massed break-through, would be replaced by diffusive penetration. These new conditions put a premium on highly mobile forces capable of operating in small self-contained units which could make up for the low troop density on the battlefield by their mobility and weapon power and which could better evade destruction by keeping the situation fluid.

The postulates of effective operation in face of tactical nuclear weapons clearly favour armoured forces, whenever mountainous or jungle terrain does not preclude their employment. For one thing, the vehicles of the armoured forces, with all their armament and communication equipment, provide the necessary basis for mobile ground tactics and effective controlled dispersion. At the same time they assure a relatively high ratio of weapon power to manpower. Moreover, the same vehicles offer the possibility of effective movement in relative proximity to nuclear explosions by virtue of their inherent protection against blast and radioactivity. In consequence, armoured forces, suitably organised and equipped, emerged as potentially most useful under conditions of tactical nuclear warfare.

The types of unit which would fit the tactical employment of nuclear weapons are small self-contained armoured battle groups organised round nuclear missile launchers as the primary weapons. Such groups might be exemplified by battalion-size units built round a battery of self-propelled launchers for rockets with nuclear warheads, supported by a company or two of light tanks or armoured cars for medium-distance security and one or two companies of riflemen in light armoured personnel carriers for close-in employment.

Small highly mobile units or battle groups of this type could operate effectively even against numerically superior forces. However, as both sides would ultimately have them their employment would lead to the impossible situation of small widely dispersed units stalking each other with over-powerful weapons and pulverising the country around them in the process. Thus, even if the tactical employment of nuclear weapons did not start a disastrous all-out nuclear war, it would, in populated districts, kill off the population which ostensibly was being defended. In other words, complete reliance on nuclear weapons implied by such units would destroy the purpose of defensive ground forces and much of their value in general. What is more, an irrevocable commitment to nuclear weapons in the organisation of tactical units not only would make their tactical employment inevitable but it would also increase the probability of the nuclear holocaust.

At the same time it is inconceivable to dispense with tactical nuclear weapons, for a definite need must remain for them, as it does for strategic nuclear weapons, as a deterrent to the use of similar weapons by the enemy. Thus, the ultimate role of tactical nuclear weapons is most likely to be that of a complement to ground units, which they would protect by their deterrent threat, rather than the basis of their weapon power under all circumstances.

But, even if tactical nuclear weapons are held back, their threat will continue to hang over fighting units, as will the threats of chemical and bacteriological warfare. In consequence, combat units will be compelled to operate dispersed and to avoid deployment which would at once tempt the enemy to exploit his nuclear weapons and run the risk of wholesale destruction.

Under such circumstances, where the threat of tactical nuclear weapons will persist but where they may not necessarily be used, the value of armoured forces will be greater than ever. On them, in fact, must devolve much of the ground defence in any territorial conflict; that is, defence against aggression aimed at conquest of territory with its population and material wealth, as opposed to a war of annihilation made possible by the advent of strategic nuclear weapons.

To meet probable tactical requirements the organisation of armoured forces needs to be recast into smaller self-contained mobile groups composed of self-propelled heavy weapons, tanks and riflemen in armoured personnel carriers. Each group ought to form a versatile mechanised ground weapon system capable of a variety of missions and of sustained operation over wide areas. Spread out in strength over critical sectors, the role of the armoured battle groups would be to pounce swiftly upon the aggressors—in all probability composed of similar units—and to beat back attempts at local penetration. Their primary aim would be to combat aggressor forces directly with skilful mobile tactics and superior equipment, rather than blowing up everything around them, and thus check aggression on the spot and in a non-suicidal way.

The potential value of armoured forces cannot be fully converted into fact, however, until their equipment and tactics, as well as organisation, have been brought in line with the demands of the new situation. As it is, few of the necessary developments took place during the first nuclear decade and subsequent progress has lagged behind the slow realisation of the potential value of armour.

In all fairness, there have been a few moves in the direction of smaller self-contained units, as shown by the American armoured cavalry regiments, the regiments of the Soviet tank divisions and the French *régiments inter-armes*, all created since the Second World War. But the small versatile armoured units, self-sufficient tactically and administratively, which are indicated by the latest operational concepts are still to be generally accepted. In fact, there have been some regressive moves right in the opposite direction, as shown by the British experimental armoured division of 1955–56, which was intended as a specialised limited-role formation of the " all-tank " type and which was the antithesis of the versatile mixed armoured battle groups envisaged under the new conditions.

On the equipment side progress in tank design during the first nuclear decade amounted to little more than refinement of basic designs evolved towards the end of the Second World War. The typical tank remained the medium of about 40 tons, armed with high-velocity guns of 3 to 4 in. calibre, which, in essence, dated back to the German Panther designed in 1942. In support of the medium, there is also the heavy gun tank of the type introduced during the Second World War by the German Tigers and the Soviet Stalins and perpetuated since by improvements of the latter and British Conqueror and American M103 heavy tanks armed with 120 mm. guns.

Lighter more mobile tanks have been advocated periodically as the answer to the pressing need for greater overall mobility but with little practical effect. One notable exception to the general trend was provided by the French AMX light air-transportable tank but even in the United States, where such progress has been made in the use of air transport and airborne operations, no comparable tank was developed for many years.

One sector of armoured equipment where genuine progress has been made in several countries since 1945 is that of armoured personnel carriers. The lack of cross-country carriers was one of the major shortcomings of the earlier armoured formations and the overdue introduction of this type of vehicle finally made it possible effectively to combine riflemen with tanks and other self-propelled heavy weapons. In other words, the development of armoured carriers has made it possible to create effective mixed armoured units and thus fulfil one of the principal requirements of successful mobile operations.

The use of armoured personnel carriers also increased the overall cross-country mobility of armoured units and thus brought them a step further in the right direction. But their development has barely touched the range of possibilities and the many urgent needs.

Among the most important needs are the exploitation of new weapons and the development of more efficient vehicles. The first includes the possibility of guided missile armed tanks to replace the heavy gun tanks and bring about a substantial weight saving all round. The second point involves more efficient engines and ought to reverse the unfortunate trend towards continuously higher fuel requirements and to reduce the dependence on the vulnerable supply lines which are the Achilles' heel of all armoured formations.

Development of lighter, more efficient vehicles and reduced logistical dependence are, in fact, imperative if armoured forces are to realise their full potential. They need them badly to develop further their mobility which, combined with weapon power, is the basis of their effectiveness and continued importance.

Part 2

Organisation and Methods

4

Basic Elements

COMMONLY spoken of as a homogeneous entity, armoured forces consist, in fact, of several different though allied elements. Apart from tanks, they generally include motorised or armoured infantry, artillery, engineers and other elements and they are at their best when these are combined into well balanced teams. In other words, when they are organised into armoured divisions, brigades and other armoured or mechanised formations, each of which, in principle, is a self-contained system of mutually complementary mechanised units and weapons and which is capable of effective independent operation.

As a result, much of the importance and interest in armoured forces centres on combined units or armoured formations. It is appropriate, however, and indeed necessary to start by considering separately the individual elements which constitute armoured forces and from which armoured formations are built.

Tanks and tank units are, of course, the most characteristic component of armoured forces and it is round them that armoured formations are generally built. Tank units themselves are built on the basis of the individual tank and its crew : 2 or more tanks form a platoon or troop, 2 or more platoons form a company or squadron, and so on.

In general, 3 tanks have come to be considered as the smallest tactical or fighting unit. A few 2-tank platoons have been used, in the Soviet K.V. or Stalin heavy tank units, for instance, but they give little scope for the platoon commander, who is occupying one of the tanks himself, and are far too easily upset by mechanical failure or loss of one vehicle. Even 3-tank platoons are considered too vulnerable, although they

41

have been used for a long time in the Soviet Army and, for a time, also in the British and French. Consequently, larger 4-tank platoons have been favoured, the fourth tank being there to some extent to ensure having an effective 3-tank platoon.

Five-tank platoons have been the largest of those commonly used and probably as large as can be effectively commanded. At any rate, larger ones have been very few, although a platoon with as many as 10 tankettes was tried during the British experiments of the early thirties.

The majority of tank companies, or squadrons, have consisted of 3 platoons, although again exceptions to this existed, in the British tank companies of the Second World War, for instance, which had five 3-tank platoons, and the post-war Stalin tank companies which had two 2-tank platoons. But they represented the extremes. British tank units later changed to four 4-tank platoons, 4 platoons per company being also favoured by French, German and, more recently, the United States Army.

As to larger units, 4-company tank battalions have been fewer than 4-platoon companies, although by all rights the senior battalion commanders should have been better able to control and use a larger number of subordinate units than the junior company commanders. Be that as it may, the great majority of tank battalions have had 3 tank companies.

By comparison with their organisation, the vehicle strength of the tank companies and battalions has varied much more widely. Companies have actually varied from 5 tanks in the case of the Stalin heavy tank units to thirty-two 2-man light tanks in the case of the British experiments of 1930 and the first German units of 1935. But these again were the extremes, if one ignores the one French battalion of six 2C heavy tanks of the thirties. In the majority of cases the companies have had between 10 and 22 tanks, that is between three 3-tank platoons and four 5-tank platoons plus command tanks. The former was adhered to for many years by Soviet medium tank units ; the latter by German light and later also medium tank companies during the period 1939 to 1940, and more recently also by American units. Most others have had between 12 and 19 tanks per company, 17 being a common figure.

Similarly, the total strength of the battalions has varied considerably, from 21 in the Stalin heavy tank units to about 90 Pz.Kpfw.II light tanks in the case of the tank battalions of the German Light Divisions in 1939. The majority, however, have had between 30 and 70-odd tanks. British heavy tank battalions of 1917–18, French infantry light tank battalions of the thirties and most Soviet medium tank battalions belonged to the former category. During or since the early forties German, British and American battalions have belonged to the latter.

The greater numerical strength of individual battalions meant, of course, that they were more powerful and less sensitive to losses but it also tended to make them unwieldy and less cohesive. It is debatable, therefore, whether the alternative of a greater number of somewhat smaller battalions is not better, for while it reduces the scope of individual battalions it makes them more manageable and manoeuvrable and shifts more responsibility to higher command level, in theory better able to cope with it.

Related to the question of scope accorded to individual battalions is also that of their equipment. The more independent they are expected to be the greater is the variety of equipment they need. Conversely, because in the great majority of cases tank battalions have not been expected to act independently, but in conjunction with other units, their equipment has been relatively simple and confined to one type of tank. This applied especially to all the tank battalions used for infantry support but it also applied to most others.

The most notable exceptions to this were the German tank battalions of 1939 to 1942, which had 2 light and 1 medium tank companies, some British tank battalions in 1942, which had 1 company of Crusader cruiser tanks and 2 of the better armed but slower Grants, and American tank battalions of

1944 to 1945, which had 1 light tank company in addition to 3 medium tank companies.

In the early British experiments in the thirties the combination of light and medium tanks was even carried down to company level and in 1940–41 German medium tank companies also had a platoon of light tanks for reconnaissance. In theory this made the individual companies more capable of independent action but, as they were generally employed in larger units and the light tanks did not prove successful for reconnoitring any more than they did for fighting, this remained in the nature of an experiment.

Another form of combination has been that of tanks which differed in armament but were otherwise similar. This started during the First World War with British heavy and French light tank units both of which had mixed platoons of machine-gun or cannon-armed tanks ; it was continued in another form in British tank units of the Second World War which had two to four 3 in. or 95 mm. howitzer armed tanks in each company to support the standard models armed with 40 mm. or 57 mm. high velocity guns. In yet another form it showed itself in the combination within companies of Centurion medium tanks with Conqueror heavy gun tanks.

All these examples show that combinations of different types of equipment are feasible within companies or even platoons. But heterogeneous equipment inevitably complicates employment. In small units it is, at best, a necessary evil and it is justifiable only if the armament of one type of tank can not be made sufficiently versatile to cover most needs. So far, fortunately, one type of armament and tank has been sufficient for the roles usually assigned not only to companies but also battalions and for this reason, as well as for the sake of operational simplicity, the great majority of tank battalions have been equipped with one type of tank.

But even where a whole battalion is equipped with one type of tank it still contains other types of vehicles. The tank platoon is about the only unit which does not, and is generally the only pure tank unit. The average company contains not only its 3- or 4-tank platoons and the commander's tank but also small command and administrative or service groups, the former principally to assist the commander in maintaining liaison with other units and reconnoitring and the latter to look after cooking and general " housekeeping " and to assist in the maintenance of vehicles.

At battalion level there are further vehicles and men to cater for the needs of personnel and vehicles by collecting, transporting and distributing food, ammunition, fuel and lubricant. In addition to the supply detachment, there is another to carry out minor repairs, headquarters staff to assist the battalion commander and a signal detachment to maintain communication within the battalion and with other units. There is also a medical detachment, a few relief tank crews and some form of reconnaissance detachment.

Combined, these indispensable units, to which others, less essential, are sometimes added, are numerous enough to constitute at least one company additional to the 3 tank companies of the typical battalion. Together with the service elements of the companies they swell the total personnel strength to between two to three times the number actually manning tanks and they and the functions they perform account for the fact that on the average there have been as many transport vehicles in most tank battalions as there have been fighting ones. In other words, for every man in a tank there is 1 or 2, less frequently more, men who perform other duties and for every tank there is a truck, which gives some idea of the composition of a typical, administratively self-sufficient tank unit.

Sometimes the service functions have not been performed at battalion level but shared between companies and regiments, which embraced 2 or more battalions. This was the case with German tank units during the Second World War and also, for a time, American. This does not alter the general picture, except that the regiment must now be taken as the self-contained unit, administratively as well as tactically, while the battalion may only be a tactical unit. On the other hand, the Russians, with their more frugal ways and smaller units, kept their companies as pure fighting units, unencumbered with administrative and service functions, which were concentrated at battalion level.

Mention of tank units larger than battalion makes it necessary to differentiate clearly between the term regiment as used in this context and its use in the British Army since the early part of the Second World War, and more recently also in the French, in place of the earlier and still more common battalion. The British and French use, or misuse, of the term regiment, which has generally meant a unit larger than a battalion, as a synonym for the latter originated with the conversion of cavalry into tank units. During the process, in deference to tradition, the cavalry regimental appellations were retained and in Britain the term armoured regiment was gradually applied to all tank units of battalion size. This fact has caused a certain amount of confusion, particularly when comparisons are made between different armies, and for the sake of consistency and clarity the earlier, more common and more explicit tank battalion is used here. For similar reasons tank company and tank platoon are used here in preference to the cavalry unit designations of squadron and troop which are synonymous in the British Army and several others but not in the United States. Otherwise the cavalry terms would be equally good, except for attempts to carry the cavalry tradition to the extent of calling tank companies sabre squadrons, which borders on the ridiculous.

The more recent British and French practice excepted, regiments had 2 or more battalions and in many cases 2 tank regiments, or one regiment plus other units, have formed a brigade. The distinction between regiments and brigades has never been very clear, however, and in practice they frequently amounted to the same thing. For instance, during the First World War a British tank brigade had the same number of tank battalions as a French tank regiment; in the original German Panzer Division the tank brigade had a total of 4 tank battalions, organised into 2 regiments, while later, when the tank brigade as such was abolished and each division reduced to 1 tank regiment, the latter could have up to 4 tank battalions. In most cases, however, the regiment tended to be smaller than the brigade, usually of no more than 3 battalions, while the brigade had at least 3 tank battalions and frequently units of other arms as well.

Tank divisions have also existed and still do in the Soviet Army but, strictly speaking, only in name. At least they are not tank units in the sense that tank battalions, regiments or even brigades have been, but are formations composed of several arms and not only tanks. This, of course, also applies to all the armoured divisions of other armies. They are the largest permanently organised bodies of troops which contain tanks but invariably they contain units of other arms as well.

Of the latter, infantry is generally the one next in importance to tanks. In the early days of the tank it was prophesied that mobile tank units would dispense with the co-operation of infantry, tank operations being visualised on naval lines and the tank as a landship. However, experience showed that tanks needed not only small detachments of " tank marines " but a substantial complement of infantry, to tackle resistance and obstacles which tanks could not overcome by themselves. Riflemen proved particularly valuable to tanks in fighting at close quarters, in protecting them from close-in attack and in " winkling out " the enemy from places inaccessible to tanks.

To begin with, tanks and infantry were usually combined by grouping a brigade of each within a division, as was the case with the German Panzer Division and the French *Division Légère Mécanique*, or by adding an infantry battalion to a tank brigade, as in the Soviet Mechanised Brigades and, later, the British Armoured Brigades. In more recent years, however, the level of combination has moved down to smaller units, as shown by the French *Régiment Inter-armes*, which consists of tank and rifle companies, and, even more, by American Armoured Cavalry Regiments where the combination of riflemen with tanks is accomplished within the platoon.

As far as infantry units themselves are concerned, their organisation has been based on the section or squad. This basic unit has been commonly defined as the largest group of riflemen that one man can control and lead, although in practice, the basic unit tended to be a light machine-gun or automatic rifle team. In either case the basic section or fire team must have a minimum of 4 or 5 men and may be considered as the light weapon equivalent of the tank and its crew. In most cases the nominal section strength has been much higher however, 10 being a common figure. Three or 4 such sections form a rifle platoon, 3 or 4 platoons a company and 3 or 4 rifle companies a battalion.

In addition to its rifle companies and its headquarters and administrative elements similar to those of tank units, infantry battalions have also had infantry heavy weapon units. These have had such weapons as heavy machine-guns, mortars, anti-tank guns and howitzers and have been usually grouped in the battalion headquarters company or one, occasionally 2, heavy weapon companies. Weapons such as these were indispensable to conventional infantry to supplement and augment the fire power of the rifle platoons, but within armoured formations most of their functions could have been performed by tanks' armament. To a large extent, therefore, heavy weapons within infantry units of the armoured formations represented a questionable duplication of effort.

However, several things conspired to perpetuate heavy infantry weapons within armoured formations, including inadequate numbers of tanks in relation to the infantry and, even more frequently, inadequate provision of cross-country vehicles which would enable the infantry to work closely with tanks.

Ideally each basic infantry unit or section should have its own vehicle with cross-country characteristics similar to those of tanks to make it possible for the two to work closely together. Unfortunately, although the development of armoured infantry carriers began during the First World War, even during the Second World War only American armoured divisions had the whole of their infantry mounted in armoured carriers, of the half-track type. Others, for the most part, had to make do with trucks. To make matters worse, the trucks were adaptations of medium-size commercial vehicles, ill suited to off-the-road operation. Consequently, infantry units of the armoured formations have had to dismount well away from the firing line and move into action on foot, instead of remaining as long as possible in their vehicles. By the same token, they could not accompany tanks closely and usually the mobility of the truck-transported or motorised infantry has been so different from that of tanks that the two were apt to operate separately.

Like the infantry, the artillery of the armoured divisions was initially also only motorised, that is truck or tractor drawn, and not mechanised, *i.e.*, equipped with vehicles from which it could fight on the move. And like the infantry, it was initially regarded by some as unnecessary, the argument being that tank operations were too mobile for the usual indirect artillery fire. The principal type of artillery support thought suitable was the firing of smoke shells and this led to the development of the 15-pounder or 3.7 in. mortar for British medium tanks of 1930 and the later close support tanks.

This kind of reasoning underestimated the value of artillery's covering fire and of high explosive shells in general ; in practice artillery proved essential. At first its guns were of the common 75 or 76 mm. variety but the Germans in their panzer divisions introduced 105 mm. howitzers and these were subsequently also adopted by American armoured divisions. Artillery of the British armoured divisions for many years retained the smallest calibre weapons in the form of the 87.6 mm. 25-pounder but in 1956 it also followed the general trend and went over to 155 mm. howitzers. Similar size weapons had already been added to the artillery of the German and American armoured divisions and in 1957 the latter even acquired 8 in. howitzers and 762 mm. rockets. The move towards larger calibre artillery weapons was inevitable in view of the fact that from the middle of the Second World War most tanks were armed with guns equal in their high explosive performance to the earlier field guns and that the smaller calibre howitzers lost much of their relative value as the calibre of tank guns increased.

Apart from moving in the direction of smaller numbers of larger calibre weapons, the artillery of the armoured division gradually became self-propelled. Up to 1942 virtually all the artillery equipment used was towed but from then on self-propelled guns increased rapidly, American armoured artillery being the first and also the only to be wholly self-propelled up to the end of the Second World War. The Russians adopted a somewhat different approach and in their armoured formations mounted most of their artillery type weapons in the S.U. vehicles, which are turretless tanks as much as anything else and lend themselves more to direct rather than indirect fire and are organised on tank rather than artillery lines.

The artillery of other armoured formations has been organised on conventional lines. For instance, that of the original Panzer Division and of the *Division Légère Mécanique* had the common organisation of 4 guns to a battery, 3 batteries forming a group or battalion and 2 and 3 battalions respectively forming an artillery regiment. From 1941 onwards American units changed over to 6-gun batteries, as did the German in 1943, but only in their self-propelled battalions; thus both American and German self-propelled battalions had 18 guns instead of the hitherto customary 12. British artillery units had 8-gun batteries organised into two 4-gun troops but there were no battalions, a regiment having 2, more often 3, batteries or, in other words, 16 or 24 guns.

In addition to their guns and gun crews, all these artillery units had their headquarters, administrative and supply units, and even larger than those of tanks or infantry. For instance, an 18-gun American battalion of the 1945 period equipped with 105 mm. M7 self-propelled howitzers, each with a crew of seven, had a total strength of 741 officers and men and 3 medium tanks for forward observers, 2 armoured recovery vehicles, 30 armoured half-tracks, 34 trucks and 21 jeeps.

Apart from field artillery, most armoured formations have also had a specialised unit of anti-tank guns. It amounted to a battalion or regiment and was originally armed with towed guns of 25 to 47 mm. but the calibre increased rapidly during the Second World War to 88 or 90 mm. and a fair portion of the anti-tank guns was self-propelled. In many ways, anti-tank units in armoured formations were an anachronism, for tanks were potentially far better anti-tank weapons. They proved useful to the relatively immobile infantry component but the need for them was another indication of a lack of close co-operation between tanks and infantry or else of a lack of adequately armed tanks. In either case it was a sign of an unsatisfactory state of affairs and again of an avoidable duplication of effort.

In contrast to anti-tank artillery units, anti-aircraft units were a functional necessity, for there were no other units within armoured formations which could perform their role. In a number of cases, as with the British and American armoured divisions during the latter part of the Second World War, they proved virtually superfluous because of the Allied superiority in the air, but that is another matter. The Germans made the most of theirs by consistently employing anti-aircraft guns as dual purpose weapons, for ground as well as anti-aircraft fire. This applied not only to their 88 mm. guns, which became famous as anti-tank weapons, but also to the 20 mm. automatic cannon which formed the original equipment of the German anti-aircraft battalions. Many others, during or since the Second World War, have been equipped with 37 or 40 mm. anti-aircraft guns.

In addition to their various artillery units, practically all armoured divisions have had an engineer unit of battalion size. Its principal tasks have been to remove obstacles and clear mines in the path of advance of an armoured formation and the construction of crossings and bridges ; during retrograde movement the principal task has been the laying of minefields and the carrying out of demolitions. In addition, engineer units have also played an important part in attacks against prepared positions.

All armoured formations have also had a signals unit of company or battalion size for radio and telephone communication within the formation and between it and others. It functions mainly for the benefit of the armoured formation headquarters, for subordinate units have their own organic means of communication.

Another unit which operates chiefly for the benefit of the formation commander and the formation as a whole is the reconnaissance battalion, or its equivalent. This, generally, has been a mixed unit composed of armoured fighting vehicles and elements for dismounted reconnaissance. Frequently its principal armoured vehicles have been armoured cars and its other vehicles wheeled also ; less frequently it has been equipped with tanks and other tracked vehicles. In the former case, under favourable conditions, reconnaissance units have had a considerable margin of superior mobility over the rest of the armoured formation but, due to lack of suitable wheeled reconnaissance vehicles, frequently have been road bound. In the latter case they had adequate off-the-road performance but lacked a sufficient margin of mobility over the other units to fulfil their role of medium distance reconnaissance and other tasks, such as screening.

Reconnaissance units and divisional headquarters complete the list of principal elements which have made armoured formations self-sufficient tactically. But even with this variety of units an armoured formation would still be incapable of independent operation.

To be able to operate independently an armoured formation must be self-contained administratively as well as tactically or, in other words, it requires its own service echelon. In the main, this is made up of 3 types of units : medical, supply or quartermaster, and workshop or maintenance. The first is responsible for collecting and evacuating casualties and surgical attention for the wounded ; the second, in the main, consists of transport units or columns which handle the supply of ammunition, fuel, food and other necessities ; the third provides spare parts and deals with major repairs of vehicles and other equipment. For an armoured formation the size of a brigade the personnel and vehicle requirements of the service functions would amount to a battalion and would most advantageously be grouped together in one. In the case of an armoured division the requirements of the 3 main functions would each amount to a battalion.

The service echelon is apt to be the target for criticism because of the numbers of non-fighting personnel and road-bound transport vehicles which it adds to armoured formations. As it is an "overhead" on the fighting units, economies in it are highly desirable and in some instances possible, even without any revolutionary changes in methods or equipment, particularly when one compares the smaller service echelon of the recent Soviet armoured formations with those of the West. Improvements are also possible in its transport equipment, as they are indeed with most other units of the armoured formations. For instance, the replacement of the road-bound trucks, which have and still form the majority of the vehicles of the armoured formations, by cross-country wheeled or tracked vehicles would remove the disparity which exists between service units and the fighting vehicles and much of the criticism that they form a drag on the mobility of the tank units. A more extensive use of helicopters and other suitable aircraft is another possible contribution towards the solution of the same problem.

In general, however, the desired and desirable economies in the size of the service echelon are to be sought not in itself as much as the armoured formations as a whole, for its size is basically a function of the ammunition, fuel and maintenance requirements of their fighting units and the needs of the total number of personnel which they contain. Were it possible to reduce any of these requirements—that for fuel, for instance, by having lighter and more efficient tanks—the service echelon could immediately be substantially reduced.

But, however reduced or transformed, the service echelon must remain, for without it armoured forces could not operate for long, if at all. Their vehicles, for instance, cannot achieve absolute reliability : however well built, they will fail in different ways and will require quick repair if they are not to become a total loss. The ability to put back into service damaged or broken down vehicles can make a major contribution to the effective strength of an armoured formation and it was the relative lead in this field which the Germans possessed during the early part of the Second World War which contributed substantially to their success in France in 1940 and in Russia in the summer of 1941.

Thus, in more ways than one, the service echelon completes the basic elements from which armoured forces are built. The list of the individual elements being complete, the way is open to consider armoured forces as a whole and, in particular, the important combination of the various elements in the form of armoured formations to which the next 6 chapters are largely devoted.

5

British Armoured Formations

THE first to build tanks, Britain was also the first to create tank units. The decision to form the first Tank Detachment was taken in February 1916, and in June of the same year the organisation of what was called the Heavy Section, Machine-gun Corps, was fixed at 6 companies each of 25 tanks. Towards the end of 1916, the companies were expanded into battalions and from the beginning of 1917 battalions were grouped into brigades. Each battalion consisted of 3 tank companies, and from the beginning of 1917, after a few changes, the strength of the predominant, heavy tank battalions settled down to 36 tanks per battalion, while others, equipped with medium tanks, had 48 tanks ; brigades usually consisted of 3 tank battalions.

Such was the organisation with which the Tank Corps, created as such in July 1917, fought in the majority of its actions. The brigades were administrative rather than tactical units and tanks usually fought by companies or battalions subordinated to the infantry formations for which they were opening the way through enemy wire and entrenchments. Even at Cambrai or Amiens, where 3 brigades were concentrated, tank units were distributed by battalions to infantry divisions or brigades with which they co-operated.

The methods and organisation of the tank units of 1917 and 1918 set a pattern which has been repeated several times in the employment of tank units in conjunction with infantry formations. However, immediately after the war, in 1919, Colonel J. F. C. Fuller, who had been Chief of Staff of the Tank Corps and who became the leading exponent of tanks, submitted a memorandum proposing a somewhat different approach. His idea was that the future employment of tanks

55

should be within the framework of reorganised infantry divisions. In particular, he suggested that infantry battalions be reorganised on the basis of 2 companies of pioneer-riflemen, one of machine-guns and one of tanks and that one such New Model Battalion be formed to carry out practical trials. The War Office accepted the proposals in rough but nothing was done about them, except for the formation, on a temporary basis, of an Experimental Brigade in 1921 and again in 1922. The brigade consisted of 4 infantry and one tank battalions and through inept handling accomplished nothing.

In 1922, another and even farther-reaching proposal was made by Captain B. H. Liddell Hart, for a New Model Division. This was, in effect, a large armoured division consisting of 3 composite mechanised brigades, each with one heavy and one light tank battalions, 3 small infantry battalions in armoured carriers and mechanised artillery. There was also to be a divisional tank battalion bringing the total of tanks per division to 300.

As it happened, this was about twice as much as the total post-war tank strength. It was only in 1923, after 4 years of uncertainty and wrangling, that the Royal Tank Corps was placed on a permanent footing with a total strength of 4 tank battalions and some independent armoured car companies. The recognition of tanks as a separate arm won them a degree of freedom for further development but, as during the war, tank battalions remained for several years as the largest tactical units.

It was only in 1926 that it was decided to proceed beyond the level of tank battalions and to form a larger mechanised force. This came into being on May 1, 1927, on Salisbury Plain, under the name of Experimental Mechanised Force. It consisted of a reconnaissance group of tankettes and armoured cars, a battalion of 48 Vickers medium tanks, a motorised machine-gun battalion, the equivalent of an artillery regiment, also motorised but containing some self-propelled guns, and an engineer company. It was the first mechanised force capable of independent operation and it opened the way for the subsequent development of armoured divisions and other mechanised formations. But its own life was short, for in 1928, after being renamed the Armoured Force, it was disbanded and superseded by different ideas.

By 1927–28 General Fuller, who was still the leading apostle of mechanised warfare, had veered towards the idea of armoured forces consisting almost entirely of tanks and the " all-tank " trend had already begun to exercise a powerful influence. It was foreshadowed in 1916 by Major (later General) G. le Q. Martel in one of the very first papers on the organisation of armoured forces and was inspired by the " landship " concept of the tank, a concept which visualised the tank as the direct equivalent of the warship and land warfare in terms of tank fleets. After a time the " landship " concept, as such, went out of fashion but the " all-tank " trend remained, inspired not only by overestimates of what the tank could do on its own but also by a desire to exploit to the utmost the mobility of tank units. The necessity of combining tanks with other arms was not recognised and the attachment of other elements was considered to be an unjustified drag on the tank units.

The experiments of 1927 and 1928 emphasised the difficulty of combining tanks with other arms and their result, combined with the theoretical predilection for the " all-tank" ideas and the associated preoccupation with mobility, led to the conception that armoured forces should be composed largely, if not entirely, of tanks. Units of other arms, such as infantry, artillery or engineers, were not to be permanently combined with tanks but would only be attached to large tank units if or when required.

Thus, after the Armoured Force was broken up in 1928, further experiments, which were resumed in 1931, were based on tanks alone. The 1st Tank Brigade, which was formed on a provisional basis in 1931, consisted of one light and 3 mixed— light and medium—tank battalions and development continued on that basis until 1934, when the brigade was made permanent. In parallel with this, the first armoured force manual, issued in

1929 under the title *Mechanised and Armoured Formations*, spoke in terms of tank brigades as the basic operational armoured units.

This concentration on tanks alone certainly speeded up the development of mobile armoured technique. But the concentration was in part only possible because the tank leaders, in their desire to exploit the newly found mobility, placed greater emphasis on strategic manoeuvring than tactical performance. In consequence, it was possible for the armoured forces to revive the mobile roles which horse cavalry could no longer perform. But, through the neglect of tactical problems and of the need to supplement tanks with other arms, armoured formations were deprived of much of their potential versatility and usefulness.

The resulting trend towards limited roles for the armoured formations was further strengthened by a decision to mechanise the cavalry and combine the mobile tank units, that is units of the Royal Tank Corps which were not assigned to close infantry support, with it. In fact, in the first Mobile Division, which was proposed in 1935 and which was actually formed in 1938, mechanised cavalry predominated. Thus, the Division was looked upon as a successor to the cavalry divisions and its role was similar to that to which horse cavalry had been reduced towards the end of the nineteenth century, that is mainly the limited role of strategic reconnaissance.

A further outcome of the limited cavalry role prescribed for the mechanised or armoured formations was the division of the available tank strength into two categories, the second of which consisted of tank units for co-operation with the main body of the army in battle. In other words, specialised infantry tank units whose development began in 1934. These units were subsequently organised into Army Tank Brigades, each of 3 infantry tank battalions, which were allotted to infantry formations in a manner similar to the employment of tank brigades and battalions in the First World War.

As for the Mobile Division, its organisation consisted of one tank brigade with one light and 2 mixed, light-medium tank battalions, 2 mechanised cavalry brigades each with 3 regiments—each equivalent to a light tank battalion—2 small artillery regiments and 2 motorised rifle battalions. With its total of 9 tank battalions and some 600 tanks, mainly light, it was a badly balanced organisation : there were far too many tank units and far too many light tanks in relation to its size and its other troops.

Some of the shortcomings of the Mobile Division were corrected in 1939, when its name was changed to that of Armoured Division and all its tank units of battalion size were called Armoured Regiments. The new organisation comprised only 2 armoured brigades : one, the Light Armoured Brigade, consisted of 3 light regiments equipped with medium or cruiser tanks and light tanks ; the other, the Heavy Armoured Brigade, consisted of 3 heavy armoured regiments with cruiser tanks only. Altogether the 2 brigades had a total of 213 cruiser tanks and 108 light tanks, or 321 tanks for the division. At the same time, divisional troops were reduced in strength and concentrated into a Support Group consisting of one motorised rifle battalion, one small 16-gun motorised artillery regiment and an engineer company. As a result, although the number of armoured regiments or tank battalions was reduced from 9 to 6, the ratio of infantry to tanks became even worse because there was now only one rifle battalion to 6 tank battalions, instead of the original ratio of 2 to 9.

The proportion of infantry to tanks was improved somewhat in the early part of 1940, when a second rifle battalion and a mixed anti-tank/anti-aircraft regiment were added to the Support Group. Simultaneously, the distinction between the 2 armoured brigades was abandoned and each was reorganised on the basis of 3 armoured regiments with cruiser tanks.

A far greater change came about in the second half of 1940, after the French campaign. A divisional armoured car regiment (battalion) was added for reconnaissance and the mixed anti-tank/anti-aircraft regiment was replaced by 2 separate regiments, one of thirty-six 40 mm. 2-pounder anti-tank guns and one of 40 mm. Bofors anti-aircraft guns. The Support

Group lost one of its 2 rifle battalions but one rifle battalion was added to each armoured brigade, so that the total number of infantry battalions per division rose to 3 against 6 tank battalions.

The lessons of the 1940 French campaign and the example of the victorious German armoured divisions went much farther, however, than an increase in the proportion of the infantry. The pre-war plans, which consigned more tanks to infantry support and comprised only 3 armoured divisions, were drastically revised. The sights were raised to 9 armoured divisions and the long-term plans grew to almost double that figure. And, what was even more important, armoured divisions were finally recognised as versatile fighting formations and fought as such from the first Libyan campaign of the winter of 1940–41 to the battle of El Alamein, in October 1942, where, for the first time, as many as 3 British armoured divisions were used.

By this time the organisation was even more similar to that of the German armoured divisions, as a result of a new organisation introduced in 1942. There was still the armoured car regiment and one armoured brigade organised as before, but the second armoured brigade was replaced by a 3-battalion motorised infantry brigade. The Support Group also disappeared, all the artillery, increased to 4 regiments by the addition of a second 24-gun field artillery regiment with towed 87.6 mm. 25-pounders, being placed directly under divisional control.

As a result of these changes the total number of tanks per division dropped to 188 from the 368 which, with anti-aircraft tanks, it had in 1941. Moreover, the number of infantry battalions for the first time exceeded that of tank battalions, as there were now 4 of the former against 3 of the latter per division. This increase in the infantry strength was inspired partly by the example of the German armoured divisions and partly by the more difficult conditions envisaged in the next theatre of operations, on the continent of Europe. The latter consideration, together with improvements in anti-tank defence and a reaction from the favourable conditions of the Libyan desert produced some weakening of faith in the fighting power of armoured formations. The number of armoured divisions was allowed to decline, from the total of 11 which were actually raised to only 5, while that of armoured units for infantry support increased. At the same time the old and once discredited concept of the limited role of armoured formations appeared again. Thus, on the eve of the invasion of Europe, a War Office manual once again proclaimed that armoured divisions were only " designed for exploitation."

Actually, once they landed in Normandy, British armoured divisions participated effectively in winning a decision, as well as exploiting the break out of the bridgehead in the drive across France and North-east Europe. The only effect of the erroneous theories about the limited role of armour was to handicap the armoured divisions by the bias in their training and by the inadequate armament of their tanks designed on the principles of the exploitation role and of under-gunned mobility.

The 1944-45 organisation was basically the same as that introduced in 1942. However, the armoured car regiment was replaced by an armoured reconnaissance regiment equipped with fast Cromwell cruiser tanks and one of the 2 artillery regiments was self-propelled, as was part of the anti-tank regiment. Including anti-aircraft, but excluding bridging tanks, an armoured division of this period had a total of 365 tanks.

The same basic organisation was retained after the war but again with a number of modifications and additions. The reconnaissance role was again taken over by an armoured car regiment and the armoured brigade was given a fourth armoured regiment, each having 57 tanks. A little later a fourth infantry battalion was added to the truck-borne infantry brigade, thus making a total of 5 infantry battalions to 4 armoured regiments per division. In addition, both artillery regiments and the anti-tank regiment were self-propelled, although subsequently the latter, renamed the Divisional

Regiment Royal Armoured Corps, was eliminated and the infantry brigade reverted to a total of 3 infantry battalions.

A greater change than in the organisation took place in the general outlook. After a period of post-war hesitation British armoured divisions were gradually accorded the importance they deserved as the most effective element in ground warfare and when, after the outbreak of the Korean war, British forces in Germany were strengthened, 3 of the 4 British divisions were armoured.

The 3 British armoured divisions represented for a time the most effective element of the NATO forces facing the Soviet ground forces, whose striking force consisted largely of armoured formations. Nevertheless, by the early fifties the organisation of these divisions left a good deal to be desired. For one thing, they had grown large and cumbersome. Their infantry, except for the organic battalion of the armoured brigade, was still carried in trucks of indifferent cross-country performance and had only limited capacity for close co-operation with tanks. And the artillery, with its 87.6 mm. gun-howitzers, was no longer in keeping with the increased gun power of tanks.

In view of all this, it was natural that a new type of organisation should have been introduced in 1955. Under it the size of the division was drastically reduced so that it came to consist of 4 armoured regiments, directly under divisional control, and one regiment or battalion each of armoured cars, infantry, medium artillery and engineers.

Many of the changes introduced with the 1955-56 organisation were undoubtedly beneficial. They included the overall reduction in size, the reduction in the number of headquarters and the replacement of the light artillery by a smaller number of larger calibre units. But this could not be said of the wholesale reduction of the divisional infantry and the return to the " all-tank " ideas. There was now only one infantry battalion to 4 armoured regiments whereas experience and logic showed that the ratio should be close to one to one.

Even more unfortunate was the tendency to restrict

armoured divisions once again to the limited role of exploitation. In fact, the limited role of armoured divisions was officially proclaimed in the 1956–57 Army Estimates. This ran counter to all the experience in the employment of armoured forces during the previous 17 years, just as the organisation of the 1956 British armoured division ran counter to many trends in the evolution of armoured formations. In fact, the policy towards armour could only be described as regressive and one which was in danger of bringing the armoured divisions back to where they started in the thirties. Or even worse, for one of the 3 British armoured divisions in Germany was broken up in 1956 and its tank units dispersed among the infantry, thus putting the clock right back to the days when tanks were a mere auxiliary to the infantry.

In the early part of 1957 British armoured divisions, as such, began to disappear altogether. But so did the infantry divisions. Their place, as the largest permanent units, has been taken respectively by armoured and infantry brigade groups. However, the change has affected armour far less than might at first appear. In fact, the 1957 armoured brigade group differs little from the small 1956 division. Basically it consists of 3 armoured regiments, one rifle battalion in armoured carriers and one artillery regiment with American-built 155 mm. self-propelled howitzers.

In general, much the same criticism applies to the 1957 armoured brigade group as to its immediate predecessor, both with regard to its organisation, inclined towards the " all-tank " principles, and its intended limited method of employment. One can only hope that it represents no more than an unfortunate but passing phase and that it will be replaced by an organisation more in keeping with the latest conditions and trends, and also that British armoured formations will be restored to their rightful place as an effective and versatile component of the ground forces.

6

French Armoured Formations

FRENCH armoured units started their life in 1916 as assault artillery and were at first designated and used as such. The original basic unit was a *groupe* of 4 batteries each of 4 tanks ; the largest unit was a *groupement* of 3 or 4 *groupes*. By the end of the First World War, however, with the appearance of the Renault light tank, the role changed to that of an accompanying weapon for the infantry. The organisation changed also : the light tanks were organised into battalions and later regiments, each battalion having 3 companies of 25 Renault F.T.

After the war the infantry support role became embodied in the official doctrine, although in the immediate post-war period General Estienne, the father of French tanks, propagated the idea of mechanised field forces based on tanks. In 1920 tanks became an integral part of the infantry, which continued to look at them as an auxiliary weapon right up to the disaster of 1940, when the majority of French tanks were still held in independent light tank battalions intended for close infantry support.

Thus, although tanks were officially assigned to the infantry, it was in the French cavalry that they first found wider scope for employment. The cavalry's interest was at first confined to armoured cars, which became associated with it during the First World War. The first few were used in 1914, and in 1917 each French cavalry division was assigned a group of 18 armoured cars, intended to act as mobile fire support for the mounted units or, in defence, as mobile pill-boxes. After the war, in 1923, the number of armoured cars per division was doubled and motorisation slowly progressed to the stage where in 1930 one of the 3 horse brigades was replaced by a regiment of truck-borne *Dragons Portés*, the divisional artillery was partly motorised and 2 years later the group of 36 armoured cars was expanded into a regiment with 80 vehicles. Some of the latter were tanks but the *auto-mitrailleuse* designation was retained for them all to avoid the impression of poaching upon the infantry's official preserves.

By 1932, also, the idea of a unified armoured force began to emerge and in that year the first combined exercises took place of cavalry and infantry mechanised detachments. No armoured force resulted from them but the cavalry continued to persevere with its efforts. In the following year the elements of a completely motorised cavalry division were assembled at Reims and in 1934 this became officially the first *Division Légère Mécanique*, or D.L.M.

As it crystallised, the organisation of the D.L.M. consisted of a reconnaissance regiment with 2 squadrons of armoured cars and 2 of motor-cyclists, a tank brigade, a motorised rifle brigade, a towed artillery regiment and an engineer battalion, as well as the usual service units. The tank brigade consisted of 2 tank regiments, each with 80 tanks, and the rifle brigade of 3 battalions of *Dragons Portés*, each of which had its own integral company of 20 light tanks in addition to one motor-cycle rifle company, 2 rifle companies in light trucks and a heavy weapons company.

The D.L.M. was the first permanently organised mechanised formation of its type and organisationally it exhibited the principal characteristics of the armoured divisions of the following decade. However, unlike the latter, which were generally formed by the addition of an infantry brigade or regiment to an independent tank brigade, the D.L.M. was evolved by a slow mutation of the cavalry division in which the armoured car group gradually grew into the tank brigade. As such, the D.L.M. could not help but retain many of the characteristics of the horse cavalry division. In particular, its operational role remained largely the cavalry role of strategic reconnaissance and security.

A few urged the adoption of a more positive and offensive role for the D.L.M., but with little effect. By 1938 a second

division was in existence and in May 1940 there were 3 with a
fourth in the process of organisation. The first 3 were used in
their textbook role of a strategic advance guard to the Franco-
British armies moving into Belgium and found themselves
pitted against the advancing German panzer corps which
proved greatly superior, principally in the co-ordinated offensive employment of their units. That this should be so is not
altogether surprising for the D.L.M. was not, unfortunately,
thought of in terms of mechanised warfare but still in terms of
the limited roles of horse cavalry. It was this outdated
doctrine, out of keeping with the potentialities of mechanised
forces and the organisational lead, which largely prevented the
D.L.M. from playing a more important role.

A further result of the outlook which limited the role of
the D.L.M. was the existence of another type of armoured
formation, the infantry's *Division Cuirassée*.

Although for 20 years the French infantry viewed its tanks
principally as accompanying weapons, it did recognise another
role for them, namely, that of *chars de manoeuvre d'ensemble*.
This implied a more concentrated use of tanks at the higher
level of division or corps, along the main line of effort of the
supported infantry formation. Only the more powerful tanks
were envisaged for this role and, in particular, the 75 mm. gun
" battle-tanks " to which General Estienne devoted much of
his energy and which eventually led to the type B heavy tank.

The need to group these tanks in bodies larger than
battalions and developments in other countries, particularly
Germany, where armoured divisions were already being
formed, led in the mid-thirties to the idea of forming armoured
divisions out of the *chars de manoeuvre d'ensemble*. The first
official thoughts were expressed in 1935 and took a more
concrete form in 1937–38 but it was only in September 1939
that 4 battalions of the type B heavy tanks then in existence
were formed into 2 *demi-brigades*, which together with two
newly formed battalions of motorised riflemen made up the
first *Division Cuirassée*, or D.C.R. as it was otherwise officially
known. Four months later the organisation was modified to

enable a second division to be formed by dividing some of the units between them. By May 1940, there were 3 D.C.R. with a fourth in the process of organisation.

The organisation by that time consisted of 2 *demi-brigades*, each with one battalion of 34 type B heavy tanks and one of 45 Hotchkiss light tanks, giving a total of 158 tanks, one battalion of motorised riflemen and two 12-gun *groupes* of motorised artillery. It was an unbalanced organisation with too high a proportion of tank to infantry units—the same, in fact, as that in the 1955 British armoured division where it too proved inadequate. Actually, the D.C.R. was meant to have 2 infantry battalions. In 1938, when the combination of different arms below divisional level had still not been much thought of, it was even proposed to allocate one rifle battalion to each *demi-brigade* and make the latter into a self-contained combat team. However, nothing was done about it in practice. It was left to the Germans to demonstrate with their improvised *Kampfgruppen* the advantages of operating in mixed sub-divisional tactical groups and to the Americans to incorporate this principle permanently into the organisation of armoured formations.

In action the shortcomings of the D.C.R. were not confined to their unbalanced organisation but even more were due to their recent formation. The latter meant that they went into action incompletely equipped and inadequately trained, especially in joint action under conditions of mobile warfare. The disadvantages of the D.C.R. in relation to the panzer divisions were thus greater than those of the D.L.M., whose basic organisation was similar to that of the contemporary panzer division and which had more time and opportunity for mobile formation training.

From almost every point of view the practical differences between the D.C.R. and the panzer divisions were thus very considerable and no less than from the point of view of the underlying ideas : the panzer division was a versatile mobile fighting formation while the D.C.R. represented principally a concentration of break-through infantry tanks. Equating the two together, as is occasionally done, is therefore quite wrong, as are close comparisons between the D.L.M. and the Panzer Grenadier Division, for the latter was essentially a motorised infantry formation while the former was a limited-role mechanised cavalry division.

In some ways, the two types of French divisions of 1940 may be regarded as having stood on either side of the contemporary panzer division, the D.L.M. leaning more towards mobility and limited combat functions and the D.C.R. towards greater striking power and limited operational mobility. Organisationally the D.L.M. was very similar to the panzer division and, therefore, on this score could prove nothing. The D.C.R. demonstrated the shortcomings of the unbalanced " all-tank " type of formation but both showed even more clearly the shortcomings of the operational doctrine of limited, specialised roles.

No direct use was, of course, ever made by the French Army of the lessons of 1940. When it was reborn in the latter part of the Second World War its armoured formations, renamed *Divisions Blindées*, were organised and equipped on American lines. In contrast to its 1940 predecessors, the operational doctrine of the *Division Blindée*, or D.B., was not much different from that of the panzer division and being modelled on the 1944 American armoured division it now had a more advanced form of divisional organisation.

Thus, each of the 3 D.B. of 1944-45 had 3 combat commands, each normally composed of one regiment or battalion of American-built M4 medium tanks, one infantry battalion and one group of self-propelled 105 mm. howitzers. In addition, each division had an engineer battalion, a regiment of M10 tank destroyers and a reconnaissance regiment with M8 armoured cars and M5 light tanks.

This organisation was the best of the various types developed up to the end of the Second World War and it was retained after the war, with minor modifications, mainly in equipment. In particular, in the early fifties, the tank destroyer regiment was replaced by a regiment of American-built M46 medium tanks and the reconnaissance regiment was re-equipped with M24 and A.M.X. light tanks. However, good as it was, the 1944-45 type of formation had a number of weaknesses. For one, in common with all the other armoured formations of the period, it was relatively large and heavy. By the late forties these points began to weigh heavily against it and the French General Staff began to search actively for a lighter and more mobile type of mechanised formation, first under the stimulus of the atom bomb and tactical air power and then of tactical nuclear weapons.

The first step towards the realisation of the new type of formation was taken during the Champagne manoeuvres of 1950. Apart from greater mobility and reduced logistical requirements considerable emphasis was also placed on the anti-tank capabilities of the new formation, in view of the utmost importance of that problem to the NATO forces, and the experimental *Division Mobile* was even described by some observers as an anti-tank division.

The Champagne manoeuvres were not an unqualified success, due largely to the lack of suitable equipment. The lightweight and highly mobile vehicles which were envisaged for the new mobile formation were not available and the obsolescent vehicles of Second World War vintage, such as American-built M4 and German Panther medium tanks, which had to be used, were simply not up to it. In 1953 and 1954, however, new French-built E.B.R. 8-wheeled armoured reconnaissance vehicles and the A.M.X. 13-ton tanks began to arrive and the experiments were resumed under the code name " Javelot." At first they were conducted by a *demi-brigade* composed of 2 squadrons of E.B.R. and 2 squadrons of A.M.X. tanks but by the autumn of 1954 they had progressed to the stage where an experimental " Javelot " brigade was formed and took part in French Army manoeuvres in Germany.

Important as it was from the point of view of marking a further positive step in the development, the importance of the " Javelot " brigade was second to that of its constituent parts. These fell into two main categories : one consisted of a highly mobile reconnaissance regiment equipped with E.B.R. and designed to cover the wide front of a mobile formation operating over a future battlefield ; the other was represented by the fighting element of the brigade in the shape of 2 *Régiments Inter-armes*, or R.I.A.

The R.I.A. represented the most novel and interesting part of the new organisation. Each consisted of a headquarters squadron, a reconnaissance squadron equipped with jeeps, 2 squadrons of A.M.X. tanks, 2 rifle companies and a battery of 120 mm. heavy mortars. The R.I.A. combined, therefore, riflemen with tanks and other heavy weapons at battalion level to form a self-sufficient battalion-size battle group.

This type of mixed, integrated or, as the French call it, heterogeneous, unit is still something new but it is not unexpected either from the point of view of the general trend in the organisation of armoured forces nor from the point of view of the development of French armour. For instance, in the early days of the *artillerie d'assaut* each group of 16 tanks had attached to it a company of specially trained *infanterie d'accompagnement* to act as assault pioneers and to provide close-in protection, while in the thirties battalions of the *Dragons Portés* had their organic tank companies. Forty years later the need for riflemen to support and complement tanks was as great as it was in 1917, while the development of the infantry has shown clearly the need for mobile heavy weapons within the framework of the smallest rifle units, a need which tanks can best meet.

The *Régiments Inter-armes* may thus be regarded as the logical outcome of both the trends in the evolution of armoured forces and of the combat experience of the infantry. From the purely traditional point of view it is easy to criticise it as being neither a tank battalion nor an infantry one. But this is precisely what the R.I.A. set out to do and it cannot be like either if it is to be an advance on both. The aim of the R.I.A. has been to produce a relatively small self-contained basic unit possessing a high degree of mobility and considerable striking power, to suit probable future conditions, and this it has largely achieved.

In 1955 the R.I.A. emerged from the experimental stage and were permanently incorporated into a new type of armoured formation, the *Division Mécanique Rapide*, or D.M.R., which superseded the experimental " Javelot " brigade. The new division did not, however, represent a complete acceptance of the new ideas embodied in the R.I.A. Its organisation was, in fact, a mixture of the old with the new : in addition to the E.B.R. armoured car reconnaissance regiment and 2 R.I.A. the division contained an infantry regiment and a battalion or its equivalent of engineers, self-propelled 105 mm. howitzers and anti-aircraft guns. The existence of these homogeneous units side by side with the R.I.A. showed that the principle of integration at battalion level still had to be fully accepted and the peculiar organisation of the D.M.R. represented, in effect, a stage of transition.

7

German Armoured Formations

In many ways, the importance of armoured forces only dates from the rise, during the thirties, of the German *Panzerwaffe*. This may seem incongruous in view of the fact that the Germans were well behind in the early application of the tank and that they were by no means the first to conceive the idea of mechanised forces. But where they proved ahead of others was in welding together the various elements necessary to form an effective armoured force and in exploiting to the full its combination of striking power and mobility.

A large share of the credit for this and for the consequent rise in the importance of armoured forces is due to General Heinz Guderian. It was he who in the twenties visualised armoured or panzer divisions as a decisive element of the German Army and it was he who largely guided their development. As others before him, he visualised armoured forces as based on tanks but—and this is where he differed from most—tanks in effective combination with other arms. Thus, the policy adopted in Germany differed both from the concept of tanks working on their own, the " all-tank " theory which prevailed in Britain, and from the doctrine of tying tanks to the infantry, of which France was the leading exponent. Moreover, panzer divisions were visualised as effective, versatile fighting formations and not merely as mechanised units for exploitation or some other limited role.

On the face of it, however, the first 3 panzer divisions, created in October 1935, did not differ much from some other contemporary developments. Each was based on a tank brigade backed by an infantry brigade, a type of organisation adopted a year earlier by the French *Division Légère Mécanique* and also tried, albeit very briefly, during the 1934 British manoeuvres.

The tank brigade, established in Britain over a period of years as the basic and largest tank unit, was the basis of the panzer division. It consisted of 2 tank regiments, each with 2 tank battalions : each battalion had 4 companies of 32 Pz. Kpfw.I light tanks, which, together with command tanks, gave a nominal total of 561 tanks for the brigade. This represented a very powerful tank component, sufficient to satisfy the most ardent tank enthusiasts.

But, as well as having the tank brigade, each panzer division also had from the very beginning a motorised infantry brigade whose role was to support and complement the tanks. The infantry, or rifle, brigade consisted of one 2-battalion truck-borne regiment and of one motor-cycle battalion. Each division also had a motorised artillery regiment with twenty-four 105 mm. howitzers, an anti-tank battalion of towed 37 mm. guns and an engineer company—quickly expanded into a battalion. There was also a reconnaissance battalion of armoured cars and motor-cyclists, as well as signal and divisional service units. The panzer division was thus a self-contained combined arms team in which tanks were backed by other arms brought up, as far as possible, to the tanks' standards of mobility.

These remained the principal characteristics of the panzer divisions throughout their existence. As time went on, how-ever, their organisation and equipment changed considerably.

One of the first changes was an increase in the infantry strength. Peacetime manoeuvres showed that 3 battalions per division were not enough and, therefore, it was decided to add a fourth. Thus, the next 3 panzer divisions, the 4th, 5th and 10th, created in 1938 and 1939, had a rifle brigade with two 2-battalion regiments while in the first 3 divisions the motorised rifle regiment was expanded from 2 to 3 battalions.

Then, on mobilisation, the actual tank strength of each division was considerably less than the original nominal total : tank battalions were reorganised into one medium and 2 light tank companies and the fourth company of each battalion became a depot and replacement unit. As a result, on the outbreak of the Second World War each division had about 320 tanks and the proportion of tanks to infantry became 12 tank companies to 12 rifle companies, instead of the original ratio of 16 to 9.

The modified organisation held good for the first 6 panzer divisions up to and including the French campaign of 1940. But 4 more divisions which were created by then differed considerably both in their organisation and their origin from the 6 created under the aegis of the Inspectorate of Armoured Troops. In fact, the 4 new divisions were the outcome of an independent development initiated by the German cavalry, as part of its own programme of motorisation. The development started in 1937, with the creation of the 1st Light Brigade, a fully motorised formation intended for the established cavalry role of strategic reconnaissance and security. A year later the brigade was expanded into a division and 3 more light divisions were created.

In essence, the light divisions were small motorised infantry formations. Their organisation, like that of the panzer divisions, varied somewhat but their principal elements consisted of 4 motorised rifle battalions and one tank battalion with a nominal strength of about 90 Pz.Kpfw.II light tanks ; reconnaissance, artillery, engineer and other units were similar to those of the panzer divisions. Otherwise, the chief characteristic of the light divisions was their strategic mobility. Thus, they had organic transporters for their tanks and, in keeping with their defensive screening role, their rifle companies had twice the normal allocation of machine-guns.

In 1938, on the formation of the Inspectorate of Mobile Troops under Guderian, the light divisions passed from the control of the cavalry and together with panzer divisions came under the new Inspectorate. Their role changed but they retained their identity until after the 1939 Polish campaign when they were transformed into the 6th, 7th, 8th and 9th Panzer Divisions. In the main, the reorganisation was confined to increasing their tank strength above the original, which was found to be inadequate. Each of the four divisions was now given a tank regiment, of 3 battalions in the case of 3 divisions and of 2 battalions only in the case of the other, the 9th Panzer Division.

Thus, on the eve of the 1940 French campaign there were 10 panzer divisions with a total of 35 tank battalions. Apart from tanks, each division had a rifle brigade, organised into one 3-battalion motorised regiment and one motor-cycle battalion or into two 2-battalion regiments, except for the 7th Panzer Division whose infantry strength had risen to 5 battalions. Other units of the divisions remained essentially unchanged.

After the French campaign, which firmly established armoured divisions as the decisive element in land warfare, a further reorganisation and expansion of the panzer forces took place. The number of panzer divisions was doubled but at the expense of the number of tank units per division. At the same time the strength of the infantry in each division was increased still further, partly to make up for the reduction in the number of tanks and partly to satisfy the usual demands for more of it. The actual order for the reorganisation was issued on September 10, 1940, and it antedated, therefore, by about two years similar reductions in the numbers of tanks and increases in the infantry strength of British and American armoured divisions.

The new organisation was put into effect before the 1941 Russian campaign. With it the 1941-type panzer division had only a single tank regiment : in the case of 6 divisions the tank regiment had 3 battalions but in all the others it contained only 2 battalions. Tank battalions themselves were organised into 2 light tank companies equipped principally with Pz. Kpfw.III 50 mm. gun tanks and one medium tank company with Pz.Kpfw.IV 75 mm. gun tanks, but there were also Pz.Kpfw.II light tanks, used chiefly for reconnaissance. The rifle brigade of each panzer division was reorganised on the lines already tried in the 7th Panzer Division, that is, with two 2-battalion motorised rifle regiments and one motor-cycle rifle battalion. Other changes included the addition of a third, medium artillery battalion with 150 mm. howitzers and 105 mm. guns and of an anti-aircraft battalion with some 88 mm. guns, which became famous as anti-tank weapons.

The principal effect of the 1940-41 reorganisation was to reduce the number and proportion of tanks. There were now only about 150 to 200 tanks per division and only 9 or 6 tank companies to 15 rifle companies, that is, a complete reversal of the original ratio. This was strongly criticised by the leading panzer commanders, who deplored the reduction in the tank strength of the individual divisions and who considered that the proportion of tanks to infantry was now quite inadequate. However, in view of the low rate of tank production in Germany at the time there was little that could be done about it. Forty-six tank battalions was all the Germans could muster for their 20 panzer divisions in 1941 and tank shortages continued to plague panzer units for the rest of the war. Of the 20 divisions, 19 were actually ready on the eve of the invasion of Russia and 17 were committed in the initial attack, concentrated in 4 panzer groups or armies.

The Russian campaign of 1941 took a heavy toll of the panzer divisions and affected seriously their strength, which began to be governed by losses and the availability of replacements as much as by their tables of organisation.

Thus, in preparation for the summer offensive of 1942, panzer divisions in the southern sector of the Eastern Front, where the main effort was concentrated, were re-equipped with 3 tank battalions, or about 170 tanks each. But those in the central and northern sectors received practically no replacements and as a rule had only 1—sometimes 2—weak tank battalions. In consequence, although the total number of panzer divisions rose further to 25, their effective strength varied considerably.

During 1942 several other changes also took place. The infantry strength was reduced somewhat with the disappearance of the motor-cycle rifle battalions which were amalgamated with the divisional reconnaissance battalions. The superfluous rifle brigade headquarters also disappeared and, like the tank regiment, the 2 rifle regiments came directly under divisional control. The designation of the rifle units was also changed, from *Schuetzen* to *Panzergrenadier*, and one of the 4 battalions in each division was by then equipped with half-track armoured personnel carriers.

The reduction in the strength of the infantry by one battalion was accompanied by a nominal increase in the strength of the tank battalions, from 3 to the original pre-war figure of 4 tank companies, except in the case of the heavy Tiger battalions which were then beginning to be formed and which retained the 3-company organisation. In practice, however, the tank strength of the panzer divisions varied considerably : tank companies commonly had less than the 22 Pz.Kpfw.III or IV, or the 10 Tigers, which they were supposed to have. Similarly, the number of tank companies per battalion varied, the increase to 4 not being immediate nor generally maintained.

In the case of the 2 panzer divisions sent in 1941 to Libya, to fight the British forces, the fourth companies arrived around May 1942. These divisions represented something of a special case, however, both on account of the long and vulnerable lines of communication and the freedom left to the commander on the spot—Rommel.

Originally, the troops sent to Libya, in February 1941, to help the Italians, consisted of one tank regiment with 2 battalions, 3 motorised machine-gun battalions, an artillery regiment with 2 battalions and a battalion each of anti-tank guns and engineers. This was clearly a group put together to meet the existing conditions. It was subsequently named the 5th Light Division, although the first 4 light divisions had already ceased to exist as such, and later still it became the 21st Panzer Division. The second panzer division in Africa, the 15th, which arrived later, had more or less a normal organisation with one 2-battalion tank regiment and two 2-battalion rifle regiments. Changes in the composition of the 2 divisions were, however, frequently made on the spot, so frequently in fact that in the end neither the command in Germany nor in Africa could find its way among them.

In 1943, following the heavy losses of yet another winter campaign and the return of Guderian to the scene as Inspector General of Armoured Troops, another reorganisation was contemplated. The losses in the Stalingrad operations were staggering but tank production was rising and in 1943 was almost double that of 1941, while that of the tank-like though turretless *Sturmgeschütz* and *Jagdpanzer* was rising even more rapidly.

Partly on the strength of the rising production figures and partly due to Guderian's firm conviction of the need to strengthen the tank core of the panzer divisions, the main change which was contemplated was an expansion of the tank regiments to 4 battalions. One of these was to be temporarily equipped with the turretless assault-guns which on the Russian plains were almost as good as turreted vehicles. Another battalion was to be equipped with Tiger heavy tanks which underlined the fact that panzer divisions were regarded as versatile fighting formations combining maximum striking power with mobility and not confined to a limited mobile role.

In addition to tanks a much more generous allocation of armoured personnel carriers was also contemplated, as was that of self-propelled guns for the divisional artillery, the first few self-propelled 105 and 150 mm. howitzers having appeared at the beginning of 1943.

However, in spite of the rising production figures, few of the proposed changes were put into effect. As a rule, from 1943 onwards, panzer divisions had no more than 2 tank battalions and only one of the 4 rifle battalions was equipped with armoured carriers. Similarly, only one of the 3 artillery battalions was self-propelled. In the summer of 1944 this was recognised as the official establishment and it may be taken as the " average " composition of army panzer divisions during the latter part of the Second World War.

There were, of course, exceptions to the rule. A few divisions, like the 10th Panzer in 1943, for instance, still had 3 tank battalions, including a Tiger battalion. In the spring of 1944 the " élite " *Grossdeutschland* Division even had 4, also including one Tiger battalion. This division and the *Panzer Lehr* also had a higher allocation of armoured carriers ; in fact, on the eve of the Allied landings in Normandy in 1944 the *Panzer Lehr* had all 4 of its panzer grenadier battalions equipped with half-track armoured carriers, as well as its engineer battalion, and the whole of its artillery was self-propelled. But even this favoured division only had 2 tank battalions, one of Panthers and one of Pz.Kpfw.IV, with a total of some 190 tanks. Other panzer divisions were by then similarly equipped with one Panther and one Pz.Kpfw.IV battalion but their total strength was seldom more than 170— usually far less. The adoption of homogeneous tank battalions equipped with one type of tank contrasted with the earlier practice of having mixed units but as late as mid-1944 the nominal strength of the battalions still stood at 4 tank companies of 22 tanks each. But, once again, the actual strength was in general considerably lower : Panther and Pz.Kpfw.IV battalions had no more than 3 tank companies whose nominal strength was reduced to 17 tanks and then, at the beginning of 1945, it was even dropped to 14 per company. As regards the turretless assault-guns and *Jagdpanzer*, in most cases one mixed battalion of them and towed anti-tank guns replaced the earlier all-towed anti-tank battalions.

Another exception to the rule were the panzer divisions which were formed by the conversion of panzer grenadier divisions which had 6 infantry battalions apiece. *Grossdeutschland* was one and the *Waffen-S.S.* panzer divisions were the others ; at their peak, in 1944, there were 8 S.S. panzer divisions against 25 army ones.

Panzer grenadier divisions started their life as motorised infantry divisions and, just as the light divisions represented the contribution of the cavalry to the development of motorisation and mechanisation, they represented the contribution of the infantry. The original pre-war motorised infantry division was a conventional 3-infantry regiment, or 9-rifle battalion, formation which had simply exchanged its horse traction, retained by other German infantry divisions to the end of the Second World War, for motor transport. After the 1939 Polish campaign the organisation of the motorised division was adjudged too heavy for its follow-up role and one of its infantry regiments was replaced by a motor-cycle rifle battalion. In this form the motorised divisions took part in the French and early Russian campaigns. By 1942, like the panzer divisions, they lost their motor-cycle battalions but in that year the divisions in the southern sector of the Eastern Front, though not elsewhere, received for the first time one tank battalion apiece.

In the following year this was extended to all motorised divisions, although some received an assault-gun battalion in lieu of the tank battalion. In June 1943 they were officially renamed Panzer Grenadier Divisions, the Panzer Grenadier designation having been already applied to the infantry of the panzer divisions. At about the same time the control of their regiments passed from the Infantry to the Inspectorate of Armoured Troops, which did not prevent Guderian from deploring the diversion of tank strength from the panzer divisions proper to the panzer grenadier divisions.

A further diversion occurred later in the same year on the formation of the first S.S. panzer divisions. Until then the *Waffen-S.S.* which originated with the armed branch of the National Socialist Party, had contented themselves with motorised infantry formations. But in 1943 the first S.S. panzer divisions were created by the transformation of some of the existing S.S. panzer grenadier divisions. In principle the only major difference between these formations and the army panzer divisions was the fact that their panzer grenadier regiments had 3, instead of 2, rifle battalions each. In practice, however, the S.S. divisions were considerably better off as regards equipment and replacements due to the political pressure which they could and did exercise and their strength was maintained much better than that of the army formations.

The existence of these formations with 6 rifle battalions each and the fact that on the Eastern Front army panzer divisions often had only one tank battalion and were thus no better off in this respect than panzer grenadier divisions resulted in demands for 3 battalion infantry regiments for the army panzer divisions also. Much of the demand was, however, attributable to the latter cause, that is the shortage of tanks. Generally, 4 panzer grenadier battalions per division were considered adequate and panzer commanders who looked beyond the immediate needs and problems emphasised the importance of increasing the tank strength of the divisions and not their infantry. Their principal aim throughout was to expand the panzer regiment of each division to 4 tank battalions.

The tank strength of the panzer divisions during the latter part of the Second World War was plainly inadequate. Not only were there no more than 8 tank companies to 12 rifle companies but the nominal—let alone actual—strength of the tank companies steadily declined, from 22 to 17, then to 14 or even 11 tanks.

Needless to say, the inadequate tank strength was a severe handicap to the panzer divisions. One of its results was an additional and in armoured formations unjustified load on their infantry units. In consequence, panzer grenadiers were burdened with all sorts of heavy weapons many of which could have been dispensed with to advantage by close integration of the rifle units with an adequate tank force.

How heavily armed the panzer grenadier units became is worth noting. The rifle companies of the original panzer divisions of 1935 were organised roughly on the same lines as the units of the contemporary German infantry formations, that is into 3 platoons with a total of 9 rifle sections and were armed with 9 belt-fed MG 34 light machine-guns. In addition to 3 rifle companies, each rifle battalion also had a machine-gun company with MG 34s on heavy mountings and 81 mm. mortars, and, unlike normal infantry battalions, a fifth company

with 37 mm. anti-tank guns and 75 mm. howitzers, as well as
a platoon of pioneers.

Both 37 and 75 mm. weapons were used throughout the
German infantry, which was among the first to acknowledge
that rifles and light machine-guns were insufficient by themselves for the needs of modern infantry combat and consequently equipped its units with a generous quantity of mortars,
anti-tank guns and infantry howitzers long before other armies
did.   In the normal infantry units, however, anti-tank guns
and howitzers were held in companies at regimental level
whereas in the panzer divisions the process was carried
farther and the same heavy weapons were distributed down to
battalion level.

This was only the beginning of the process of increasing
the use of heavy weapons and of their progressive decentralisation within panzer grenadier units.   By 1942, for instance, the
machine-gun companies were abolished and the machine-guns
on heavy mountings and 81 mm. mortars were redistributed
among rifle companies.   With the addition of these weapons
each rifle company had 22 machine-guns, 4 of them on heavy
mountings, and two 81 mm. mortars while each battalion
heavy weapon company had four 75 mm. howitzers and three
50 mm. anti-tank guns.   In addition, each 2-battalion panzer
grenadier regiment had a heavy gun company with six 150 mm.
self-propelled infantry howitzers.   By 1944 battalion heavy
weapon companies were rearmed with four 120 mm. mortars
and 75 mm. anti-tank guns and in those battalions which were
equipped with armoured half-tracks 75 mm. guns were issued
even down to companies.

The organic fire power of the panzer grenadier units was
thus formidable.   Not only regiments but even companies had
at their disposal an impressive array of weapons and were
quite capable of effective independent action on a limited scale.
This was important in itself but it had an even greater general
significance.   The increasing number of heavy weapons was a
clear indication of the need for them and of their growing
importance.   They were no longer a mere supplement or

support for the riflemen but the means by which an infantry action was actually decided. Their decentralisation was further in keeping with the German doctrine, and battlefield necessity, of providing the highest degree of self-sufficiency to even small units. This proved particularly important in mobile operations but later also in all forms of action over extended fronts, such as those in Russia, and in face of enemy air superiority.

In the latter stages of the war there were attempts to reverse the general trend, that is to relieve rifle companies and battalions of most of their heavy weapons by concentrating them in heavy weapon companies or even heavy weapon battalions. However, these attempts were dictated mainly by shortages of trained personnel and other contemporary difficulties. Although theoretically attractive, centralisation of heavy weapons was found to create serious difficulties in the way of close and rapid co-operation between them and riflemen, especially in the kind of mobile operations which panzer grenadier units had to carry out.

Nevertheless, rifle units of the panzer divisions could have been relieved of some, if not most, of their heavy weapons with advantage had there been more tanks, which could have taken over the role of many of these weapons far more efficiently. In fact, some of the panzer commanders were of the opinion that, had sufficient numbers of tanks and self-propelled guns been available, the rifle companies should be armed almost exclusively with the 7.92 mm. M.P. 44 assault rifle, a promising infantry weapon roughly half way between a sub-machine-gun and a conventional calibre rifle, which was copied after the war by the Soviet Army. The task of providing medium and heavy fire power would then have fallen entirely on tanks and other self-propelled heavy weapons which were better suited to it. But, as long as there were serious shortages of tanks and of armoured infantry carriers, the necessary combination and optimum results could not be achieved.

Similarly, shortages of tanks and armoured carriers hampered the development of the system of mixed battle groups, which the German panzer divisions introduced and, in spite of difficulties, used with considerable success. In many ways, the mixed battle groups, or *Kampfgruppen*, were an extension of the principles on which panzer divisions were founded. As the latter formed a combination of different arms at division level so the armoured battle group represented a combination of tanks, riflemen and guns at the level of smaller units, of brigade, regiment or battalion size.

Judiciously applied, the use of mixed battle groups enhanced the effectiveness and mobility of the panzer divisions and for a time gave them an advantage over the more rigid, and therefore slower, methods of their adversaries who confined co-operation between arms to the level of large units. It was also one generally better suited to the conditions of the modern battlefield than the employment of a whole division in one body, particularly in face of strong enemy air forces.

The Germans did not carry the system of mixed battle groups to its logical conclusion and did not refashion their divisional organisation in line with it. The only attempt to combine permanently different arms below division level, in the form of the independent panzer brigades which were created in the second half of 1944, was only an emergency measure and proved shortlived. Thus, it was left to the American armoured divisions to be the first to do it with their system of combat command tactical headquarters and self-contained battalions, which made possible rapid formation of mixed teams of tanks, armoured infantry and artillery.

Several years after the end of the Second World War, when the question of re-creating panzer divisions arose, the Germans adopted a modified form of the American organisation. The new panzer division was based on 2 combat command tactical headquarters and 3 battalions each of medium tanks and panzer grenadiers supported by self-propelled artillery. The general proportion of tanks and infantry were clearly those which long experience proved best but this time great stress was laid from the start on providing panzer grenadiers with suitable cross-country armoured carriers so that they could co-operate more effectively with tanks in mobile fighting teams. In general, the new panzer division, although derived in part from the organisation of the American armoured divisions, also represented further development of the ideas which the Germans themselves pioneered.

8

American Armoured Formations

UNLIKE its later, more original forms, the organisation of the first American armoured units raised during the First World War followed closely the pattern of the British Tank Corps. In view of the British lead and the experience already gained this was a very sensible move and in January 1918 it led to the creation of a British-type tank corps with brigades as its largest units. Each tank brigade was to consist of one battalion of British-type heavy tanks and 2 light battalions with French Renault-type tanks and a total of no less than 15 brigades was planned.

Only 3 tank battalions were in the field when the Armistice of 1918 intervened, however, and shortly after the war the independent Tank Corps was abolished. Under the 1920 National Defence Act tanks became an integral and subsidiary part of the infantry, as they did at about the same time in France. The infantry organised them into 2 tank regiments with light and heavy tanks and 7 divisional light tank companies which were retained until the late thirties when the infantry tank units were reorganised into 6 independent battalions. Similarly, the role assigned by the infantry to its tanks remained static for many years. It was principally the infantry-accompanying role, very similar to that of the French *chars d'accompagnement*, although for a time a second, or " leading," role was also recognised for the more powerful tanks which corresponded roughly to the French *chars de manoeuvre d'ensemble*.

Under these circumstances little progress could take place either towards a more mobile employment of tanks or in organisation and it was almost inevitable that the impetus for new developments would come from elsewhere, as it did. In

1927 the then Secretary of War, D. Davis, witnessed the manoeuvres of the first British Experimental Mechanised Force and on his return gave instructions for the setting up of a similar force in the United States. This was done in 1928, when a mixed brigade-size force was assembled at Fort Meade, Maryland. It consisted of one battalion each of heavy and light tanks, one battalion of infantry and one of artillery, as well as smaller units. It did not prove a success, however, due partly to its unsuitable, obsolete equipment and after 3 months it was disbanded.

Two years later, in 1930, the experiment was resumed at Fort Eustis, Virginia, where a second Mechanised Force was assembled. It was smaller than the first, being roughly of regimental strength, but again it was mixed, consisting of tank and infantry, as well as cavalry armoured car and artillery detachments. The second force proved to be longer lived and was not disbanded until 1932, by which time the development of mobile mechanised forces was assigned to the cavalry. A part of the Fort Eustis force became the nucleus of a mechanised cavalry unit organised at Fort Knox, Kentucky, where it was absorbed in 1933 into the 1st Cavalry Regiment, Mechanised.

From this there gradually grew a mechanised cavalry brigade, the 7th Cavalry Brigade (Mechanised), which was called into being in 1932, but which did not become effective until the late thirties. By 1939, however, the brigade was complete. It consisted of 2 mechanised cavalry regiments, which were, in effect, light tank battalions, with a total of 112 light tanks and a small motorised artillery regiment with 75 mm. howitzers.

The role envisaged at the time for the brigade was a mechanised form of the traditional and limited cavalry role of exploitation, raids on enemy flanks and rear and so on. This narrow outlook on the role of mechanised forces was not, fortunately, destined to remain in force for long, particularly under the impact of the successes of the German panzer divisions. The decisive role which the latter played in France

showed convincingly the value of armoured forces as the
spearhead of modern armies and the 1940 French campaign
was barely over when the United States Armoured Force was
created. The Armoured Force put an end to the earlier
division of tanks between the infantry support units and the
mechanised cavalry and, like the German *Panzerwaffe*, it was
visualised by its founders as the decisive arm in land warfare.
Its principal element were to be armoured divisions, versatile
fighting formations made up of all arms, like the panzer
divisions.

Some steps towards the organisation of the armoured
divisions had already been taken before the creation of the
Armoured Force. During the 1940 spring manoeuvres in
Louisiana the expanded 7th Cavalry Brigade had attached to
it an infantry regiment carried in trucks. Various shortcomings
were found in this first joint employment of armoured units
and motorised infantry, including the need for half-track
personnel carriers and howitzers to support the infantry units.
Nevertheless, the combination formed an acceptable basis for
an armoured division and it became one when the first 2
armoured divisions were called into being in July 1940, the 7th
Cavalry Brigade becoming the 1st Armoured Brigade of the
1st Armoured Division.

As originally organised, the armoured divisions consisted
of a reconnaissance battalion, an armoured brigade, a 2-
battalion infantry regiment, an artillery battalion with 105 mm.
howitzers, an engineer battalion and service units. The
armoured brigade itself, which was the main element of each
division, consisted of 2 light tank regiments each with 3
battalions of M3 light tanks, one medium tank regiment with
2 battalions of M3 medium tanks and one artillery regiment
with 2 battalions of self-propelled 105 mm. howitzers.
Altogether the division had 108 medium tanks and 273 light
tanks.

Basically, the organisation of the original American
armoured division with its armoured brigade and a supporting
infantry regiment was similar to that of the original German

panzer division. The influence of the latter was unquestionable but the American armoured division also showed several original features, as well as the influence of the earlier mechanised cavalry brigade organisation, and thereafter it evolved along increasingly independent and original lines.

The original divisional organisation was tried during the 1941 manoeuvres and, not unexpectedly, a number of defects was noted. The chief was a lack of balance due to the large number of tank units relative to other arms : there were no less than 25 tank companies and only 7 rifle companies, illustrating an underestimate of the importance of infantry common to most early armoured formations. There was also overlapping of responsibility between the divisional and armoured brigade headquarters. In consequence, the organisation of the armoured divisions was remodelled to give them better balance and greater flexibility and striking power. The number of tank units was reduced, infantry was increased by one battalion and the armoured brigade headquarters were eliminated.

The reorganised division consisted of a reconnaissance battalion, 2 armoured regiments each with one light and 2 medium tank battalions, one armoured infantry regiment with 3 battalions, 3 self-propelled 105 mm. howitzer battalions and, as before, one engineer battalion and service units. In general, the organisation was much tidier and the effectiveness of the division greater. The total number of tanks was reduced slightly, from 381 to 375, but the number of medium tanks was actually doubled and the division gained in every other respect also.

The most significant and novel feature of the new organisation, however, was the introduction of 2 tactical headquarters, of roughly brigade headquarters status. These, the Combat Commands A and B, came directly under the divisional headquarters and were intended to assume command of any combination of the division's units.

The creation of the combat command headquarters recognised the need, brought about by tactical conditions, to operate in combined-arms battle teams of smaller than divisional size. It also, of course, bestowed a high degree of operational flexibility. This, combined with the fact that the whole of the divisional artillery was self-propelled and that all the infantry was carried in armoured half-tracks, made possible a much more efficient, flexible and more mobile employment of the American divisions than that of the armoured formations of other armies which were neither so equipped nor organised.

From some points of view the combat command system of combined-arms tactical teams was not, however, entirely new. The Germans had already practised much of it in the form of their mixed battle-groups, or *Kampfgruppen*, of which panzer divisions made so much use throughout the Second World War. It could be traced back even further, to the older German system of splitting divisions into march-combat groups and there is no doubt that these German methods exerted a considerable influence on American developments, as did the German emphasis on the tactical self-sufficiency of small units.

But, although the Germans may have anticipated the combat command system, they never carried it to its conclusion. Nor did they have the means to put it into practice as fully as the Americans did. With few exceptions, German panzer divisions had only a fraction of their artillery self-propelled and only a fraction of their rifle units equipped with armoured carriers. The role of the combat command headquarters was performed by panzer and panzer grenadier regimental head-quarters, which worked reasonably well but which could not be as efficient as the American system where the combat command headquarters were fully equipped and trained to assume command of combined-arms teams.

Admirable as it was, the combat command system intro-duced in 1942 was capable of further improvement, as were other aspects of the divisional organisation. Changes in both came in 1943, as part of a general reorganisation of the American armoured forces.

The atmosphere in which the reorganisation took place could hardly be described as favourable to the armoured divisions. The Armoured Force had by then lost a good deal of ground and the decisive role originally envisaged for it was neglected. Control passed into the hands of the Army Ground Forces and men with far less vision and understanding of the value of armoured forces. The commander of the Army Ground Forces in particular had some very definite and unfortunately also very limited ideas about armoured divisions. In fact, according to him armoured divisions were " of value only in pursuit and exploitation " and he seemed as oblivious of their achievements in other, more important, roles as of their future possibilities.

Under these circumstances it is hardly surprising that the overall effect of the 1943 reorganisation was to restrict the scope of the armoured forces and to shift the major portion of the American tank strength from armoured divisions to the support of the infantry. Armoured divisions themselves were tied more closely to infantry formations by a new corps organisation of 2 infantry and one armoured divisions, rather in contradiction of the highly mobile exploitation role envisaged for them in some quarters.

As regards close infantry support, G.H.Q. tank battalions intended for this role existed all the time, but up to the 1943 reorganisation they were relatively insignificant. The result of the reorganisation was such, however, that by the end of the Second World War there were no less than 60 independent tank battalions against about 50 in the armoured divisions. When it is remembered that there were also 68 tank destroyer battalions equipped with tank-like vehicles and for the most part attached also to infantry formations it is clear what a high proportion of the armoured strength was diverted to infantry support.

Apart from a lack of understanding of the full potentialities of armoured divisions there were also other factors which affected their general position and organisation. There was, for instance, a desire to economise at their expense and the fairly general contemporary overestimate of the power of anti-tank guns. Then there were the known changes in the organisation of the German panzer divisions, which increased considerably the proportion of infantry to tanks and which were wrongly interpreted—in Britain as well as the United States—as a major combat lesson and not, as they were in fact, chiefly the result of shortages of equipment.

Lastly there were the shortcomings of the existing divisional organisation which was still considered somewhat unwieldy and suffering from a surfeit of headquarters. The situation was not as bad as in the early panzer divisions where there were as many as 5 brigade and regimental headquarters for only 7 tank and infantry battalions, but the 3 (armoured and infantry) regimental headquarters in the American divisions were considered largely superfluous.

The problem of superfluous headquarters was remedied in the new organisation issued in September 1943, which also brought in other changes and reductions. The division now had a third but smaller combat command headquarters, three battalions each of medium tanks, armoured infantry and self-propelled artillery and one battalion of engineers, as well as a reconnaissance battalion and service units.

The main reduction was in the number of tank battalions, from 6 in the 1942 organisation to only 3 in that of 1943. However, 2 of the 3 battalions which were eliminated were light tank battalions whose equipment had become of doubtful value, so effectively the loss in tank strength amounted to only one medium tank battalion. Most of the other reductions affected the " overhead," such as the 3 regimental headquarters rather than fighting units, and so the division came through the ordeal looking leaner but not much less powerful.

In general, the new 1943 organisation was only a further development of the system introduced in 1942. By eliminating the regimental echelon, by making battalions into self-contained basic units and by giving more emphasis to the combat command system the organisation was made even more flexible and adaptable. So flexible and elastic in fact that the new divisional organisation was described as a federation of 13 battalions.

With two exceptions, all American armoured divisions in 1944 and 1945 were organised on those lines and it was with this organisation that they fought in Europe. The two exceptions were the 2nd and 3rd Armoured Divisions, which retained a modified form of the old 1942 organisation and which, because of their size relative to that of the new divisions, were sometimes referred to as " heavy divisions."

All told, 16 American armoured divisions were in the field by the end of the Second World War and their organisation was thus given full trial. It came through well, just as the armoured divisions themselves proved capable of performing effectively in a variety of roles, disproving the views that they were only suitable for exploitation.

As a result of the high degree of flexibility inherent in the system of combat commands and self-contained battalions, the divisions in the field had ample opportunity to try several forms of tactical grouping. Some divisions, for instance, tended to have combat commands of fairly fixed composition, while others altered the grouping for every new operation or even for every phase of one, which was apt to lead to confusion. Of those which tended towards more permanent grouping of battalions, some had most of the infantry in one command and most of the tanks in another, to obtain a concentration of striking power on the one hand and a good base in the collected infantry battalions on the other.

This last system, which resembled the contemporary British armoured division organisation and the original organisation of the panzer divisions, had few disadvantages in theory but in practice it was found that each command tended to get involved in a private battle of its own. On the whole, therefore, the " unbalanced " formation, that is, one with a preponderance of infantry in one command and tanks in another, was found inferior to the more common " balanced " formation having at least 2 similar mixed tank-infantry combat commands.

Having proved itself in battle, the divisional organisation based on combat commands and separate self-contained battalions was retained after the war. The alternative 3-regiment divisional structure which had been used by most armies and which was retained in the American infantry divisions was briefly considered after the war but only to be finally rejected in 1946.

But, although the basic organisation established in 1943 was retained, a number of modifications was introduced with the post-war division. The 3 combat commands were placed on an equal footing and a number of units was added, the principal additions being a battalion each of armoured infantry, of heavy tanks, of 155 mm. self-propelled howitzers and of anti-aircraft artillery. The last 3 took the place of units which previously were often attached to the armoured divisions but never formed part of them. The heavy tank battalion, for instance, was intended to take over the role of the tank destroyer battalion which used to be attached earlier. Of infantry, not only was a fourth battalion added, but each infantry battalion received a fourth rifle company as well.

The result was a return to something like the 1942 level, in personnel and in tanks, there now being 361 light, medium and heavy tanks against some 248 of the 1943–45 division. Changes in organisation were also accompanied by several changes in equipment. The original post-war division had 76 mm. gun M4A3E8 medium tanks in its 3 medium battalions in place of the earlier 75 mm. gun M4 tanks, and the heavy tank battalion was equipped with the 90 mm. gun M26 Pershing. After 1949, when new tanks became available, all 4 tank battalions were re-equipped with successive models of the Patton medium tank series, the M46, M47 and then M48, all developed from the earlier M26 and like it armed with 90 mm. guns. The reconnaissance battalion also received new M41 light tanks to replace the earlier M24. The 4 armoured infantry battalions, too, received new equipment in the shape of M75 and M59 full-track armoured personnel carriers which replaced the earlier half-tracks. The new carriers made possible even closer teamwork between tanks and infantry, while the ratio of 4 infantry battalions to 4 tank battalions ensured a good overall balance between the two.

In general, except for its size and equipment, the post-Second World War armoured division introduced in 1947 had similar characteristics to its 1943-45 predecessor. It was still based on the system of combat commands and self-contained battalions and had the same equal proportion of tanks and infantry. And, like its predecessor, it was a versatile fighting formation, only more effective, thanks to its more powerful armament.

Unfortunately, the post-war changes also made the armoured division larger and heavier. This added further difficulties to the already formidable supply problems and inevitably affected its overall mobility. These facts and the general trend towards smaller, more compact divisions raise the problem of reducing the overall size of the armoured division. Within the system of combat commands and self-contained battalions something can be done by reducing the number of tank and infantry battalions from 4 to 3 of each and a proportional reduction in the strength of other units. Beyond that, any reduction in the overall size of the division would inevitably involve reductions in the size of the battalions.

An alternative to the latter course would be to abandon the system of combat commands and self-contained but homogeneous battalions for one of mixed, or integrated, battalions directly under divisional control. Something of a precedent for this exists in the American armoured cavalry regiments— highly mobile 3-battalion units intended principally for security and reconnaissance roles—where, in fact, the mixed tank-infantry organisation is carried right down to platoon level. The adoption of an organisation based on mixed battalions would mean some loss of flexibility at divisional level but, on the other hand, it would increase the effectiveness of its constituent units. Moreover, it would be much more in keeping with the demand for far greater tactical and administrative self-sufficiency on the part of battalion-size units than had been the case earlier. This, more than anything else, would argue in favour of mixed tank-infantry armoured battalions, or small armoured regiments, which would, in addition, make possible a greater number of smaller but more mobile armoured divisions.

1. The first armed motor vehicle, a powered quadricycle with a Maxim machine-gun, being demonstrated by F. R. Simms in June 1899. (*Simms Motor & Electronics Corporation Ltd.*).

2. Rolls-Royce armoured car built in 1914 for the Royal Naval Air Service. (*Imperial War Museum*).

3. Little Willie, the first British tank, completed in September 1915. (*William Foster & Co. Ltd.*).

4. Big Willie, or Mother, the prototype of the first tanks used in battle. (*Imperial War Museum*).

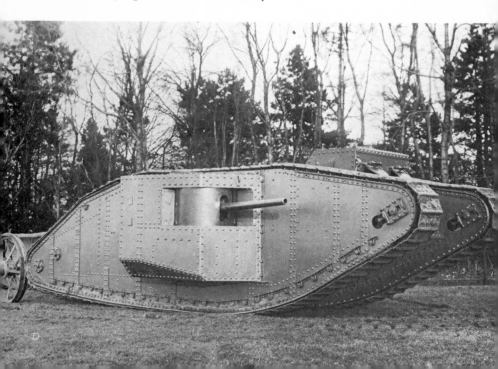

9

Soviet Armoured Formations

THE development of Soviet armoured formations, like that of most others, dates from the late twenties and early thirties. It was then that the Soviet Union began to build its tank strength and to expand its armoured forces beyond the few units it hitherto possessed.

At the time there were in existence two diametrically opposed schools of thought on the use of tanks. One, and the older of the two, subscribed to the concept of limited employment of tanks in the role of a subordinate auxiliary to the infantry. The French Army was then the chief exponent of this theory but it was also widely accepted elsewhere. In deference to it the Russians allotted one light tank battalion to each regular infantry division and for a few years there was even one tankette battalion to each frontier infantry regiment. Tank brigades of light and of medium-heavy tanks were also created, for infantry support at the higher level of corps or army. Each brigade usually consisted of 3 tank battalions and no other units.

The other of the two contemporary schools of thought subscribed to the theories first advanced by a handful of British pioneers of the more independent and mobile employment of tanks. They visualised them either in the role of mechanised cavalry or of an all-tank mobile field force and strove towards this in the experiments carried out, within the limits of the available resources, on Salisbury Plain.

The more revolutionary aspects of this theory were bound to appeal to some of the Soviet doctrinaires and being able to afford the luxury of masses of tanks the Red Army was able to subscribe to it, as well as to the more conservative theory. Thus, in addition to the other armoured units, it formed independent mechanised brigades whose role became that of mechanised strategic cavalry. In this they resembled the Tank Brigade of the Royal Tank Corps and they followed closely the " all-tank " principles which dominated at the time British ideas on the organisation of armoured formations. In other words, Soviet mechanised brigades consisted largely of tanks, usually 3 battalions of fast Christie-type B.T. tanks, to which was added a small infantry-automatic weapons element and auxiliary units.

In the tracks of the mechanised brigades came larger armoured formations, called mechanised corps, the first, according to some Soviet statements, being formed as early as 1932. The corps embraced 2 or 3 mechanised brigades, each with its 100-odd tanks, together with a motorised infantry brigade and a rather large motorised field artillery regiment. In this form the mechanised corps bore some resemblance to the contemporary German ideas on the organisation of armoured divisions. However, the Soviet mechanised corps was never the versatile closely integrated fighting unit of tanks, infantry and artillery which the panzer divisions were, and the mechanised brigade, with its preponderance of tanks and its accent on the cavalry role, was more typical of Soviet ideas on the organisation and employment of mobile armoured units.

The relative importance of the mechanised corps, of which there were 7 by the end of the decade, was further weakened by the doubts which the Soviet command began to share with others on the eve of the Second World War. Partly because of erroneous deductions drawn from the Spanish Civil War, it lost some of its faith in large armoured formations and shifted its emphasis to small tank units and infantry support.

It was only after the success of the German panzer divisions in Poland in 1939 and in France in 1940 that the Soviet command recognised the error of its ways. The position had to be reconsidered hurriedly and the outcome was a far-reaching programme of reorganisation, with the emphasis on armoured divisions modelled after the German pattern.

The new armoured, or tank, division established in 1940, consisted of 2 tank regiments, with a total of some 400 B.T.,

T-34 and KV heavy tanks, one motorised infantry regiment and one artillery regiment. Two tank divisions and a motorised infantry division formed a tank corps, the motorised division being similar in its organisation to the tank division but with the position and ratio of tank and infantry units reversed.

Never parsimonious where tanks were concerned and haunted by nightmares of German tank strength, the Soviet command planned to have 20 tank corps, or 40 to 50 tank divisions, by the autumn of 1941. These, however, never materialised as planned for the German attack caught the Red Army still in the throes of reorganisation. A year earlier, at the time of the Finnish winter campaign, Soviet armour was still organised into mechanised corps and brigades, as well as heavy and medium tank brigades, and in 1941 the tank divisions were only just coming into being.

Apart from anything else, the figure of 40 or 50 tank divisions which were planned serves to emphasise the strength of the Soviet armoured forces and, with the 20,000 or so tanks which they then possessed, makes ridiculous the contemporary German estimate of the total Soviet strength at 46 armoured brigades.

Nevertheless, ignorant as they were on the eve of " Operation Barbarossa " of the Soviet tank strength and of the new T-34 and KV tanks, the Germans managed to destroy practically the whole of the Soviet armoured forces arrayed against them. In this they were undoubtedly helped by the hurried organisation of the new Soviet armoured formations, as well as by the legacy of the inferior infantry-support Soviet tank methods and the inept operational handling of their armoured forces by the Soviet commanders.

The magnitude of the German success is perhaps best shown by the fact that by the end of the first campaign, in the winter of 1941, the German high command had identified 35 Soviet tank divisions destroyed in action and a further 30 disbanded as a result of heavy losses. At the time there were virtually no large Soviet armoured units left.

The exhaustion of the German forces and the stabilisation of the Eastern Front in the winter of 1941-42 gave the Soviet command a chance to raise some more armoured formations, from the units left in the interior of the country and the equipment coming from the Ural factories unaffected by the German invasion.

The new formations, however, were of an entirely different type from their immediate predecessors and represented, in fact, a return to the earlier brigade basis. No doubt, Soviet commanders were much more capable at the time of handling brigades than the larger and more complicated divisions and, of course, brigades were more in keeping with the much reduced tank resources.

The new tank brigade, as at first reported, had a tank regiment with 3 small mixed tank battalions, a motorised infantry-machine-gun battalion, a company each of anti-tank guns and mortars and small reconnaissance and anti-aircraft units. However, most of the brigades used in 1942 and 1943 were considerably smaller still, with only 2 tank battalions of 23 tanks each, a motorised rifle battalion and some smaller supporting units.

It was only in 1944 that the tank strength of the brigades began to rise to a more respectable level. The brigades of that period had either 3 battalions, each with two 10-tank companies, or 2 battalions, each with 3 tank companies, in either case representing a total of 65 T-34 medium tanks. By then also the infantry unit assumed the novel form of a sub-machine-gun battalion.

The operational capabilities of such small formations as the Soviet tank brigades were extremely limited and there was little option but to use them for some time in the limited infantry-support manner. But as time went on their number grew: already in the late spring of 1942, some 14 tank brigades were used during the abortive Soviet Kharkov counter-offensive. In 1943 the Germans estimated Soviet strength at 138 brigades and by the end of the Second World War they had identified no less than 258 different tank brigades, including 49 of the Guards.

What they lacked in individual strength and quality, the Soviet tank brigades thus partly made up in quantity. The limited operational capabilities of the individual brigades were further made up by grouping them together in larger armoured formations, the so-called tank and mechanised corps and tank armies. The first of the new-type corps appeared in action in the autumn of 1942, during the Stalingrad operations, and marked the beginning of a process of differentiation between the independent brigades which were retained mainly for infantry support and those grouped within the framework of corps for more mobile operations.

The actual composition of the tank corps varied considerably but generally it was based on 3 tank brigades and 1 motorised rifle brigade. At maximum strength, in addition to these the corps also had one reconnaissance and 1 motorcycle battalion, 1 or 2 heavy tank battalions, 2 assault gun and 2 towed anti-tank regiments, and a battalion each of anti-aircraft guns, mortars and rocket launchers. With all these units and a maximum strength of some 300 tanks the tank corps corresponded roughly to a Western armoured division.

The mechanised corps, on the other hand, was basically a motorised infantry formation, somewhat similar, in principle, to the German panzer grenadier divisions. In other words, it provided the infantry follow-up force for the tank corps, which the ordinary infantry formations, with their horse traction, were unable to provide. The organisation of the mechanised corps resembled that of the tank corps but with the position of the tank and infantry brigades reversed ; that is, it had 3 motorised infantry brigades, each with its own tank battalion, and one tank brigade.

The independent tank brigades were generally similar to those in the tank and mechanised corps and like the latter were chiefly based on the T-34 medium tanks, there being a maximum of 107 of these per brigade. However, being principally intended for co-operation with the infantry, they did not have organic infantry units. Apart from these brigades there were also independent heavy tank regiments, with 23 heavy KV or JS (Stalin) tanks each, and independent assault gun or S.U. regiments, which were allotted as required for the support of infantry or armoured formations.

By the end of the Second World War Soviet armoured forces thus consisted of the following four categories : the tank corps, the mechanised corps, the independent tank brigades and the independent heavy tank and assault gun regiments. According to some German estimates, there were 25 tank and 13 mechanised corps at the end of the war in Europe, representing over one half of the total Soviet tank strength in the field. Powerful as this force was, it was still small in relation to the mass of the Soviet infantry formations. It also represented a smaller overall degree of mechanisation than that in the armies of the Western Allies, or even the German Army which made the most of its tanks by concentrating practically all of them in its panzer divisions.

Also unlike the German, the Soviet operational doctrine was still inclined towards tying tanks down to the pace of the infantry mass. But the increasingly successful employment of armoured forces in more independent roles in the closing stages of the war encouraged Soviet protagonists of armour as the mobile spearhead of ground forces.

In the immediate post-war period Soviet armoured forces had to face the additional problem of doubts raised about their future by various new developments in armour-piercing weapons and other fields. In this they were no different from other armoured forces. But, unlike the American, for instance, which found their strength reduced from 16 to only one armoured division, the Soviet armoured forces emerged in the post-war period not only undiminished in number but, in fact, occupying a far more important position than ever before. Estimates of the total Soviet strength have varied somewhat but there is little doubt that armoured formations represent about one-third of the Soviet field forces and their most effective mobile striking force.

To fit them for this new role the organisation of the Soviet armoured formations was very thoroughly overhauled and they changed considerably from their wartime predecessors. Divisions were again introduced, for instance, and shortly after the war they replaced brigades as the basic armoured formations and, also, the rather loose corps organisation.

As in the case of the earlier divisions and the wartime corps, there were, however, still two types : the tank division with a preponderance of tanks and the mechanised division with a higher proportion of infantry. The basis of the former have been 3 medium tank regiments originally with tanks of the T-34/85 type but more recently with T-54, one heavy tank-assault gun regiment with Stalin tanks, and one rifle regiment. The 4 tank regiments represent a total of some 300 tanks and S.U.s and the other units of the division include a towed 122 mm. howitzer regiment, a light anti-aircraft regiment, and a regiment each of heavy mortars and rocket launchers ; there is also a reconnaissance battalion and the usual divisional service units.

The organisation of the mechanised division is based on 3 mechanised regiments, each of one medium tank and 3 rifle battalions, and one medium and one heavy tank regiment. Broadly speaking, the division stands in the same relationship to the tank division as the motorised division did to the tank division of 1940 and as the mechanised corps did to the tank corps during the war. The need for such an intermediate formation between the tank division and the infantry division has been less clear than that for its predecessors in view of the increasing motorisation of regular Soviet infantry divisions, which since the Second World War have dispensed with horse traction. The infantry divisions have also re-acquired their own organic tank units, usually in the form of a regiment of medium tanks with some S.U.s. This shows that the Russians did not abandon the idea of using a portion of their tank strength for infantry support but in view of the large number of tanks at their disposal this diversion detracts little from the strength of the armoured formations.

It is probable that the existence of the two types of Soviet armoured formations is only an interim measure and that the two will, eventually, merge into one or else that the mechanised division will supersede the infantry or rifle division. As it is, in spite of the different proportions of riflemen and tanks, tank and mechanised divisions are similar.

In principle, they are both closely integrated formations of tanks and infantry with considerable fighting power. In this last respect, illustrated clearly by the inclusion of heavy gun tanks and powerful assault guns, they are at one with the earlier German ideas on the subject and well away from the Second World War Anglo-American principles of under-gunned mobility.

In trying to assess Soviet formations from other points of view allowances must be made for the smaller size of some Soviet units and for differences in terminology. For instance, a Soviet tank battalion has had only 21 tanks and a 3-battalion regiment was not much different from a Western tank battalion. The rifle battalions too have been smaller. Thus, although the number of units is different, the effective overall ratio of tanks to infantry in the Soviet tank divisions had not differed much from the one to one unit ratio generally considered desirable.

In the mechanised divisions the proportion of infantry is, of course, higher—almost double that in the tank divisions. At that it is similar to the proportion of the two elements with which the German panzer divisions operated during the latter part of the Second World War, although as a result of shortages of tanks rather than by design.

In the case of both the tank and mechanised divisions, however, the degree of integration between riflemen and tanks is close, probably closer and more permanent than in any earlier armoured formation. The inclusion of an automatic rifle battalion in each medium and heavy tank regiment is somewhat similar to the British practice of having a rifle battalion in each armoured brigade but, in view of the smaller size of Soviet units, it represents a higher proportion of infantry within the armoured units and a closer tie-up between the two. Similarly, a close degree of integration is met with in the mechanised divisions where each mechanised, or rifle, regiment has an organic medium tank battalion, the latter being additional, of course, to the divisional medium and heavy tank regiments.

Apart from their organic infantry battalions tank regiments have their own assault guns and rifle regiments have their guns, mortars and other heavy weapons. With all these means at their disposal the regiments form self-contained battle groups and each division can thus readily operate in 4 or 5 such groups, in line with all the recent trends in tactical employment. The permanent existence of such regimental battle groups also shows that Soviet divisions have advanced well beyond the earlier system of armoured formations based on separate tank and infantry echelons.

In other respects, Soviet divisions seem able to dispense with some of the paraphernalia found in other armoured formations. This lightens their whole structure and contributes to their smaller size, although admittedly some of it has been due to shortages of equipment. Armoured infantry carriers of a wheeled truck type did not appear until about 1950 and tracked armoured infantry carriers later still. On the credit side one must put the diesel engines used in all the heavier armoured vehicles and the resulting fuel economy and operating range, and the availability of powerful and versatile assault guns, such as the JSU-152.

Taken as a whole, the organisation of Soviet armoured formations reflects the sound lessons of experience and up-to-date development. First, there is the accent on fighting power and on well armed fighting vehicles, born out of the hard school of the Eastern Front and its armoured battles. Then there is the close integration of tanks and riflemen, developed gradually from the days of the original mechanised brigades. Finally, there is the relatively small size of the divisions and their self-contained regimental battle groups, which were born out of wartime necessity and have been brought up on a sound assessment of future needs and conditions.

10

General Trends

INTERESTING and instructive as may be the study of the armoured formations of individual countries, it is even more important to consider their development as a whole. The broader the field of observation or analysis the more likely it is to bring out significant points or trends and the more likely it is to lead to valid conclusions regarding armoured formations in general.

To be able to generalise one must, however, first form a synthesis of the development of armoured divisions. As a first step towards this, the evolution of the organisation of armoured divisions may be grouped into 4 fairly distinct phases which mark the successive, if somewhat overlapping, stages of the development.

Of these 4 phases the first was that of the tank brigade. There were exceptions but, nonetheless, most of the early development of mobile armoured forces was based on what were, in fact or in effect, tank brigades. In other words, units which consisted of 2 to 4 tank battalions and little else. Such was the British Tank Brigade of the early thirties, the early Soviet Mechanised Brigades and the American 7th Cavalry Brigade. Even some of the later and larger formations, such as the British Mobile Division and the Soviet Mechanised Corps, were little more than groupings of tank brigades.

The second phase was ushered in with the appearance in 1934 of the first French *Division Légère Mécanique* and, a year later, of the first 3 German panzer divisions. These divisions were still based on tank brigades but in each case the tank brigade was permanently combined with an infantry brigade, or its equivalent, and units of other arms.

This type of organisation based on a tank brigade and a complementary infantry brigade was adopted almost universally in the early part of the Second World War. The Italian Army adopted it in 1939 for its 3 *Divisioni Corazzate* and so, in essence, did the Soviet Army in its shortlived tank divisions of 1940-41. The organisation of the original 1940-41 American armoured divisions was also of this type and so was that of the Japanese armoured divisions. The British Army adopted it also and only abandoned it in 1956.

However, battlefield experience brought about a different type of organisation in the latter part of the Second World War and the third phase of the development. Instead of being combined at divisional level, as had been the practice until then, the combination of different arms moved down to brigade or combat command level.

This development was first officially recognised in the 1942 and 1943 reorganisations of the American armoured divisions which, from 1943 onwards, were based on self-contained battalions and combat commands combining battalions of different arms. American armoured divisions have been typical of this third phase of the development but their basic structure was also adopted by French armoured divisions towards the end of the Second World War and, much more recently, by the new German armoured divisions.

Even where this type of organisation was not officially recognised it was still used in the field and the armoured divisions operated in 2 or 3 mixed brigade-size groups. This was the case during the Second World War with the German panzer divisions, which actually pioneered the system of mixed armoured battle groups, or *Kampfgruppen*, and it was also the case with British armoured divisions.

In 1957 the British Army went over permanently to this system, replacing its earlier armoured divisions by mixed armoured brigade groups, albeit rather unbalanced in their composition. Armoured brigades permanently combining tanks, infantry and other arms have also been used for some time by the Swedish and Turkish Armies and, in a somewhat rudimentary form, they were used even earlier by the Soviet Army.

The fourth and latest phase of the evolution of the organisation of armoured formations was also introduced in the latter part of the Second World War. It has been characterised by the formation of mixed inter-arm battle groups at an even lower level than that hitherto accepted, namely the level of the battalion. Formed by *ad hoc* combinations of tank and rifle companies and other units, these mixed battalion-size battle groups, or reinforced battalions, were used on some scale during the Second World War by American, German and British armoured divisions.

However, this tactical development was not incorporated into the organisation of armoured formations until after the war. American armoured cavalry regiments and the post-war Soviet tank divisions were the first to permanently incorporate in their organisation mixed units below brigade or combat command level. A little later they were followed by the French *Régiments Inter-armes*. The different unit designation may cloud the issue somewhat but in all three cases there is the common and essential feature in the permanent combination of riflemen with tanks and other heavy weapons within battalion-size units. This is certainly something new and peculiar to the fourth phase of the evolution of armoured formations.

Considering the four phases of the development, an obvious trend running through them is that of progressively closer co-operation between arms and of their integration at progressively lower unit level. From the " all-tank " tank brigades of the first phase, through the combination of several arms at the level of the armoured division of the second phase and the mixed brigade-size groups or combat commands of the third, to the appearance of the self-contained battalion-size groups in the fourth phase the trend is clearly towards closer teamwork and integration.

The original British "all-tank" ideas over emphasised the tank and ignored the need to combine it with other arms into an effective mobile weapon system. As a result, the tank brigades or divisions based on the " all-tank " ideas proved inferior to and were displaced by others in which tanks were combined with mobile infantry, artillery and other arms. In other words, armoured divisions of the type so successfully introduced by the German panzers in the lightning campaigns of 1939, 1940 and 1941.

Once the interdependence of tanks, infantry and other arms was recognised their combination did not stop at the level of the armoured division. Instead it spread down to smaller units, urged by the combined pressure of mobile operations and the growing power of modern weapons.

Of the two, mobile operations, with their rapid movements and changing situations, demanded rapid and close co-operation between mutually complementary arms and, by the same token, rendered ineffective the necessarily slower co-operation confined to the level of large units. As for the second factor, the destructive power of modern weapons has precluded the old-fashioned massing of forces and fostered the development of small self-contained battle groups. The latter actually originated before the advent of tactical nuclear weapons but their importance has, of course, increased since.

The combination of tanks with other arms and their integration at progressively lower unit level has not been without opposition. Even today there are still some who favour armoured formations composed almost entirely of tanks, as was shown by the recent British experiments. A common argument against the combination with other arms, and in particular infantry, has been that it reduces the mobility of armoured formations by comparison with that which they would have if composed of tanks alone. Examined closely, the argument is only valid, however, if the organic infantry of armoured formations is not properly equipped with cross-country vehicles and the adverse effect on mobility is not inherent in the combination as such. Moreover, in the field, combination of tanks with riflemen had proved essential and from the panzer divisions of the thirties to the American,

Soviet and French divisions of the mid-fifties approximately equal proportions of tank and infantry units have been found best.

Otherwise the biggest bone of contention is the level down to which permanent combination of riflemen with tanks and other self-propelled heavy weapons should be carried out. Integration down to and including brigade or combat command level has become widely accepted but that below, at battalion level, has not. On the other hand, there is a significant body of opinion that the mixed battalion offers the best solution to future tactical requirements, particularly from the point of view of the possible employment of tactical nuclear weapons and the attendant necessity for dispersed operation.

Were the mixed, or combined-arms, armoured battalions generally accepted they would bring about further considerable changes to the organisation of armoured formations. A probable first step would be a smaller basic formation, or armoured division, composed of five, or so, mixed armoured battalions or small combined-arms regiments. Such an organisation, based on multiples of five, strikes a reasonable balance between the conflicting requirements of a minimum number of headquarters and of the allowable number of units within the span of effective executive control and, in general, offers the advantages of economy and flexibility.

Apart from the structure and composition of the armoured formations, the other and even more important aspect of their development is their role and employment in the field. Here again a trend might be discerned running through the four phases of evolution—a trend towards more versatile employment and increased scope.

To be true, some of the original British ideas on the employment of tanks did envisage armour as the effective basis of ground forces. Unfortunately, they did so in terms of tanks alone—in terms of " tank fleets "—and failed to recognise the need for combination with other elements into an effective multiple weapon system. Tanks alone were only capable of performing a limited mobile role and it was this limited role that the early armoured units assumed.

The adoption of a limited role by the early mobile armoured units was strongly influenced by the example of their immediate predecessors, the horse cavalry, whose role they partly took over. Initially too, the adoption of a limited role was a sound practical course, when mechanisation was still struggling for recognition and much of the operational technique still had to be evolved. But there was no reason why armoured formations should continue to be confined to the limited roles to which horse cavalry was reduced towards the end of its existence, in the late nineteenth and early twentieth centuries.

Yet this policy of limiting the role of armoured forces continued well beyond the initial period. In essence it was based on two things : first, the failure to recognise the full potentialities of armoured formations and, secondly, on the historical fallacy that mobile forces were never more than an auxiliary arm of exploitation and pursuit.

As a result of all this armoured formations, such as the first British Armoured Division, the Soviet Mechanised Brigades and the French *Division Légère Mécanique*, were confined to the limited " cavalry " role right up to the early stages of the Second World War. It was the Germans who were the first to recognise and demonstrate that armoured divisions were capable of much more. In the first two years of the Second World War—in 1939 to 1941, in Poland, France, the Balkans, Russia and Libya—their panzer divisions proved to be far more than a mere instrument of exploitation : no less, in fact, than the principal striking force of the German Army, more powerful as well as more mobile than its other divisions.

The brilliant example of the panzer divisions convinced most. In 1940 and 1941 most armies recognised armoured divisions as the versatile and decisive element in ground warfare and concentrated on creating as many of them as possible. The Germans themselves formed 6 up to the outbreak of the Second World War ; for the 1940 French campaign they raised the total to 10 and for the 1941 attack on Russia doubled it to 20. In 1942 they increased the total further, to 25, and later still created 8 additional *Waffen-S.S.* panzer divisions.

The Soviet Army followed the example of the German, recognising the decisive role played by the panzer divisions, although for a time it remained well behind the Germans in the effective use of its masses of tanks. Stalin himself told Harry Hopkins, the special representative of President Roosevelt, that in June 1941 the Soviet Army had 60 tank divisions and the Germans did, in fact, identify 65 up to the end of the 1941 campaign. For a time thereafter the Russians abandoned the divisional organisation but they continued to build their armoured forces and by the end of the Second World War had 6 tank armies in the field.

In 1941 the United States were thinking of equally large-scale and decisive employment of armoured divisions. In fact, the Victory Programme of that year envisaged no less than 61 armoured divisions. However, the total actually in the field by the end of the war was only 16. Several factors contributed to the difference between the target and achievement but, whatever the reason, the two figures are symbolic of the ground lost by armoured divisions during the latter part of the Second World War.

Much the same thing happened in Britain. After 1940, following the successful example of the panzer divisions, the British Army raised 11 armoured divisions but in the latter part of the Second World War it only maintained 5.

The main reasons were a loss of faith in armoured divisions born out of the contrast between the favourable conditions in Libya and those in Italy where contemporary operations shifted, the slowing down of operations on the Eastern Front, in Russia, as a result of the temporary exhaustion of both sides, and one of the periodic waves of exaggerating the importance of anti-tank weapons. As a result of all this, in 1943, in both Britain and the United States, armoured divisions were again

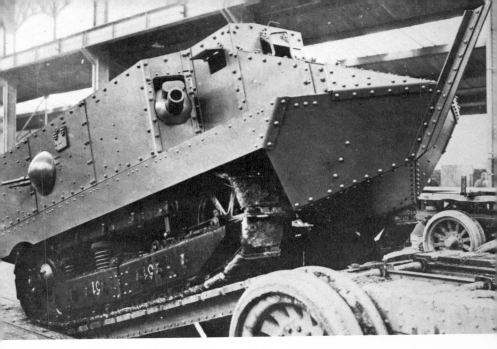

5. The original type of French tank built by the Schneider Company in 1916. (*Imperial War Museum*).

6. Renault FT light tank of 1918. (*Imperial War Museum*).

7. British Light Infantry Tank which attained 30 mph during trials in 1922.

8. Vickers Medium Mark I built in 1923. (*Vickers-Armstrongs Ltd.*).

thought suitable only for a limited exploitation role and the once discredited concepts crept back into official doctrine.

In fact, of course, once they landed on the Continent of Europe, in 1944, both British and American armoured divisions fought as versatile fighting formations and contributed their share to winning the battle, as well as to the subsequent exploitation. The part played by armoured divisions in the final victory was large and by the end of the Second World War Western armies comprised 28 of them : 16 American, 5 British, 3 French, 2 Canadian, 1 South African and 1 Polish.

On the other side armoured divisions were no less important. As Germany's situation deteriorated, panzer divisions became the core of the German defensive system, just as earlier they had spearheaded German offensives, and their performance on the defensive emphasised further the versatility and effectiveness of armoured formations.

Nevertheless, in the West the harmful limited-role theories persisted. After the Second World War the fixation on the limited exploitation role for armoured divisions and another of the periodic waves of exaggerating the importance of anti-tank weapons contributed to American and British armoured forces being cut down to one armoured division each—a ridiculously low strength in total or even in relation to the much reduced post-war American and British Armies.

In contrast, the Soviet Army consistently continued to emphasise the importance of its armour, reorganising its armoured divisions and increasing their strength in relation to the rest of the Soviet ground forces. So much so that by the early fifties the total number of tank and mechanised divisions rose to over fifty, representing almost one-third of all Soviet field forces and the principal armed threat of the Soviet *bloc*.

It was only the slow realisation of these facts and the havoc wrought by North Korean manned Soviet armour in the early part of the Korean war which brought about a reawakening to the importance of armoured divisions in the West. Once again the Western nations turned their attention to them and in the early fifties NATO could count on something like 11 armoured divisions being available in Europe : 3 British, 3 French, 3 Italian, 1 American and 1 Belgian.

But after 1954-55 Western policies towards armoured divisions have again shown signs of lacking in firm and full understanding of their value. In contrast to the consistent Soviet attitude, the effectiveness of armoured formations has again been denied and their number reduced, particularly in Britain.

This is probably no more than yet another unfortunate passing phase but the vacillations do no credit to anyone and are a constant reminder of the failures to grasp the full value of armoured formations as an effective mobile ground weapons system. Recognised and treated as such they need fear no loss of value. Their size, organisation and equipment are bound to change with time but given adequate development there is no reason why armoured or mechanised formations should not retain their importance in ground warfare.

11

Tactics

By comparison with their organisation or equipment, the tactics of armoured forces are less tangible and the advances made in this field more elusive. Nevertheless, over the years, progress as important as that in tank design has taken place in the art of employing armoured forces in battle and the latest operational methods are as far removed from those of 1916 as the equipment on which they rely is from the tanks of the First World War.

The first tanks were born in an atmosphere of continuous fronts and static, almost siege-like conditions. It was natural, therefore, that their original method of employment should have been in frontal assaults. The first, delivered by British tanks on September 15, 1916, was actually executed by advancing behind a rolling artillery barrage and just ahead of the attacking infantry; the principal task of the tanks was the destruction of machine-gun nests which survived the artillery bombardment and which usually took such a heavy toll of the attacking infantry waves. The tanks were too few and too scattered to score a major success but in essence their first action set a pattern for the simplest form of employment in a conventional artillery-infantry assault.

From the frontal assault and the shallow penetration which it produced the employment of tanks graduated to the tactical break-through. This was accomplished by British tanks at Cambrai in 1917 and at Amiens in 1918, in each of which over 300 fighting tanks were used over relatively narrow fronts. In this way hostile defences were saturated, that is attacked with more tanks than they could possibly cope with. Moreover, every attempt was made to secure surprise and the usual long artillery bombardment, which had hitherto heralded every

115

major offensive, was dispensed with : the considerable concentrations of artillery, amounting to almost one gun to every 10 yards of the front, opened fire only just prior to the tank assault and concentrated mainly on counter-battery work. Tanks themselves destroyed the barbed wire belts in front of the hostile trenches and the hostile strong points, opening the way for the infantry which followed closely behind the single wave of assaulting tanks, one tank to every 40 or 70 yards of the front.

In both cases a break through the hostile defence lines was achieved but the overall success was limited through lack of suitable means of exploitation : horse cavalry could make no headway even against a few scattered machine-guns and the existing tanks were too slow and had a very limited operating range. However, with the development of faster medium tanks a means appeared both for exploiting the success of the heavy assault tanks and of elaborating the assault technique. Both features were embodied in the " Plan 1919 " put forward by the Chief of Staff of the British Tank Corps, Colonel J. F. C. Fuller. In essence the Plan envisaged an extension of the tank assault by sending platoons or companies of fast Medium D tanks through the hostile lines to attack command posts, while heavy tanks assaulted frontally and opened the way for the bulk of the medium tanks which were to exploit the break-through, followed by truck-borne infantry.

The First World War came to an end before " Plan 1919 " could be put into effect. The same applied to an elaboration of the frontal assault tactics evolved by the French Army. Its principal feature was a division of roles in the assault between tanks leading it and those which followed, shepherding the infantry, and the creation of two corresponding categories of tanks. The latter category already existed in the shape of the Renault F.T. light tanks, well suited to accompanying the infantry ; for the leading role in the break-through the French were building powerful 68-ton 2C tanks, about twice as heavy as the largest contemporary British tanks.

Something of this assault technique was actually foreshadowed in the proposed 1918 organisation of American tank brigades which were to consist of one battalion of British-type heavy tanks and 2 of French-type light tanks, and was perpetuated after the First World War in the existence of American tank units equipped with British-designed Mark VIII heavy tanks and the Renault-inspired M1917 light tanks. The French themselves, however, built only 10 of the 2C heavy tanks and after the war, as methods of trench warfare were gradually supplanted by ideas based on more open fighting, the heavy break-through tanks fell into neglect.

This left the field to the light infantry-accompanying tanks which came to dominate it through the twenties and most of the thirties. Having originated them and saddled itself with a stock of some 3,000 Renault F.T. the French Army was the chief exponent of this type but it was also adopted by most other armies, due partly to its low cost and the fact that it fitted best with the established order of things.

The typical method of employment of the light accompanying tanks was the attachment of a battalion to an infantry division and the allotment of one tank company to each assaulting infantry battalion ; the normal company front was 300 to 600 yards and its advance in a single wave slightly ahead of the infantry. The employment of the accompanying tanks was closely tied to the foot-slogging riflemen, being governed by the speed and endurance of the latter, and their principal task was to neutralise hostile automatic weapons holding up the advance of the infantry.

The capabilities and effectiveness of the light accompanying tanks were extremely limited and after a time the concept of leading an attack with more powerful tanks regained strength. But this time they were no longer called break-through tanks. Instead, the new or revived category of more powerful tanks was collectively designated by the French Army as the *chars de manoeuvre d'ensemble*, which corresponded roughly to the contemporary United States Army concept of " leading tanks " and which were best exemplified by the French type B heavy tanks of the thirties.

Like the light accompanying tanks, these more powerful

tanks were also used by companies or battalions but not in such close contact with infantry units. Instead of being subordinated to small infantry units, these more powerful tanks were committed under divisional or corps control along the main line of effort. Being better armed and better able to stand up to punishment they generally moved ahead of the light infantry-accompanying tanks, destroying enemy heavy weapons, anti-tank guns and tanks.

Tactics such as these, based on 2-tank echelons, became the pattern for the more advanced type of employment of tanks in frontal assaults in conjunction with the infantry, even where two separate categories of tanks were not available. In either case the basic feature was the echeloning of tanks in two waves, the first penetrating as quickly as possible on to the objective and dominating it while the second remained close to and brought on the infantry.

The Russians went one better than the French. During the thirties they adopted a very similar tactical system but they added to it something akin to the raiding tactics proposed in 1918 for the British Medium D tanks. Thus, in contrast to the two categories of French tanks, the Russians had three. First, they had the *N.P.P.*, or close infantry support, tanks whose role corresponded to that of the *chars d'accompagnement* and which were typified by the divisional light tank battalions. Then they had the *D.P.P.*, or distant support, tanks which corresponded roughly to the *chars de manoeuvre d'ensemble* and which were supposed to attack more deeply and more independently of the infantry. Finally, there were the *D.D.* tanks which were supposed to penetrate rapidly and deeply into the hostile defensive zones to shoot up command posts, artillery and reserves.

The Soviet tank tactics of the thirties represented the most highly developed system derived directly from the methods of the First World War and the most elaborate form of tank employment under the control of infantry. The tactics did, in theory, envisage attacking with tanks the entire depth of the hostile defensive system and the *D.D.*, and to a lesser extent the *D.P.P.*, tanks were able to operate more independently and make better use of their mobility. However, the overall tempo and depth of the attack were still governed by the foot-fighting infantry. Moreover, although the use of up to 2 tank brigades was envisaged in support of one infantry division, tanks were not used in mass but were parcelled out by companies or battalions to infantry units. Thus, although tank brigades or even tank corps existed, in battle they hardly operated as such and their staffs, like those of the British tank brigades in the First World War, were little more than advisory bodies to infantry formation commanders.

While the French and Soviet Armies were elaborating tank tactics aimed at penetrating continuous static fronts and closely tied to the infantry, the British took the lead in developing more independent and mobile methods. Experiments began in 1927 and the development took a large step forward with the formation of a tank brigade as an operational mechanised unit, and not merely an administrative grouping as were the tank brigades of the First World War. This provided the first instance of as many as 4 tank battalions manoeuvring together under one command and the first example of a massed mobile employment of armour.

The tank brigade of the Royal Tank Corps consisted only of tanks—light tanks for scouting, medium tanks for attacking and howitzer-armed tanks for putting up protective smoke screens—and it was envisaged for mobile employment against hostile flanks or rear, in harassing raids and in exploitation. In the absence of convenient openings or flanks it was to operate through gaps made for it by other units. In other words, the employment of the tank brigade was to be limited to favourable circumstances. Given the chance it could, no doubt, have created havoc shooting up hostile rear installations, as the Medium D would have done in 1919, but it could not achieve decisive results unaided. Based only on tanks, and not very powerful tanks at that, and innocent of other arms it could not perform more than a limited mobile role. Similar reservations applied to the first American mechanised formation, the 7th

Cavalry Brigade of the thirties, and to the Soviet mechanised brigades of the period, when they were being used in a cavalry role and not in break-through operations.

As a first step towards a more mobile employment of tanks the assumption by the early armoured formations of the limited horse cavalry role was sensible enough. But there was no reason why the scope of armoured formations should not be gradually extended. Instead, what happened in Britain, for instance, was that an arbitrary division was drawn between offensive operations against strongly held enemy positions and mobile operations, and troops divided accordingly into two parallel categories : the tank brigade was assigned to the limited mobile role and, to cope with what was regarded as the distinct task of fighting, the retrograde step was taken of creating a special category of heavily armoured " infantry " tanks to be used by battalions in simple frontal assaults in close support of the infantry.

In consequence, it was in Germany and not in Britain that the next step was taken in the evolution of armoured tactics, beyond the confines of the limited mobile role. In essence, what the Germans did was to combine the functions of penetration, on which the French and Soviet armoured forces had concentrated, together with mobile exploitation in a single versatile armoured formation—the panzer division.

To the extent that its organisation and employment were based on a tank brigade, and in its general mobile character, the panzer division followed the course set by the British tank brigade. However, the Germans expected more of the panzer division than a limited mobile role and they recognised that tanks alone were insufficient to achieve decisive results. In consequence, they backed the tank brigade of the panzer division with a motorised infantry brigade which would follow and complete the work of tanks or assist their passage through obstacles. They also added units of other arms and produced a mobile division which had both greater striking power and greater mobility than other contemporary formations of comparable size and which was equally capable of obtaining a decision in battle as of mobile exploitation after it.

In some other respects the contemplated use of the panzer division on a narrow front against strong hostile defences also resembled the contemporary Franco-Soviet doctrines at their best. The differences were, however, greater than similarities. For one thing, under the German system tanks were not parcelled out among infantry units but were concentrated under one command. Secondly, the whole tempo of operations was geared to the speed of tanks and not that of the foot-fighting infantry.

The actual method of operation envisaged for the panzer division on the eve of the Second World War was an attack by its tank brigade of 4 tank battalions and over 300 tanks on a front of 3,000 to 5,000 yards. The tanks were echeloned in depth in several waves and, in theory, each main wave was assigned a specific task, such as penetrating to attack hostile command posts and reserves, or attacking hostile artillery, or neutralising hostile infantry positions until the arrival of the panzer division's infantry echelon.

The success of the panzer division was thought—and proved —to depend on the fire power of the tank brigade and the speed with which it attacked. The rapid tempo of the attack gave a minimum of time to hostile defences and the concentration of the tank brigade on a narrow front ensured their saturation at the point chosen for the break-through. This accomplished, an even more rapid follow up enabled the panzer divisions to convert tactical breaks-through into major strategic successes and they struck deep, advancing at up to 60 miles per day. To achieve this high overall tempo of operation and to make full use of their mobile striking power the panzer divisions did not, as a rule, wait for infantry formations to open the way for them but attacked on their own, where necessary opening the way through obstacles with their own infantry and engineers.

Normally the organic motorised infantry, or panzer grenadiers, followed closely at the heels of the massed tanks, their task being to mop up resistance by-passed by tanks and, together with anti-tank guns, consolidate the success. They followed tanks in their vehicles as long as possible but being equipped with trucks they had to dismount whenever they encountered hostile fire and move into action on foot. However, from the 1940 French campaign onwards, part of the infantry was equipped with half-track armoured personnel carriers which enabled that portion of it to work really closely with tanks while the remainder, still equipped with trucks, had to content itself with a less mobile and more passive follow-on role.

For the sake of speed the participation of the artillery in armoured attacks was remoulded also, the customary and necessarily slow massed artillery preparation being dispensed with and whenever necessary and possible replaced by the far more rapid massed dive bomber attacks. The role of the relatively small artillery component of the panzer divisions was to concentrate on selected targets inaccessible to, or most dangerous to, tanks, such as anti-tank guns.

All this applied to the Polish, French, Balkan, Russian and Libyan campaigns of the 1939-42 period, in all of which the panzer divisions played a leading and decisive role. When the tide of war turned against Germany and opportunities for large scale offensive operations vanished the principal role of the panzer divisions became that of delivering swift and powerful counter-blows against hostile penetrations. As the general situation deteriorated, panzer divisions became the backbone of the German defence as much as they had been the spearhead of the earlier offensives. They took to defending critical sectors, holding key points with their infantry and counter-attacking with their tanks, and to delaying defence in small mobile battle groups.

The far reaching extension of the role of the panzer divisions during the course of the Second World War emphasised the versatility in which they led and which was only slowly matched by other armoured formations.

For instance, the versatile and effective employment of the panzer divisions contrasted sharply in 1940 with the French tactical system, with its battalions of light infantry-accompanying tanks scattered over a wide front, its *chars de manoeuvre d'ensemble* grouped in the *divisions cuirassées* but used equally in penny packets and its separate mechanised cavalry divisions —all used separately and defeated piecemeal. A year later the same fate met the Soviet armoured forces, built on a similar system to the French. When the Germans struck, the Russians were trying hurriedly to organise tank divisions on the model of the panzers but their methods, if not their organisation, were still rooted in the earlier system.

Both the Soviet and French systems, with their different categories of tanks and different roles and with their parcelling out of tanks in small units, compared badly with the logical simplicity of the German methods of concentrating all the available tanks in the panzer divisions and concentrating panzer divisions at the decisive points. Both might have achieved a limited degree of success given favourable static conditions but with their over-specialisation and complication they failed utterly under the mobile conditions imposed by the Germans.

After the heavy losses of 1941, Soviet armoured forces virtually had to go back to the beginning and retrace the general course of armoured tactics. Thus, to begin with, they reverted to the system of straightforward frontal assaults with small tank units leading the infantry. Necessity became a virtue and the official doctrine became that of close co-operation with other arms.

From frontal assaults Soviet armoured forces graduated to progressively deeper penetrations and from tactical breakthrough to mobile exploitation and envelopment on a strategic scale. In the closing stages of the Second World War in Europe the rate of advance of Soviet armour began to approach that of the German panzer divisions in 1940 and 1941 and in Manchuria, in August 1945, it exceeded it by a dash of some 700 miles in 5 days through collapsing Japanese resistance.

The breaks-through which preceded the mobile exploitation were created at times by infantry divisions supported by massed artillery and independent tank units but on other occasions Soviet armoured formations penetrated through on their own. In such cases they attacked with 200 to 300 tanks on a narrow front of 1,500 to 2,000 yards, usually in three main waves, preceded by artillery preparations lasting several hours.

Against strong enemy defences both the Russians and the Germans led on occasions with heavy tanks but more often heavy tanks followed the mediums, supporting the latter with their heavy long-range guns. Thus the role of the more powerful tanks was gradually transformed from that of heavily armoured assault vehicles to lead the break-through to that of heavy gun tanks supporting the medium tanks with their heavier fire power. This transformation was initiated by the tactics of the German Pz.Kpfw.IV medium tank in relation to the lighter German models before the Second World War and completed with the use of Tiger and Stalin heavy gun tanks within German and Soviet armoured formations.

The powerful heavy gun tanks such as the Stalin played a particularly important role in meeting hostile armour, an event considered unusual in the early days of armoured forces but with time increasingly frequent and important. Equally important in meeting hostile armour were the heavy S.U. assault guns or turretless tanks. On such occasions Soviet medium tanks usually tried to retire and to manoeuvre on to the flanks leaving the fire fight to the less manoeuvrable but more powerful heavy gun vehicles.

In contrast to the effort which the Russians devoted to heavy gun vehicles and the progress they made in increasing the direct mobile fire power of their armoured formations, they remained well behind in the effective mobile employment of infantry in conjunction with tanks. The best they could do was to mount infantry on tanks, usually those of the second and third waves, and it was only after the Second World War that they began to produce armoured infantry carriers.

Nevertheless, in the final stages of the Second World War Soviet armoured formations already closely approached the standard set earlier by German panzer divisions as the decisive element in ground warfare, capable alike of obtaining a decision in battle as of mobile exploitation. Their ideal became a massed attack on a narrow front delivered by several waves of tanks echeloned in depth, an attack which would smother hostile defences by its mobile fire power and minimise counter-action by its speed. The rear echelons of tanks would bring on part of the infantry, riding on tanks, the rest, together with motorised artillery, following on behind to consolidate the success of the tanks.

By the end of the Second World War, however, this partic-ular form of employment was already being superseded by other, more flexible methods based on closer co-operation between different arms in smaller tactical groupings than an armoured division or its contemporary Soviet equivalent, the *bronye-tankovyj korpus*.

The changeover from the earlier tactical system centred on the offensive employment of whole armoured divisions to the more flexible methods based on smaller closely knit teams of several arms took place gradually in all the major armies. For instance, for eleven years after the Second World War British armoured divisions retained an organisation based on a separate tank and infantry echelon, although already in 1944 British armoured divisions fought in mixed tank-infantry brigade or battalion groups. And up to the end of the Second World War British official doctrine still insisted on confining armoured divisions to the role of exploitation, leaving the harder task of fighting and breaking-through to infantry divisions and special " infantry " tank units. The latter practice of retaining tank units outside armoured divisions for use with infantry divisions was not, of course, confined to the British Army. Both the Soviet and United States Armies—but not the German—practised it in the latter part of the Second World War but neither went to the extreme of specialised " infantry " tanks nor drew such sharp distinction between the two roles.

The British system of the two separate and distinct categories of tanks proved, in fact, unnecessarily specialised and complicated. Like the earlier French and Soviet systems it might have worked given reasonably static and favourable conditions, including a wealth of equipment. Under average conditions it meant a dispersion of tank effort between two separate categories, ill suited to co-operating with each other and, as happened in Libya in 1942, a piecemeal defeat. It is noteworthy that the more successful German methods were evolved in an atmosphere of limited resources and that the concentration of all the available tanks in the panzer divisions and the use of the panzer divisions in a variety of roles were based on the principle of making the most of the available resources.

As for the Second World War British doctrine that armoured divisions should be retained for exploitation after the enemy had been defeated, this was an unjustified and unworkable luxury. In practice, British armoured divisions proved as capable of participating in the different phases of the fighting as the others. Any shortcomings which they might have displayed were not fundamental but were due to such avoidable handicaps as their tanks, designed on the principle of under-gunned mobility. The under-gunned tanks proved a particular handicap in Normandy, in 1944, where 3 British armoured divisions were used in a series of frontal attacks and, in spite of the handicap, managed to pin down the bulk of the opposing German armour and thus help the break-through by American forces on the right flank of the Allied bridgehead.

The doctrine with which American armoured divisions entered into action was somewhat less inhibited than the British but between 1940, when the first American armoured divisions were created, and 1944, when the majority of them was committed, there was a definite trend towards limiting their role, mainly to exploitation. In practice, however, this doctrinal tendency to regard armoured divisions as a single purpose arm proved unfounded and unworkable. They had to and did engage in different types of operations, from the break-through at St. Lo and the drive across France, to the hard fighting on the German frontier, as well as the defence of

Bastogne and the final push into Germany. They even took part in attacks against permanent fortifications, although, as a German armoured force manual pointed out several years earlier, this was an exceptional form of employment and, since their potential mobility could not be fully used, wasteful if other less mobile divisions were available.

In the variety of operations in which American armoured divisions participated the predominant tactical form were mixed subdivisional groupings of several arms. The same applied to British armoured divisions during the latter part of the Second World War and to the German panzer divisions, which pioneered the system of mixed armoured *Kampfgruppen*. However, neither could use it as fully as the American divisions which alone had armoured half-track carriers for the whole of their infantry and self-propelled guns for the whole of their artillery.

On the face of it, the subdivisional groups of tanks, infantry and other arms did no more than reproduce on a smaller scale the basic pattern of the armoured divisions. However, the processes associated with this miniaturisation and its consequences have been farther reaching, particularly in the light of the post-Second World War developments.

For one thing, the combination of different arms in smaller groups has made co-operation far more intimate and quicker. It assures far more rapid co-operation under fluid conditions of highly mobile warfare over wide fronts and ensures the benefits of mutual support whenever the terrain or other conditions prevent the operation of an armoured division in one body and make smaller tactical formations imperative. Moreover, smaller mixed groups make it easier to change from leading with tanks to leading with infantry, or vice versa, according to the needs of the situation.

In addition, smaller self-contained tactical groups have become essential for dispersion in face of the destructive power of modern weapons, first in the form of massed aerial bombing and now that of single nuclear devices. The Germans were the first to experience the former and to discover that attempts to mass in face of hostile air superiority were an invitation to disaster, as it was at Mortain in 1944. On the other hand, delaying defence in small mobile battle groups, often consisting only of a tank platoon and a depleted rifle company, could be highly successful, even under unfavourable conditions.

The more intimate grouping of different arms has also altered their relative position and roles. Thus, the earlier fairly well defined separation and co-operation between the tank and infantry echelons of the armoured divisions has given way to close integration between the two elements and co-operation between a number of mixed tank-infantry teams. Tanks themselves have ceased to be a distinct assault element, which they were thought to be for a long time, and have assumed instead the more general role of a source of mobile medium-weight direct fire power within the closely knit weapon system represented by an armoured battle group.

The relative position of the infantry had to alter also. Within small armoured battle groups it can neither play the role of the dominant element to which tanks are subordinated, as they were in the early days, nor that of a passive follower merely occupying or holding ground, as it was inclined to be in the early armoured divisions. Instead, it has to assume the role of an active partner, alternately leading or following, depending on whether the conditions favour it or the tanks. In other words, where visibility is reduced and fighting at close quarters, as in woods, built-up areas, hills and so on, the infantry has to lead and the tanks support it ; in more open country, where vehicular mobility is unimpeded and fighting generally at longer ranges, the tanks lead with the infantry following as closely as possible in their vehicles and completing the work of the tanks.

The smaller closely knit tactical groupings of tanks and armoured infantry have made it possible not only to change more rapidly from leading with one to the other, and thus better able to cope with a variety of situations during offensive operations, but also to pass from the offensive onto the defensive. Their ability to protect themselves effectively at close quarters as of engaging targets at longer ranges with the heavier weapons have made them equally adaptable to both.

Until relatively recently defence has been one of the neglected aspects of armoured operations, in spite of several successful examples of defence by armour, notably German. For many years it has been customary to describe armoured units as offensive in character and, by implication, to rule out defensive missions. This outlook was largely inspired by the conception of defence as static rather than dynamic, aimed at holding a particular piece of ground rather than inflicting a maximum of casualties on the enemy and wresting the initiative from him. From the latter point of view armoured units are well suited to defence. This is particularly true in the light of the destructive power of modern weapons which puts a premium on the ability to keep the situation fluid and where prolonged static defence—exemplified by the recent concept of defensive " bastions "—runs the risk of total annihilation. Thus, the description of armoured forces as offensive has been unnecessarily restrictive and it would have been far better to define them as mobile, though even this ought not to be interpreted too rigidly as meaning movement at all times and at all cost.

At the same time, while the close co-operation of different arms in small mixed battle groups has increased their ability to participate in various types of engagements, it has also simplified their form. Obviously, the smaller the unit the simpler must its tactics be : a small battle group could not indulge in trying to attack simultaneously several successive layers of a hostile line, as was envisaged, for instance, under the pre-Second World War Soviet break-through doctrine. Nor should there be any need for such tactics in view of the destructive power of present-day weapons, which render obsolete any system of linear defence and its counterpart of a massed break-through—which is neither possible nor necessary.

This does not, necessarily, preclude massed mobile employ-ment of armour and to that extent battle group tactics need not represent a break with the concepts introduced by the German panzer armies and Soviet tank armies. But any concentration could no longer take the form of a slow build up of large homogeneous blocks of men and material but would call for the swarming in of small mobile fighting teams.

With the proliferation of small self-contained battle groups and their dispersal armoured tactics are bound to move farther and farther away from their original linear character to that of area fighting. With both sides disposed over considerable areas fighting must tend towards probing, blocking and infiltrating. This type of fighting places greater emphasis on the resourcefulness and initiative of small units rather than elaborate technique but, at the same time, it poses before higher commanders the difficult task of ensuring that the dispersion involved in area fighting does not lead to piece-meal defeat and that the multitude of small actions fits into a pattern of overall success.

12

Logistics

IT is impossible to consider armoured forces without giving some thought to the system which provides the means for their existence and operation or, in other words, to logistics.

Logistics embrace a wide range of activities, from the acquisition of raw materials, through their processing into the desired products and the transportation of troops and equipment to the zone of operations, to the supply of day to day necessities. In the broadest sense logistics also embrace questions of manpower but in relation to armoured forces their meaning may be legitimately restricted to the more common one, which is confined to material problems.

Within this meaning the tank provides a good example of the range and sequence of logistical activities. Each one requires tens of tons of steel and smaller quantities of other materials and thousands of man-hours, involving many skills, spread over hundreds of industrial facilities ; when manufactured it becomes a heavy and bulky object which has to be stored and transported to the units in the field and for every mile it moves it requires fuel and lubricant and, periodically, spare parts.

The technique of tank production is a subject in itself and best discussed separately. The more general aspects of production are, however, part and parcel of logistics, not only as they concern the requisite materials and resources, but also the time necessary to translate a requirement into an actual item of equipment or supply in the hands of the user. This, or in American terminology the procurement lead time, has been growing steadily with the increasing complexity of equipment. During the First World War, for instance, tanks

131

were delivered to the troops within a year, or less, of the initiation of their design. Forty years later a new model requires at least two years from the laying down of a specification to the delivery of the first production vehicles and under peacetime conditions usually much longer.

The growing complexity and the longer lead time place increasing responsibility on the logisticians who must plan further and further ahead of the actual need. The growing complexity also calls for more extensive resources and multiplies the ramifications of logistics.

Ultimately much of the logistical effort is reflected in terms of money and its growth in the rising cost of tanks. Thus, during the First World War the cost of a typical British heavy tank was estimated at about £5,000 ; in the latter part of the Second World War a medium tank of comparable weight cost around £15,000 to £20,000 and since then some of the large and more complex models have exceeded £100,000. Even when allowances are made for monetary depreciation, these figures indicate the increase in costs which has taken place as a result of the steadily growing complexity of tanks.

Tanks and their procurement are, of course, only a part of the logistical problem, although an important one. The requirements of a self-contained armoured formation extend to many items and can perhaps be gauged from the size of some typical armoured divisions. For instance, the French *Division Légère Mécanique* of 1938 had a total personnel strength of 10,400, 220 tanks, 80 other armoured vehicles, 1,700 trucks and 1,500 motor-cycles ; the panzer division of 1939, at maximum strength, had 11,797 men, 328 tanks and 97 other armoured vehicles, 1,998 cars and trucks and 1,294 motor-cycles ; the American armoured division of 1941 had 12,697 men, 381 tanks, 759 armoured half-tracks and wheeled vehicles and 2,235 trucks, while the British armoured division of 1941–42 had 14,371 men, 340 tanks and 2,704 other vehicles. The much more recent, 1950, American armoured division had 15,973 men, 373 tanks, 636 other armoured vehicles and 2,094 trucks.

As in the case of individual tanks, so in that of whole armoured divisions costs have been going up. Thus, the cost of equipping the 1944 British armoured division was estimated at £18,000,000 and that of the contemporary and somewhat smaller American division at £10,000,000. But in 1951 the cost of equipping the contemporary American armoured division had risen to £70,000,000.

Figures such as these give a further indication of the magnitude of the logistical effort required to create armoured forces and of their growing cost. The only small consolation lies in the fact that they are not alone in this. For instance, the most complex type of tank still costs far less than a supersonic fighter aircraft and the total number of vehicles required by an armoured division is not much different from that of a motor- ised infantry division of comparable size.

The equipping of armoured forces brings in another phase of logistics. Once organised, armoured formations frequently have to be moved long distances by rail or by sea, which calls for considerable railway or shipping resources. To give an example, it has been estimated that the rail transport of a complete American armoured division of the 1944–45 type would require 71 trains with a total of 2,302 carriages and wagons, while to move by sea the same division would require 45 troop and cargo ships of the " Liberty " type.

Movement by road, on the other hand, requires consider- able quantities of fuel, the supply of which is one of the major problems of logistics. Here again the total requirements have been rising. For example, the French *Division Légère Mécan- ique* required 32,000 imperial gallons to move 100 miles ; the 1941 British armoured division required about 60,000 gallons to move the same distance and the 1944 American armoured division 120,000, while the requirements of its post-Second World War counterpart rose to no less than 190,000. All these figures apply to 100-mile moves by road. For cross-country operation they would be twice as high, or more, and even under favourable tactical conditions the last mentioned American division would require 290,000 gallons, or 930 tons, of fuel to move 100 miles.

Human requirements are about the only ones which have not increased significantly over the years, the daily ration per man weighing about 4 lb. In other words, the total ration requirement of an armoured division has been a relatively modest 20-odd tons per day. But this weight adds its share to the total requirements. In the closing stages of the Second World War it was estimated that in action an American division required about 600 tons of fuel, ammunition and other supplies per day. Similar figures applied to the contemporary British armoured divisions which under conditions of mobile operations required about 360 tons of fuel and 150 tons of ammunition per day and during heavy fighting a slightly smaller total but with the relative quantities of ammunition and fuel interchanged.

The huge quantities of supplies and the complete dependence on them sharply set off armoured units from the mobile forces of earlier days. The latter, based on the mobility of the horse, could largely live off the land and operate for long periods with negligible or no re-supply. Mechanised forces, on the other hand, depend not only on large quantities of supplies but also on their continuous flow.

If, for any reason, the flow of supplies is interrupted or even reduced the operation of armoured forces is almost immediately impeded. The difficulties of supplying armoured formations may have been exaggerated at times, as they were before the outbreak of the Second World War, but, nevertheless, on several occasions they proved to be very real. For instance, the inability of the logistical support to keep up with the tactical situation acted as a powerful brake on the advance of the German armoured divisions into Russia in 1941 and was principally responsible for stopping the Anglo-American armoured forces on the German frontier in the autumn of 1944. The dependence of tactical operations on logistics was shown even more clearly by Rommel's *Afrika Korps* whose operational decisions came to depend on the success, or otherwise, of

Italian tankers to run the gauntlet of British ships and aircraft. On a lower level, a good many tanks have been lost, particularly during retrograde movements, not through enemy action but because of failure of arrangements to re-supply them with fuel.

The problem of logistical support of armoured forces is not, of course, confined to fuel, although this aspect is probably the most striking. Spare parts are but one of several others. As early as 1917, French tank units experienced a severe crisis due to lack of spare parts. At that early stage of the development a failure to provide for an adequate supply of spare parts was understandable, for nothing like it had been met before. However, in varying degree, provision of spare parts has continued to be a problem ever since. That it is not an easy problem is perhaps best illustrated by the fact that a typical contemporary wheeled transport vehicle requires no less than 4,000 separate maintenance items and a typical tank almost 6,000.

The number and the total volume of the items required make the problem of logistical support of armoured forces formidable under the most favourable circumstances. Under enemy attack on the producing centres, storage depots, distributing points and on the lines of communication the difficulties are multiplied many times. In addition, the logistics system itself requires considerable resources for its operation. Depots, distributing points and the communication lines between them have to be manned and ships, trains, trucks and aircraft which carry the supplies require considerable quantities of fuel, as well as many other things.

There is, therefore, every incentive to keep supply requirements of armoured units down to a minimum. Every reduction brings in not only a reduction in the quantity which has to be delivered but also in the logistical facilities and the supplies necessary to operate them. Consequently, every saving in the primary requirements brings in a compounded saving in the overall expenditure of effort, reduces the size of the vulnerable logistical system and makes more certain the delivery of the reduced quantity of essential supplies. Conversely, every increase in the supply requirements of armoured units brings about a disproportionate increase in the total amount of effort and makes their operation even more difficult and precarious under the threat of enemy attack.

There is no easy solution to the problem but there are several ways of reducing logistical requirements and difficulties, apart from avoiding obvious waste and supply discipline.

One approach is through constant and careful scrutiny of armoured forces to ensure that every unit or item of equipment really justifies its logistical cost. Whenever opportunity occurs there is a tendency to acquire additional means which might be desirable but which, more often, constitute an ill-justified burden. Opportunities for this natural but insidious process grow as the wealth of the available equipment increases but often having less is being better for it. This applies in particular to overlavish equipment with vehicles which, far from increasing mobility, usually hampers it by creating traffic problems, and by swelling manpower, fuel and maintenance requirements. A question once asked whether every second lieutenant had to have a jeep may have been largely rhetorical and perhaps unfair to second lieutenants, but it contained a grain of truth and an indication where some of the possible economies lay.

Maximum versatility is another obvious approach to reducing the logistical burden by making the most of every single item. That it has not been universally recognised is illustrated by instances of developing parallel narrowly specialised categories of tanks and of deliberately confining armoured units to limited roles, instead of making the most of their potentialities. Duplication of effort has not been unknown either. For instance, tank battalions have carried infantry mortars and infantry battalions high velocity anti-tank guns when both could have been dispensed with by close combination of tanks, with all their guns, with infantry, with its usual mortars.

Standardisation, or concentration on a minimum number of types of equipment, is another and related question. Its lack was a weakness of the British tank development in the early part of the Second World War, when several different tank designs were being simultaneously produced, unnecessarily complicating supply and maintenance. Some of the savings possible through a reduction of models are illustrated by the change from the five different engines used in American medium tanks of the Second World War to a single standardised engine type which reduced the number of engine spare part items from 5,000 to less than 1,000.

Another aspect of the same question is that of reducing the variety of vehicles used within armoured formations. For instance, through force of circumstances, some German armoured divisions in Russia, during the latter part of the Second World War, had to use as many as 54 different types of vehicles, which seriously hampered their operation. The Germans wistfully remarked that, in contrast, their Russian opponents seemed to use only 2 types of vehicles in their armoured formations : the T-34 medium tank and a simple Ford-type truck. This over-simplified the facts but a reduction in the number of vehicle types has been a fruitful field for economy.

Yet another approach is through simplicity of equipment, to reduce the amount of maintenance and avoiding at all cost over-complicated models which may be theoretically superior but which require excessive attention. Another stepping stone towards the same ultimate objective of reduced logistical requirements is greater operating efficiency of individual vehicles so that they require less fuel and can operate longer between one refuelling and another. From this point of view, it is most unfortunate that more attention has not been given in general to the more efficient diesel engines which could have made a substantial contribution towards reducing the total fuel requirements of armoured units.

The way fuel is handled is also a field in which some economies have been made and others, such as bulk refuelling, are possible. For instance, the flimsy tin cans used by the British Army up to the early stages of the Second World War led to a considerable wastage of fuel and, therefore, increased overall requirements. The 4-gallon jerrican introduced by the Germans shortly before the Second World War and subsequently copied by most others, has been a great improvement but it is still relatively inefficient as a means of transporting large quantities of fuel because of the manpower involved in handling and the relative weight of the container.

A similar problem of dead weight to useful load besets other modes of transport. Better transport vehicles with a higher payload to dead weight ratio and greater individual load carrying capacity could make a further substantial contribution to easing logistical problems. So could a reduction in the amount of handling of supplies on their way from the supply depots to the units in the field by reducing the number of staging points, reloading and so on.

These are some of the many problems and ways of achieving greater economy and effectiveness in the field of logistics, which are so important to armoured forces and on which armoured forces depend for their life blood.

Part 3

Tank Development

13

Britain

THE first tank came to life in Britain in September 1915. This vehicle was still only fitted with a dummy turret and was quickly superseded by another, improved, model. But it was the first tank designed and built as such and the first tracked armoured vehicle ever to operate.

Like most new devices, the first tank was preceded by a long series of invention and experiments. As early as 1855, at the time of the Crimean War, J. Cowan took out a patent for a turtle-shaped wheeled armoured vehicle based on the contemporary steam tractor, and towards the end of the South African War of 1899 to 1902 armoured steam tractors were actually introduced, but only for hauling supplies. In 1899, at an exhibition of motor-vehicles in Richmond, Surrey, F. R. Simms demonstrated a powered quadricycle which he had fitted with a machine-gun and shield and in 1902 exhibited a boat-shaped armoured car built for the armament firm of Vickers and Maxim. In 1905 a fully tracked tractor built by the British firm of R. Hornsby & Sons was taken up by the military transport authorities, who experimented with it and a lighter model until 1914, but through lack of financial support from the War Office, Hornsby abandoned further development in 1912 and sold many of their patents to the Holt Manufacturing Company, which was pioneering the tracked agricultural tractors in the United States. At about the same time, two years before the outbreak of the First World War, an Australian, L. E. de Mole, submitted to the War Office detailed proposals for a fully tracked armoured vehicle, which in several respects anticipated the wartime British tanks, but only to have them rejected.

None of these early ideas or experiments had any direct connection with the birth of the first tank, although they did represent a general trend towards it and the evolution of mechanical components which made the automotive fighting vehicle possible. The actual chain of events which resulted in the first British tank started with Colonel E. D. Swinton some 2 or 3 months after the outbreak of the First World War.

At the time Colonel Swinton was acting as the official correspondent with the British Expeditionary Force in France and from his observations of the losses inflicted on the British infantry by German machine-guns conceived the idea of an armoured machine-gun destroyer built on the Holt tractor, of which he had heard but not yet seen. His original suggestion, put out in October 1914, met with no response from the military authorities but eventually found a very receptive mind in Winston Churchill, who was then the First Lord of the Admiralty. Unlike the Army, the Royal Navy was already using armoured vehicles, armoured cars developed since the outbreak of the war for the advanced units of the Royal Naval Air Service operating in France. Some of these armoured cars were remarkable in themselves—the Rolls Royce type was so successful that it was used for more than twenty years—and when the earlier opportunities for road operation disappeared the naval armoured car units began to turn their attention to the problem of cross-country movement. This, together with an indirect influence of Swinton's proposals, inspired Winston Churchill to set up, in February 1915, a Landships Committee to investigate armoured cross-country vehicles. With the setting up of this purely naval committee began the actual development work which led to the first tank.

The first steps consisted of experiments with the only available English track, the Diplock Pedrail type, and the design of a vehicle with very large wheels but in July 1915 Foster & Company of Lincoln were instructed to build an armoured vehicle on the basis of an American track assembly and the engine and transmission of an earlier Foster wheeled tractor. The tracks actually came from a Creeping Grip tractor, a type similar to the early Holts, but built by the Bullock Tractor Company of Chicago. The resulting vehicle was first tried on September 6, 1915 and consisted essentially of an armoured box with a fixed dummy turret mounted on short tracks and having two steering wheels carried on a projecting tail. The tracks were subsequently modified and lengthened and what was originally called the Bullock track machine became Little Willie but even the modified vehicle could not meet a newly stated requirement of the War Office. From June onwards the latter began to take an interest in landships and in August 1915 it stipulated that tanks should be able to cross trenches 5 feet wide. This requirement was translated into the dimensions of a sufficiently large wheel and from the latter came a new track layout, which gave the early British tanks their peculiar rhomboidal silhouette. In turn, the track layout led to the mounting of the main armament of 2 naval 57 mm. 6-pounder guns in sponsons projecting out of the side of the tank.

The second landship, designed on the new lines and later called Mother, was completed in December 1915. Although based on the same mechanical components as Little Willie it was much longer, 31 ft. 3 in. overall including tail wheels, and weighed 28.4 tons. Its trials were encouraging and in February 1916 an order was placed for the production of 100 machines, subsequently raised to 150 : 75 Mark I Males armed with 2 6-pounders and 4 machine-guns and 75 Mark I Females armed with 5 machine-guns only, each manned by a crew of 8.

As a result of the successful trials of Mother the first tank units were also organised, as the Heavy Section, Machine-gun Corps, under the command of Colonel Swinton. The original establishment was set at 6 companies, each of 25 tanks, and little over a month after the first production tanks were delivered in August 1916, 2 of the newly raised tank companies were sent to France. The General Headquarters, hitherto lukewarm towards tanks, were now anxious to use them, to bolster the British offensive on the Somme and to try a few at the earliest opportunity, instead of using them in a massed surprise assault. Thus, in spite of warnings against premature employment, the first 2 tank companies were sent into action on September 15, 1916.

The first tank action was not a great success. Used piecemeal, in twos or threes, the tanks did some useful work in support of the infantry but the overall result was negligible in relation to their possibilities. Forty-nine tanks were actually available and of this number 32 reached the starting line and 18 actually took part in the attack.

Small as it was, the success of tanks in their first battle was sufficient to induce the Commander-in-Chief to demand an expansion of the tank forces, with the result that 1,000 tanks were ordered shortly afterwards and the unit strength expanded to 9 battalions. The 9 battalions were to be formed into 3 tank brigades and each battalion, of 3 tank companies, had a nominal total of 72 tanks, shortly afterwards reduced to 36.

Needless to say, the expansion programme took time to become effective. Deliveries of new tanks, improved versions of the original Mark I, did not begin, for instance, until 1917 : that of the 100 Mark II and III in January and of the 1,000 Mark IV in March. In the meantime, the limited number of the available tanks continued to be used, in driblets and over some of the worst possible ground, changed by shell-fire and rain into a morass of mud. Even when new tanks arrived and numbers increased, as at the third battles of Ypres, or Passchendaele, in July 1917, inept employment and swampy conditions prevented the newly created Tank Corps from achieving any significant results. It was only on November 20, 1917, at Cambrai, that tanks were finally able to establish their value beyond any doubt and win recognition.

In essence, the battle of Cambrai originated with the Tank Corps and consisted of a massed assault over suitable ground without the usual forewarning artillery bombardment. The whole of the Tank Corps then in France was concentrated and took part in the battle, 3 brigades of 9 battalions with a total of 474 tanks. The result was a spectacular break-through and although the initial success was not exploited, through the failure of the cavalry and lack of other suitable means, Cambrai more than vindicated the Tank Corps.

After its success at Cambrai the Tank Corps in the field grew to 13 battalions but its next employment was on the defensive, against the German offensive in March 1918. Against its wishes, it was strung out in a defensive cordon and the dispersed tank units used mainly to cover the retreat. In the course of it many tanks had to be abandoned after mechanical breakdown or after running out of fuel, a story which repeated itself in several later retreats in which tanks took part.

But when the Allies returned to the offensive in the summer of 1918, the tanks came into their own again. At Amiens, in August 1918, the whole of the available strength was concentrated again, to the tune of 11 tank battalions and 604 tanks of all types, and the success of Cambrai was repeated. From then until the Armistice of November 11, 1918, tanks participated effectively in numerous smaller actions, opening the way for the advancing infantry and the total number of battalions in the field rose to 18, including one armoured car battalion, with a further 8 tank battalions training in England.

The most numerous of the vehicles used in the final phase were Mark V and Mark V* heavy tanks, of 28 to 33 tons, similar to but considerably improved on the earlier Marks, which they replaced. Just over 1,000 of these two were made. However, there were also some lighter vehicles, the 14-ton Medium A, which were capable of a maximum speed of 8.3 m.p.h., compared with 4.6 m.p.h. of the Mark V. They also differed from the latter in their layout, which included a fixed turret, with 4 machine-guns, above the tracks.

Successful and large scale as was the use of tanks in the closing stages of the war, even bigger things were being planned for 1919. In spite of the continued lack of understanding on the part of several military authorities, including the Commander-in-Chief, Sir Douglas Haig, tanks had found full support in the Government and the Allied Supreme War Council. In consequence, tank production, which had fallen below the 1917 peak of 200 tanks per month, was considerably increased in the latter part of 1918. At the same time, the Chief of Staff of the Tank Corps, Colonel J. F. C. Fuller, proposed a new method of operation.

Colonel Fuller's proposal, embodied in his " Plan 1919," envisaged a considerable extension of the methods hitherto employed. Cambrai and Amiens had already demonstrated the ability of heavy tanks, properly used, to break through the strongest entrenched positions. What was now proposed was to combine the frontal assault of massed heavy tanks with a deep tactical penetration by units of the new and faster medium tanks, which would strike at enemy headquarters and communications. The total number of tanks required to put the new tactics into effect was estimated at 5,000, or 90 heavy and medium tank battalions, of which the British Tank Corps would supply about one-third.

To provide the necessary force for 1919, the Tank Corps was to be expanded to 34 battalions. But the expansion had barely begun when the Armistice intervened and in the hurried demobilisation which followed the strength of the Tank Corps rapidly melted away. In fact, for a time after the war, the very existence of the Corps was in doubt. It was not until 1923 that the Tank Corps was put on a permanent peacetime basis with an authorised strength of 4 tank battalions.

In the immediate post-war period it was armoured cars which were principally in demand, for service in the various trouble spots, in Ireland, India and Iraq, and their total rose rapidly to 12 independent armoured car companies. Armoured cars, taken over from the Royal Naval Air Service, had already proved successful in the Middle East and after the war in Iraq they further demonstrated their value and that of mechanised units in general, as well as the possibility of aerial supply, in a series of far-ranging reconnaissance drives. In one particularly noteworthy operation, called the Ramadi Reconnaissance, in March 1922, a column of 7 Rolls-Royce armoured cars and 9 other vehicles operated in the desert for 21 days maintained entirely by aircraft.

In the meantime, at home, the tank battalions of the Tank

Corps, which was still struggling for survival, were also faced with the problem of equipment. Immediately after the Armistice it was decided to discontinue the production and development of all tanks, except the Medium C and D. The total number of British tanks produced up to the end of 1918 amounted to 2,636 but many of these had become casualties and such tanks as remained were only built for a short useful life under the particular conditions of the Western Front. There was, consequently, no stock of serviceable wartime tanks which would compare with the 3,737 Renault F.T. with which the French Army was left or the 952 M1917 light tanks of the United States Army. Later this proved a blessing, for it meant that there was no dead weight of obsolete equipment, but it made the immediate equipment problem acute.

Of the two designs which were retained for further development, Medium C was designed in December 1917 to fulfil a Tank Corps specification for an " ideal " medium tank. It was a relatively large 19.5-ton vehicle, 25 ft. 10 in. long overall, with the rhomboidal unsprung track layout characteristic of the earlier Mark I to V heavy tanks. However, it had no sponsons but a single fixed turret mounting either one 6-pounder and 3 machine-guns or 4 machine-guns only.

The other model, the Medium D, was conceived together with " Plan 1919 " and figured largely in the latter as the fast medium tank which would strike at the hostile headquarters. The principal requirement originally laid down for it was speed, 20 m.p.h., or more than twice the maximum of 8.3 m.p.h. of the Medium A or the 7.9 m.p.h. of the Medium C. The actual design of the Medium D was tackled by Lt.-Colonel P. Johnson, who was on the engineering staff of the Tank Corps and who in 1919 was asked to form the first government Tank Design Department. Colonel Johnson rose to the occasion and in mid-1920 produced the first prototype capable of the specified maximum speed, having already demonstrated its possibility a year earlier, in a demonstration at Leeds, with a stripped-down Mark V. However, the design of the tank was still within the wartime conception of a short useful life, while after the war much longer trouble-free life began to be demanded. Moreover, after the war, Colonel Fuller added the requirement that the Medium D be amphibious. The modified conception demanded considerable further development effort and ruled out such features as the original wire cable inter-dependent suspension.

Nevertheless, Colonel Fuller, who was responsible for initiating tank policy at the War Office, felt sufficiently confident first to abandon the Medium C, of which only 36 were built, and then, in 1920, on the strength of preliminary experiments, to recommend the adoption of the Medium D as a cavalry tank and of a similar but lighter infantry tank. The Light Infantry Tank was produced in 1921 and on trials attained the remarkable for its day speed of 30 m.p.h. But, like the Medium D, it had a number of troublesome features, including the cable suspension and its own novelty, and further cause of undoing, in the form of curved track steering by means of laterally flexible " snake tracks."

In the meantime, an order was also placed with the armament firm of Vickers Ltd., for the design of a tank similar to the Light Infantry Tank. Designed and built in 1921, the 8.75 ton Vickers tank looked like a smaller version of the Medium C but, for the first time on a British tank, it had a 360° traverse turret, domed in shape and mounting a 47 mm. 3-pounder gun, and it had a sprung suspension. Its speed was disappointing and it was handicapped by the use of a hydro-static transmission, which had already been tried on some of the wartime heavy tanks and abandoned. In consequence, this design was rejected but, nevertheless, a production order was placed with Vickers, who in 1922 designed a second tank which weighed 11.75 tons but which had a designed speed of 15 m.p.h. and in practice proved capable of more. And it was this tank which became the post-war vehicle of the Tank Corps and not the Medium D or the Light Infantry Tank of the Tank Design Department, which was closed down in 1923 as an economy measure.

The Vickers tank was originally called Light Tank Mark I but it became far better known under its second designation of Medium Tank Mark I, or, more generally, as the Vickers Medium. Its production, begun in 1923, amounted to some 160 Mark I and II and it became virtually the only tank in service with the Royal Tank Corps throughout the twenties and it remained as the standard medium tank well into the late thirties. Its general layout was not as good as that of the first Vickers design and this was not compensated by the fact that a machine-gun was mounted in either side of the high super-structure—its 3-pounder gun and the 2 to 4 ball-mounted Hotchkiss machine-guns in the turret should have been enough, even for those machine-gun minded days. But, to offset its failings, the Vickers Medium did initially have three virtues : it was considerably faster than any tank in service at the time, it was reasonably reliable and there was just about enough of it to equip the four battalions of the Royal Tank Corps. In consequence, it could and did serve as the vehicle with which the Royal Tank Corps pioneered new methods in armoured warfare and, in a way, motivated the development through its improved performance.

The development of the new methods in armoured warfare was initiated chiefly by Colonel Fuller, who in 1919 submitted the first post-war memorandum on the organisation of the army in relation to tanks. In it he proposed that each infantry battalion be reorganised to include one tank company and suggested the formation of one such new model battalion to carry out practical tests. The War Office accepted the idea in rough and even decided to form a new model brigade but nothing was done about it, beyond some half-hearted experiments in 1921 and 1922, until 1926, when it was decided to form an Experimental Mechanised Force. A year later, on May 1, 1927, this force came into being, assembled for trials on Salisbury Plain.

But even then, in 1927, the Experimental Mechanised Force was the first properly constituted self-contained force based on automotive vehicles. It set a new pattern which was followed throughout the world and, together with the theoretical writings of Colonel Fuller and then Captain Liddell Hart, gave Britain another lead in the field of armoured warfare.

The Experimental Mechanised Force itself consisted of a reconnaissance group of 2 armoured car and one tankette companies, one battalion of 48 Vickers Mediums, one motorised machine-gun battalion, the equivalent of a large artillery regiment which included some self-propelled 18-pounder guns, and an engineer company. Both during the 1927 manoeuvres and those of 1928, when it was renamed the Armoured Force, this experimental formation provided valuable experience in the mobile employment of mechanised units, including the important and new problems of movement of large numbers of vehicles under tactical conditions and their supply. But at the three main tasks set before it—strategic reconnaissance, co-operation with infantry divisions and independent operations—it was not considered an unqualified success. For each of these roles a somewhat different composition could be shown best. Moreover, the unarmoured elements of the force were considered to be a drag on the armoured ones and Colonel Fuller was already advocating armoured formations composed almost entirely of tanks. As a result, what emerged from the 1927-28 trials was the unfortunate idea that the best line of future development of mechanised forces lay in " all-tank " tank brigades, to which other elements, such as infantry, artillery and engineers, would be attached if or when required for particular operations.

The " all-tank " trend was embodied in the first armoured force manual, *Mechanised and Armoured Formations*, issued in 1929, which considered armoured, or tank, brigades as the basic mechanised formations. In addition, the manual divided the army into " mobile troops " and " combat troops," as if the two could not be one. It showed that the idea of a versatile and self-contained mechanised force had not taken root and that it was being supplanted by a division of armoured troops into two separate specialised categories, which grew into the mobile all-tank formations and tank units for infantry support.

In consequence, it was not in Britain but in Germany that the idea of effective versatile armoured formations was brought to fruition in the form of the panzer divisions.

In Britain, after the Armoured Force was disbanded in 1928, further experiments, resumed in 1931 and 1932, were on a tank brigade basis, the brigade consisting of one light and 3 mixed light-medium tank battalions. After a break of one year, in 1934, the tank brigade was permanently established and for the following 4 years it constituted the one mechanised formation of the British Army, as well as a major portion of its tank strength. During the period of tank brigade development considerable progress was made in new methods of operation and mobile tactics of tank units. But the all-tank composition of the tank brigade, which greatly helped the development of new armoured technique, also limited its tactical capabilities as a mechanised formation and this went hand in hand with a tendency to concentrate on the strategic potentialities of the newly found mechanised mobility to the detriment of the tactical essentials of fighting power. During the 1934 manoeuvres the tank brigade was temporarily combined with a motorised infantry brigade and a motorised artillery brigade into a mobile force, but the short-lived experiment was not considered a success, and tank and other units, which should have complemented each other to achieve maximum effectiveness, went their separate ways.

The preoccupation with mobility and the relative neglect of striking power could also be observed in tank design, where considerable progress took place except in tank armament. Almost up to the outbreak of the Second World War there was no British tank more powerfully armed than the light experimental Vickers tank of 1921, in spite of the fact that several vehicles much improved in every other way were designed and built.

One of the most important early developments was actually that of very small and very lightly armed vehicles. This originated with the idea of a cheap, partially armoured one-man machine which could be used to assist the infantry. The development of this type was initiated by Major Martel, who built the first one himself in his private workshop, in 1925, and the work was then carried on by Messrs. Carden and Loyd. This type of vehicle was taken up officially in 1926 and 8 Martel-type Morris-built 2-man vehicles and 8 Carden Loyd Mark IV, also with a crew of 2, were built for the 1927 Experimental Mechanised Force, and used as reconnaissance tankettes.

At this stage it was decided that what was really wanted were two types of light armoured vehicles : a small turreted reconnaissance vehicle for the armoured units and an armoured machine-gun carrier for work with the infantry. The latter led to the Carden Loyd Mark VI, a low 2-man vehicle weighing 1.5 tons and capable of 25 m.p.h. Introduced in 1928, it attracted world-wide attention as a thoroughly practical, low-cost vehicle with a performance above the contemporary average and it was purchased and copied by several countries. It was also issued to the Royal Tank Corps battalions pending the development of the turreted light tank and was used in the contemporary mechanised infantry brigade experiments which revived something of General Fuller's New Model Brigade of 1919. Development of the armoured machine-gun carrier was temporarily abandoned in 1933 but it was revived about 2 years later and in 1935 a new and larger model was built, the forerunner of the Bren Gun Carrier, 10 of which were allotted to each infantry battalion shortly before the Second World War.

The first of the light tanks with a turret, the Carden Loyd Mark VII, came out in 1929. It was a 2.5-ton, 2-man machine armed with a .303 in. Vickers machine-gun and capable of no less than 35 m.p.h. The next model—Carden Loyd Mark VIII—was considered sufficiently satisfactory to be put into service in 1930 as the Light Tank Mark I, and from it stemmed a long line of Vickers Carden Loyd light tanks, the Carden Loyd Company having been absorbed in 1928 by the newly formed Vickers-Armstrongs organisation. As the 4.75-ton Mark V of 1935 it became a 3-man tank with a .5 in., as well as a .303 in.,

Vickers machine-gun, and in its final Mark VIC form it weighed 5.3 tons and was armed with coaxial 15 mm. and 7.92 mm. Besa machine-guns.

The Vickers Carden Loyd light tanks were mechanically successful and they were also inexpensive ; their fighting power was limited but they were considered suitable for reconnaissance and also for colonial service, in which they gradually replaced the armoured cars. As a result, they were produced in some quantity during the thirties, although as time went on their cost increased and their soundness decreased with growing size, and they became overloaded top-heavy vehicles. They were not intended to be the principal equipment but they almost became that, for it was only in 1938 that the 1922-designed Vickers Mediums began to be replaced by a new gun-tank, the first production vehicle for many years with anything more powerful than a machine-gun.

The reason for this delay lay in a combination of circumstances and tank policies. Once the production of the Medium Mark I and II was completed, Vickers designed a new medium tank known as the Sixteen Tonner, the first of which was built in 1928 and the second in 1929. It was a considerable step forward on the Medium Mark I and II, except for its main armament which still consisted only of a 47 mm. gun. But guns were then regarded as a mere appendage to machine-guns, and of these it had no less than 5 : one in the main turret and a pair in each of the 2 auxiliary turrets placed forward on either side of the driver's position. There was general satisfaction with it and a third vehicle was ordered in 1931, intended to be followed by others. But a financial crisis intervened and as a result of drastic cuts in defence expenditure the development of the Sixteen Tonner was abandoned at the third vehicle.

When it became clear that the Army could not afford this rather expensive type of medium tank in peacetime, many favoured concentrating production on the other extreme of the cheap machine-gun-armed light tanks and this is virtually what happened. By an odd coincidence, at about the same time the Germans also temporarily concentrated on the production of this type of light tank, but principally because they had no tanks at all and because the development of the more powerful vehicles which they wanted was taking a long time. In either case, but particularly so the British, there was a far more sensible solution close at hand.

This was represented by the Vickers-Armstrongs Six Ton Tank, a highly successful private venture. The prototype, which was ready in 1928, suffered from a touch of the contemporary machine-gun complex, having 2 machine-gun turrets mounted side by side. But the second variant had a single 2-man turret with a 47 mm. gun and machine-gun, that is, the same armament as the turret of the Sixteen Tonner. It also had the same maximum armour thickness and the same 100-mile operating range ; it was not quite as fast, being capable of a maximum speed of 22 m.p.h. as against 30 m.p.h. of the Sixteen Tonner, but it was fast enough for most practical purposes and it had some compensating features, including a much better and more durable short-pitch track. It was certainly not as luxurious as the Sixteen Tonner but it cost far less. Altogether, the second variant of the Six Ton Tank represented a very sensible design based on essentials, a type which carried the same main armament as the medium tank at a fraction of the cost and yet which was far more useful than the lighter machine-gun-armed light tanks. This type was evolved in the United States into the M3 light tank, which the British Army was glad enough to get in 1941, and in Czechoslovakia into the Pz.Kpfw.38t, which served the Germans well enough in France in 1940 and in the first Russian campaign.

However, this type of tank was not even considered in Britain. At the time the Army was inclined to go to extremes, shown by the large and expensive Sixteen Tonner on the one hand and the small and cheap Carden Loyds on the other, or, a little later, by the division into the two narrowly specialised categories of mobile and infantry tanks, instead of a single versatile type of tank and armoured unit.

There was also some lack of appreciation of the primary importance of gun power and a tendency, inherited from the

Mark I Female of 1916, to over-value a multiplicity of machine-guns. This showed itself best on the A.1, or Independent, 31.5-ton experimental heavy tank built by Vickers in 1926, which had four small machine-gun turrets but which in its fifth and main turret only mounted a 47 mm. 3-pounder. It was virtually a Female version of the First World War heavy tanks translated into more modern idiom. The same tendency was responsible for the fact that when a compromise solution—a cheap medium tank—was attempted as a successor to the Sixteen Tonner it reproduced most of the latter's bulk and the unnecessary complication of three turrets. It proved to be neither a good enough light-weight nor a good enough medium, although, in all fairness to its designer Sir John Carden, its chassis proved useful for other vehicles.

Design of this new medium tank began in 1934 to the A.9 specification, the prototype was completed in 1936 and the tank was put into limited production in 1937. It became the Cruiser Tank Mark I, a 12.5-ton vehicle with a crew of 6. In addition to 3 machine-guns, it had a new 2-pounder 40 mm. gun, which represented a further decrease in the calibre of British tank guns since the First World War, although, of course, the muzzle velocity of the new gun was higher.

The designation of the A.9 as a cruiser, instead of a medium, tank not only introduced a new name but also marked a parting of the ways in the development of the more powerful tanks. Throughout the twenties and early thirties the same Vickers Mediums were used both for co-operation with the infantry and for mechanised force experiments. In 1934, however, one of the 5 battalions to which the Royal Tank Corps had grown was set aside specifically for infantry support. In 1934, too, shortly after work on the A.9 began, Vickers-Armstrongs were asked to produce a special infantry version, the A.10. Its main characteristic was thicker armour, 30 mm. instead of the 14 mm. of the A.9, and it dispensed with the 2 auxiliary machine-gun turrets. But by the time it was ready even thicker armour was deemed essential for infantry support tanks and it was consequently re-designated and produced as a heavy cruiser tank.

The new specification for an infantry tank was largely the work of General Elles, the wartime commander of the Tank Corps, who in 1934 became Master General of Ordnance and who brought back with him some of the First World War ideas. In short, he asked for a tank whose principal characteristic would be armour protection, a tank which would not be much faster than the infantry but which would be immune to the contemporary 37 mm. anti-tank guns. At the same time, money was still short and the tank was designed strictly down to a price. The result was what one might have expected: an 11-ton tank with a crew of 2, a single machine-gun and a maximum speed of 8 m.p.h. It was heavily armoured, having armour up to 60–65 mm. thick, but its usefulness was extremely limited. Nevertheless, beginning with the pilot model built in 1936, 139 were produced and it became the Infantry Tank Mark I.

When the gathering war clouds loosened the Treasury purse strings a more ambitious infantry tank was embarked upon, which combined the armament and general layout of the A.10 with even thicker, 75 mm. maximum, armour. Mechanically it was derived from an experimental series of 3 A.7 medium tanks built at the Woolwich Arsenal in the mid-thirties and it became the Infantry Tank Mark II or, later, the Matilda. Up to 1941 this 26.5-ton tank was the most heavily armoured vehicle in service anywhere but its general effectiveness was limited by its low mobility and its main armament of only the 40 mm. 2-pounder, which fired solid shot only, while its immunity proved to be temporary.

A larger calibre weapon than the 47 mm. and later 40 mm. tank guns was introduced in the late twenties but only for a limited role in a specialised type of vehicle called the Close Support Tank. The first of this type was a Vickers Medium rearmed with a 15-pounder mortar and this was later followed by others which were standard cruiser or infantry tanks rearmed with a 3.7 or 3 in. howitzer in place of the 40 mm.

tank gun, or, finally, with a 95 mm. howitzer. All the howitzer-armed tanks were strictly support vehicles intended for firing smoke or high-explosive shells only and quite incapable of anti-tank fire. They could not, therefore, be compared in any way, as has sometimes been done, with the contemporary German or Soviet medium tanks, whose 75 or 76.2 mm. guns were short barrelled but general purpose weapons, and whose equivalent was conspicuously missing in British tank development.

One further significant step was taken before the outbreak of the Second World War, namely the development of a new series of cruiser tanks to replace the A.9 and A.10 and based on the American Christie independent suspension. It is a revealing reflection on the contemporary interest in what was happening in other parts of the world that the Christie system was only looked into after the visit of a British mission to Russia, in 1936, when Soviet B.T. Christie-type tanks were seen, some 8 years after the first demonstration of the original Christie vehicle in the United States. However, thereafter events moved with commendable speed, a chassis was purchased from Christie and the first of the new series of cruiser tanks, built to the A.13 specification by the newly created Nuffield Mechanisation Ltd., was completed in the second half of 1937. This became the Cruiser Tank Mark III, a vehicle with the same general layout as the A.10, or Cruiser Mark II, but with a Christie-type suspension and a Nuffield-Liberty V–12 engine which gave it a maximum speed of 30 m.p.h. It weighed 14.2 tons and had the same 14 mm. armour as the Sixteen Tonner and the A.9, although on its second version, called Cruiser Mark IV, this was raised to 30 mm. Another, somewhat later and lower silhouette design to the A.13 specification, the 18-ton Cruiser Mark V, or Covenanter, had even thicker armour and so did the 19-ton Mark VI, or Crusader, which first appeared in 1939, just before the outbreak of the Second World War. But none of these had more powerful main armament than the 2-pounder of the A.9 or A.10. Yet one auxiliary machine-gun turret reappeared on the Crusader and 2 on the contemporary experimental A.14 and A.16 heavy cruisers, showing how strong the machine-gun complex still was.

As a result of all this, on the eve of the Second World War there were under development two distinct categories of cruiser tanks and infantry tanks, the former distinguished by their relatively high maximum speed of 30 m.p.h. and the latter by their thick armour but both armed with the same 40 mm. 2-pounder gun main armament. Exactly the same main armament was also used on a new light tank, the 7.15-ton Tetrarch, but this tank hardly counted. Although its prototype was completed in December 1937, the first production vehicles were not delivered until July 1940 and the Tetrarch was practically never used except as an airborne tank in the 1944 Normandy landings when it became the first tank ever to go into action by air.

As for the policy of the two categories of cruiser and infantry tanks, it was basically unsound. It meant that tanks were not being developed to achieve an optimum combination of their principal characteristics of fire power and mobility but that they were being channelled into specialised fields to suit preconceived ideas based on the traditional division into infantry and cavalry. As later events amply proved, what was required was not the same armament on two or more different types of vehicles but one good well-armed tank followed by the development of another and even more powerful vehicle.

For the cruisers the 2-pounder main armament was initially adequate and the cruisers were generally well up to the standard of contemporary light-medium tanks. But what was lacking was a more powerful tank which would supplement and eventually supersede the 2-pounder gun cruiser, a type exemplified by the 75 mm. gun medium tanks which other countries were developing. The infantry tank could never fill this need because, with one single experimental exception, it was never more powerfully armed than the cruiser and, of course, because it was not mobile enough. Its own basis was a negative one of armour protection. Yet in infantry support, as in mechanised formations, successful employment of tanks depended chiefly on skilful combination of fire and movement and not on ambling forward relying on thick armour. What the division into the two categories of cruiser and infantry tanks really produced was a dispersion of design and production effort over two types whose primary offensive characteristics were no different. In addition, the emphasis on mobility in one case and on armour protection in the other obscured the even greater importance of gun power. The effects of this were to plague British tanks throughout the Second World War.

Of the two main categories, the infantry tank was initially in the ascendant. In 1938 a Mobile Division was finally formed, embracing the Tank Brigade of the Royal Tank Corps and 2 mechanised cavalry brigades equipped with light tanks. A year later it was renamed the Armoured Division and two more such divisions were planned. But 5 army tank brigades, each of 3 battalions of infantry tanks, were also planned and it was to infantry tank production that greater effort was being devoted both immediately before the war and during the period of Phoney War preceding the German offensive in the West, in May 1940. The reason was that the infantry tanks fitted far better with the prevailing Franco-British ideas of slow-motion infantry warfare, while armoured divisions were considered suitable only for a limited role and not as the versatile decisive formations which the panzers were proving to be. Indeed, such was the effect of the earlier preoccupation with operational mobility of the Tank Brigade and of the traditional ideas of the cavalry, which was mechanised and combined with the Royal Tank Corps into the new Royal Armoured Corps, that the Mobile Division and its immediate successor was considered chiefly for the very limited role of strategic reconnaissance.

During this period, another infantry tank was accepted, the Valentine, a redesign of the A.10 with 60 mm. armour and a 2- instead of 3-man turret, and a new A.20 specification was issued in September 1939 for an even more heavily armoured infantry tank than the Matilda. Apart from its armour, the

main characteristic of the A.20 was to be trench-crossing
capacity, a requirement compounded from memories of the
First World War and the contemporary static trench-warfare-
like conditions.   The A.20 did not get beyond two prototypes
but its basic features were incorporated in the next or A.22
design.   This became the Churchill infantry tank, a 38.5-ton
vehicle with 100 mm. frontal armour but still armed with
nothing more powerful than the 40 mm. 2-pounder !

The pre-eminent position of the infantry tanks was radically
altered by the German victory in France in 1940 and the
decisive part played in it by the panzer divisions.   Attention
turned to armoured divisions, of which 9 were now planned and
which were now looked upon as suitable for more than strategic
reconnaissance or even more than exploitation.   As a further
consequence, the emphasis shifted to cruiser tanks.   But,
although the requirement for infantry tanks was reduced
considerably, Britain's strategic position and the threat of
invasion precluded any drastic change which would reduce the
total output of tanks.   Consequently the change over from
infantry to cruiser tanks was slow and three newly raised
armoured divisions initially had to be equipped with Valentine
and Matilda infantry tanks.   The crumbling importance of
infantry tanks was also propped up by a single successful action
of the Matildas in France and their successes against the
ill-equipped Italian troops in Africa in 1940 and early 1941.
But the most important consideration, with regard to infantry
tanks and in general, was an uninterrupted output of the largest
possible quantity of tanks.

Great efforts were made to increase tank production and
they were crowned with considerable success.   As a result the
Army received increasingly large quantities of tanks.   Four
years earlier, in 1936, the total strength amounted to 375, 164
of which were the obsolete Vickers Mediums and the rest light
machine-gun-armed tanks built since 1929.   When the
war broke out in September 1939 there were 1,000 light tanks
but only 146 of the new cruiser and infantry tanks.   However,
production of the latter was rising and in total in 1939 more

tanks were produced in Britain than in Germany. In 1940 the output in the two countries was almost equal : 1,399 in Britain and 1,460 in Germany.

This, however, was not known at the time. For a long time German tank strength was grossly overestimated and there was a tendency, all too common everywhere, to ascribe enemy successes to superior numbers and not superior methods or equipment. Moreover, Dunkirk and the rest of the 1940 campaign in France, in which one armoured division, one infantry tank brigade and 7 mechanised cavalry reconnaissance regiments were used, cost the loss of almost 700 tanks. In addition to the German threat there were also the requirements of the Middle East, where British forces were facing the Italians. All this combined to urge the greatest possible output of tanks. During 1941 the rate of tank production trebled and the total for the year amounted to 4,841, or over 1,000 more than Germany's output for that year. In 1942 British tank production rose further, to its annual peak of 8,611 tanks, or more than double the contemporary German output.

The production of these quantities of tanks was a great achievement. Unfortunately, a good deal of the effort was wasted. None of the many Covenanter cruiser tanks was ever considered battle-worthy because of mechanical shortcomings ; the Churchill, rushed into production when invasion seemed imminent, took a long time to become reliable and fit for use in the field. The one notable exception in this respect was Vickers-Armstrongs' Valentine, which showed the great value of an adequate development background and what might have been achieved had policy allowed a concentration of effort on one basic design, instead of dispersing it in the simultaneous production of two categories of cruiser and infantry tanks and five different designs no different from each other as regards their main armament. As it was, the two principal types of tanks used in the field, in Libya, in 1941 and early 1942, the Matilda and the Crusader, not only required a considerable amount of maintenance effort but, by the contemporary

H.A.

standard of the Eastern Front, their main armament was already obsolete.

However, the Germans happened to be in the same boat. Also outclassed by the new Soviet T-34 medium tank, they had, at the time, no significant advantage over British tanks. Contrary to once widespread belief, the 5 cm. KwK L /42 gun of the most numerous German tank, the Pz.Kpfw.III, was similar in its armour-piercing performance to the 2-pounder. The short-barrelled 7.5 cm. KwK L /24 of the Pz.Kpfw.IV was a better general-purpose weapon but at sheer armour punching it was no longer superior to smaller calibre guns and, in any case, there were not very many of it. Thus the reverses suffered by British forces at the hands of the German *Afrika Korps* were not due to superior tank guns but to tactics. While the Germans concentrated their tanks in their two panzer divisions and supported them closely with other arms, British tanks carried the dispersion between infantry and cruiser tanks into battle and fought divided. Moreover, the armoured brigades of the armoured divisions tended to be employed on their own, on the lines of the earlier all-tank principles, instead of fighting in well-knit divisional teams.

The relative armament position held good even in the second half of 1942, when, as a result of their experience in Russia, the Germans started bringing out better armed tanks. But this was not due to the appearance of correspondingly better armed British tanks but due to the arrival of new medium tanks from the United States, the Grant and then the Sherman. The former was a modified version of the American M3 medium first ordered in the second half of 1940, and the latter was the standard American M4 medium tank. The Sherman made its début at the battle of El Alamein, in October 1942, where it played an important part in the final defeat of the *Afrika Korps*. Subsequently, in 1943, when deliveries of American-built tanks exceeded British production and when, in spite of the continued high rate of production, few battle-worthy British tanks were available, the Sherman became the principal tank of the British armoured forces.

The fact that few, if any, battle-worthy British tanks were available in 1943 out of the many produced was due to the earlier concentration on mobility or armour protection, to the detriment of tank armament, and the subsequent preoccupation with quantity. The need for a more powerful tank gun than the 2-pounder was not appreciated sufficiently and as late as 1943 tanks were being produced with this no longer adequate weapon. A more powerful 6-pounder gun, of the same 57 mm. calibre as the tank guns of the First World War, was conceived as early as 1938 but its design was not pursued with any urgency. In mid-1940 a tentative specification was issued for a cruiser tank with this gun but no firm decision was taken for its design until January 1941, with the result that the first prototype of what were to become the Centaur-Cromwell cruiser tanks was only ready in January 1942. In the meantime, in an attempt to put the 6-pounder more rapidly into service, it was decided in March and April 1941 to mount it in modified Crusaders and Churchills. The first of these up-gunned versions, or Crusader III and Churchill III, were produced in May and March 1942 respectively.

The 57 mm. 6-pounder was a great improvement on the 40 mm. 2-pounder but by the time the up-gunned Churchills and Crusaders began to appear in the field, towards the end of 1942, it was outdated by the new longer-barrelled 75 mm. gun of the rearmed German Pz.Kpfw.IV and completely outclassed by the 88 mm. gun of the Tiger I heavy tank. At the beginning of 1942 the War Office began to consider a more powerful tank gun, the 76.2 mm. 17-pounder, for a proportion of infantry and cruiser tanks. This was a timely move because, as it happened, the Germans were already working on a medium tank with a similar gun, the Panther. But again the development of the British tank gun was not pressed with sufficient urgency and, in any case, the 17-pounder model was only intended to form a small proportion of cruiser tanks and not to replace the lighter armed models in general. The first model of a cruiser tank with a 17-pounder, the A.30 or Challenger, was completed in August 1942 but it proved unsatisfactory.

Although a few were made for 1944, it was only in 1945, too late to be used in the war, that a satisfactory 17-pounder tank was produced—the original Centurion.

In production during 1943 and in battle in 1944 the equivalent of the Panther was the 27.5-ton Cromwell. With a maximum speed of 38 m.p.h. the Cromwell was mobile enough but it was completely outgunned by the German medium tank, in spite of a change from the original 6-pounder to a medium-velocity 75 mm. gun. The latter was the outcome of a new official policy adopted in January 1943 and inspired by the success of the medium-velocity 75 mm. guns on the American-built Grants and Shermans. Unfortunately it was a policy more than 2 years behind the American and at least 3 behind the Russian. What was good in 1941 and 1942 would no longer be adequate in 1944 and this time no help would come from the United States, where the more powerful successor to the Sherman, the T20 medium tank, was being pushed with as much energy as the British 17-pounder cruiser tank. The reasons were much the same : that the role of armoured formations should again be limited to exploitation, that they should not fight enemy tanks and similar chimerical ideas. Only a few months before the invasion of Europe was an attempt made to redeem the situation by grafting the 76 mm. gun and turret of the T20 series on to the Sherman chassis. Virtually the same thing happened in Britain : standard Sherman tanks were rearmed with 17-pounders and these hurried conversions became for a time the most potent Allied tanks in the field.

But for the 17-pounder Sherman, the close nature of the Normandy battlefield, which robbed the Germans of some of the advantage of their powerful tank guns, and the overall Anglo-American superiority in resources the tank situation might have been critical. As it was, the armoured divisions were badly handicapped by the majority of their under-gunned tanks. However, in spite of this and the official doctrine, 3 armoured divisions made a major contribution to winning the Normandy battle, as well as to the subsequent drive across north-east Europe.

Altogether there were 5 armoured divisions in existence in the latter part of the Second World War out of the 11 raised. Some of the others were disbanded because of losses but the principal reason for the reduction in the number of armoured divisions was a lack of appreciation of their potentialities and a continued diversion of a considerable portion of armoured strength to infantry support. In spite of the obvious versatility and effectiveness of the panzer divisions and the fact that the British armoured divisions were employed in a similar manner in Libya and later in Normandy, official doctrine still regarded armoured divisions as only " designed for exploitation." And because armoured divisions were regarded capable only of a limited role there existed a large number of tank units for use under other circumstances, namely in conjunction with infantry formations. To this category belonged army tank brigades, each with 3 battalions of infantry tanks, and the so-called " swinger " armoured brigades organised on the same lines as the armoured brigades of the armoured divisions and equipped with Sherman medium tanks.

Fortunately, in spite of the continued division between armoured units for mobile operations and tank units for co-operation with infantry formations, infantry tanks were fighting a losing battle. Ever since 1940, when their production was cut, infantry tanks as such were gradually losing ground and the Churchill turned out to be the last produced. The Libyan campaigns of 1941 and 1942 undermined further the policy of building a slow infantry tank whose thick armour did not compensate for its lack of mobility. However, the infantry tank was not abandoned at this stage but only as a separate vehicle design. In 1942 a new policy emerged of a single vehicle design produced in two versions : one heavily armoured for infantry support and the other, the cruiser tank intended for exploitation, less heavily armoured but more mobile. The armament was still the same for both and was not considered as the primary requirement.

From this came the design of the heavily armoured infantry versions of the Cromwell to partner the standard cruiser model. Even the Americans caught a touch of this disease and designed a heavily armoured experimental version of their Sherman, the T14 assault tank.   It had thicker, 102 mm. armour and weighed 41 tons, but its offensive power was no greater than that of the standard M4 medium and it was very wisely abandoned in September 1943.   The only infantry derivative of the Cromwell to be actually built, the A.33 experimental tank, was also distinguished by thick, 114 mm. armour but for all its 40-odd tons it carried no heavier armament than the 27.5-ton Cromwell.

Even when the design of the A.41, or Centurion, 17-pounder cruiser tank began in 1944, a more heavily armoured but no more heavily armed infantry tank, the A.45, was still envisaged.   But wiser counsels finally prevailed.   Out of the original and unsuccessful A.30 17-pounder cruiser and the infantry versions of the Cromwell came a single new type of cruiser, the Comet, armed with a derated version of the 17-pounder called the 77 mm. gun.   First used in the winter of 1944-45, the Comet was still behind the Panther in armament but it made up some of the leeway, it was mobile and it was thoroughly reliable.

The Churchill infantry tank lingered on, however, its life prolonged by a brief spell of popularity in Tunisia in 1943, where the country was close and enemy tanks few.   Its further modification, Churchill VII, was loaded with up to 152 mm. of armour but only armed with a medium velocity 75 mm. gun and thus completely outclassed by such contemporary heavy tanks as the German Tigers and the Soviet Stalin.   Altogether 5,640 Churchills were produced and they found their best use as specialised vehicles : A.V.R.E. engineer assault tanks, Crocodile flamethrower tanks, bridgelayers, recovery vehicles and so on.

Since 1942 work was proceeding on a heavy turretless assault tank, the A.39 or Tortoise, proposed by some as a successor to the Churchill.   It weighed 76 to 78 tons, had armour up to 230 mm. thick and was armed with a 94 mm.

32-pounder gun, thus being the only infantry or assault tank ever to be more heavily armed than a contemporary cruiser. But it was completed too late and did not get beyond 6 prototypes. The same applied to a belated 17-pounder version of the Churchill, the A.43 or Black Prince, of which again only 6 were built.

In July 1944, Field-Marshal Montgomery, the commander of the 21st Army Group in Europe, officially proposed the abolition of the division between cruiser and infantry tanks. The proposal was not immediately accepted but in 1946 it became official policy and thus, at long last, the division into infantry and cruiser tanks, which had blighted British tank development since the mid-thirties, came to an end.

Less happy and unnecessarily restrictive was Field-Marshal Montgomery's insistence on a single type of tank, which he called a Capital Tank. A well-armed medium tank, the equivalent of the German Pz.Kpfw.IV of 1939–40, the Soviet T34 of 1941, the Sherman of 1942 and the Panther of 1943, was undoubtedly the primary requirement. But there might still be need for another vehicle. Not a slow and thick-skinned infantry tank but a more heavily armed heavy-gun tank, to back up the basic medium tank. In other words, the equivalent of the Tigers and Stalins which were used within German and Soviet armoured formations to support the Panthers and T-34s. As it was, because of the insistence on a single type of tank, the 42.5-ton Centurion I cruiser tank, which was introduced just as the Second World War ended, was thought of as a Universal Tank. In practice this meant no more than the existence of a single well-armed medium tank. Although the Centurion came to be used in more than one role it was no more " universal " than the Sherman was in 1943, when it was used alike within armoured divisions and in armoured brigades for co-operation with infantry formations.

The immediate post-war development concentrated on the Centurion. After 1948 the introduction of Centurion III and later models armed with a high velocity 83.9 mm. 20-pounder in place of the original 17-pounder increased further its value and represented a successful combination of the type of powerful armament hitherto carried on the Tiger II heavy tank with the mobility of the Panther, and this in spite of an increase in weight up to 49 tons. By the fifties, however, the need for a more powerfully armed version to complement the basic medium gun Centurion was recognised, with the result that a heavy-gun tank was brought out, the 120 mm. 60-pounder gun Conqueror of 65 tons.

The principal role envisaged for the Conqueror was that of a " tank killer " and it was combined with Centurions within armoured regiments, which ensured that the latter were really well armed. In a broader sense, the Conqueror showed a healthy emphasis on gun power which had been lacking in much of the earlier British tank development. The only question which remained by the time the Conquerer began to be introduced into service in the mid-fifties was whether tanks as heavy as it was could live up to the changing tactical conditions.

Since then the Conqueror also has been challenged by further development of the Centurion series whose armament has been increased from the 83.9 mm. 20-pounder to a much more powerful 105 mm. gun, thus reducing the relative value of Conqueror's 120 mm. gun.

14

France

THE French were a close second in evolving the tank. The development was quite independent of the British but, as in the case of the latter, the construction of the first French tank was preceded by experiments with other types of armed or armoured vehicles. Of these the first semi-armoured car built by the Société Charron-Girardot et Voigt in 1902 and the unarmoured *autos-mitrailleuses* pioneered by Captain Genty and successfully used in Morocco from 1908 onwards deserve to be mentioned. So does the employment of a few improvised armoured cars in the opening stages of the First World War and the experiments conducted during 1915 with unarmed barbed wire crushing tractors.

It was, however, with the appearance on the scene of Colonel J. E. Estienne that French tank development took definite form. Having seen a Holt tractor used by British artillery he conceived the idea of a tracked armoured fighting vehicle armed with machine-gun and cannon. Undismayed by an initial lack of response, he managed to secure the support of the French Commander-in-Chief, General Joffre, and on this basis, in December 1915, took his ideas to the Schneider company of Le Creusot. Schneider had already done some preliminary studies of the application of the Holt tractor chassis to armoured cars and in collaboration with Colonel Estienne soon had a tank project under way. The need to convince various military and industrial sceptics, as well as labour and material shortages, delayed the execution of the original order for 400 vehicles, given in February 1916 and rather optimistically scheduled for delivery by November 1916. However, 2 months after the acceptance of the Schneider tank project, another order was placed for a further 400 tanks

169

to be designed and built by the Compagnie des Forges d'Homécourt, better known after its location as Saint Chamond.

Both the Schneider and the St. Chamond tanks were of the turretless variety and both had a 75 mm. gun as main armament. The Schneider also had 2 machine-guns, weighed 13.5 tons and was operated by a crew of 7; the larger St. Chamond weighed 23 tons, had 2 more machine-guns and a crew of 9. The first vehicles of both types were delivered to the French Army centre at Marly in September 1916 and several shortcomings became immediately apparent. But, since the British Army had made its first use of tanks on the Somme in the same month—which the French, with justification, regarded as premature—it was decided to proceed with production without waiting for modifications.

In the meantime, General Estienne, who had been placed in command of the *Artillerie d'Assaut*, as the French tank units were called at first, paid a visit to Britain, in June 1916, on receipt of the first news of British tank development. After seeing something of British heavy tanks he suggested that the two countries divide their efforts, France concentrating on lighter models. On his return he pursued his idea with Louis Renault, the head of the French motor firm bearing his name, which immediately started work on a light tank design. The first Renault light tank was delivered in April 1917 but bickering and delays resulted in quantity production not getting under way until almost a year later. Eventually 7,820 were ordered, one-half of the total with firms other than Renault, and 3,177 were actually delivered by the end of the war.

The Renault F.T., as it became known, was a light 2-man tank of about 6.5 tons, capable of a maximum speed of 4.8 m.p.h. and with an operating range of 25 to 30 miles. Instead of the 75 mm. gun of the two earlier tanks it had either one machine-gun or one short 37 mm. gun, but while the Schneider and St. Chamond were little more than armoured boxes placed on copies of the Holt tractor chassis the Renault was a much more advanced design with a turret; it was, in fact, the first tank in service with an all-round-traverse turret.

The first French tank action took place on April 16, 1917, with 128 Schneiders organised into 8 *groupes* of 16 tanks each. Like subsequent engagements of the St. Chamonds, it was not a conspicuous success. Their original method of employment was in keeping with the designation of the tank units, that is as assault artillery carrying forward the fire power of field guns with the advancing infantry. The poor performance and lack of success were not, however, due to the method of employment as much as to mechanical weaknesses and limited obstacle-crossing ability of the vehicles, which were greatly inferior in this respect to the contemporary British tanks. As a result, the first two models were abandoned on completion of the original orders and production was concentrated entirely on the light Renault F.T., one of the lessons with the earlier tanks being that a number of less powerful machines was preferable to one heavy tank.

The original intention as regards the employment of the Renaults was to wait until considerable numbers were produced and to launch them into action *en masse*. The German offensive in the spring of 1918 upset these plans and the light tank battalions, which had hardly completed their organisation, were sent to support the hard-pressed infantry units. In spite of being employed in small packets under unfavourable circumstances they acquitted themselves well in the defence of the Retz Forest and by their counter-attacks contributed to the checking of the German offensive. In July 1918 some 480 were concentrated and used with great success in the French counter-offensive at Soissons and they continued to be used successfully thereafter in numerous smaller engagements, leading or working in close co-operation with the infantry units to which they were attached.

The Renault light tanks were, in a way, fortunate in their actions in that they operated over ground which had not been heavily shelled—initially by accident and then partly by deliberate choice of ground—and they also proved remarkably reliable, apart from their troublesome cooling fan drive. Thus, although they were not much different in speed or armour from the two earlier tanks and were far less powerfully armed, they were able to perform more successfully and while the number of serviceable Schneiders and St. Chamonds dwindled away that of the Renaults increased rapidly. At one stage a complete battalion of Renault light tanks was being formed each week, the total up to the end of the First World War being 27 battalions.

Out of the total of some 3,900 tanks produced, the end of the hostilities found few of the earlier machines in working order but, in spite of battlefield casualties, there were about 3,000 Renault F.T. Since the production of armoured vehicles stopped soon after the Armistice of 1918, they became the main and almost only equipment of French armoured units of the post-war period.

They held this position for the following 18 years, although in a report written less than a year after the end of the war General Estienne warned about the capabilities of the F.T. As he pointed out, the Renault F.T. was constructed and used at a time when the enemy had nothing comparable and was able, therefore, to enjoy an uncontested superiority. After the passing of this phase the F.T. ought to be replaced by a more powerful vehicle, a real battle tank and not merely an accompanying model. Powerful battle tanks operating in mass would become the decisive factor in future operations, in attack and in counter-attack, and would counter enemy anti-tank guns not merely by the sheer thickness of their armour but by their concentrated employment and mobility. The value of accompanying tanks, those " armoured skirmishers " which he predicted would ultimately replace infantry fighting on foot, was not rejected, especially if they would become more mobile. But, as they would be designed to engage infantry targets they would be less powerful and therefore, however useful, their construction should on no account interfere with that of the battle tanks, which could never be too numerous or too powerful.

Speaking 2 years later, in 1921, in Brussels, General

Estienne drew in vivid colours the changes which mechanisation would bring to the armies of the future and the potentialities of a mechanised force of 100,000 men, made up of tanks,
mechanised infantry and self-propelled artillery, operating as
a single arm. Again he reaffirmed his faith in the decisive role
which armoured forces would play in the future and made a
plea that they should be kept in peace and in war as a separate
arm and not made subservient to the infantry.

Unfortunately the plea went unheeded. Only a little
earlier the headquarters of the *Artillerie d'Assaut* were abolished
and tanks were placed under the care of a subdivision of the
Infantry Department. This reaffirmed the use of tanks in
their accompanying role and was hardly a move towards the
development of an independent armoured arm, which General
Estienne demanded. However, once having found in tanks
a useful auxiliary the infantry was not going to relinquish its
claims on them lightly and, in all fairness, the Renault F.T.
tanks were suitable for little apart from an accompanying role.
Yet the creation of a separate arm, such as the Royal Tank
Corps in Britain or the German *Panzerwaffe*, was the only way
of ensuring that the new problems would receive due attention
and that tanks would not be regarded solely as an auxiliary to
the foot soldier.

While the tactical development was thus destined to
remain static, there was at least some technical development
in the field of armoured vehicles. First of all, the construction
of ten 2C heavy tanks begun during the war was completed.
Design studies of this type started as early as the end of 1916
and originally led to the 1A 41-ton heavy tank. This experimental model was superseded by the heavier, 68-ton 2C, 300
of which were planned for 1919, for a special break-through
role. Although, in the event, only ten were built these tanks
excited a lot of interest for years being the heaviest in service
anywhere in the world. Their number was commonly overestimated and when in the late twenties one of them was
modified into a 2C *bis* and rearmed with a short 155 mm. gun,
in place of the standard turret-mounted 75 mm. gun, it gave

rise to a new imaginary series of French super-heavy tanks which has been mentioned in several tank books !

Other French developments of the 1921–27 period included attempts to improve the performance of the Renault F.T. by fitting it with the Kegresse continuous rubber tracks, which proved unsuccessful although the same type of track was satisfactory on a number of half-track armoured cars.   In 1926 development began of a *char de bataille*, a medium tank of 19 to 20 tons armed with a 75 mm. gun, to which General Estienne had devoted a good deal of attention since the war. This vehicle could trace its ancestry to a modification of the original Schneider tank and several years later it resulted in the type B1 heavy tank. At about the same time Renault produced a greatly improved version of the original F.T., the N.C. light tank which had armour up to 30 mm. thick and a maximum speed of 11 m.p.h.   It was not adopted by the French Army but some were sold to Japan and it served as the basis for the development of the D-1, which was adopted in 1930 and 160 of which were ultimately produced. This was a tank of some 14 tons with armour and speed similar to those of the N.C. but with a turret-mounted 47 mm. gun and machine-gun and another machine-gun in the hull served by the third crewman, who also operated a radio set with which this tank was fitted.

Except for three type B1 tanks, the D-1 was the only new type issued to the French tank units between 1921 and 1935, and during the whole of that period the majority of the units were equipped with the Renault F.T. Within limits the F.T. was a serviceable and economic machine and there were few armies of any consequence which during the twenties did not have at least a few or close copies of it, the American M1917 and the Italian Fiat 3000 being good examples of the latter category. Yet its long life—some went into action against Allied troops during the Anglo-American landings in North Africa in 1942—was a very mixed blessing for had it dropped to pieces earlier the dead weight of obsolete equipment might have been less. The absence of a progressive doctrine was partly responsible for the lack of understanding of the need for new equipment but, at the same time, the lack of modern tanks was partly responsible for the lack of understanding of the potentialities of mechanised warfare : it was not easy to visualise it and almost impossible to demonstrate it with a tank whose maximum speed was short of 5 m.p.h.

Together with a lack of understanding of the need for new equipment, and partly because of it, went another very important reason for the absence of modern tanks : a lack of money for the purchase of new vehicles. With Germany defeated and the League of Nations in full swing France paid less attention to her land forces and the greater part of the defence budget was spent on building up the navy. A good portion of such money as the Army had was used for the maintenance of obsolescent material and what was left went for the provision of such basic needs as new light machine-guns and gas masks. Then, when the horizons in Europe began to darken, milliards of francs were poured, from 1932 onwards, into the permanent fortifications on France's eastern frontier, which grew up in keeping with the defensive attitude and the belief that future operations would be largely on the lines of those of 1918. In vain did the commanding general of the French tank units appeal in 1932 that a fraction of the money sunk into the steel and concrete of the Maginot Line be spent on the production of new tanks. It required 3 more years and the appearance of the first new-series German tanks before new models of French tanks were finally adopted and put into production.

By this time the infantry had also lost its monopoly on tanks because the cavalry also took them up in the early thirties. The cavalry's association with armoured vehicles began as early as 1914, when some French cavalry corps received their first detachments of armoured cars. From 1917 each cavalry division was assigned 18 armoured cars and after the war motorisation progressed to the stage where, in 1930–32, the cavalry division had a regiment of armoured cars, a regiment of truck-borne riflemen and some motorised artillery, as well as its horse elements.

The mixture of the 5 m.p.h. mounted units with 20–30 m.p.h. motorised elements was not a happy one yet it was one with which many armies experimented, unwilling for various reasons, often mainly emotional, to give up their horses. In France, as elsewhere, mixed formations of this type survived until 1940, but the next logical step in the evolution of the mobility and power of the cavalry was a homogeneous, fully motorised formation which came into being in 1934, with the creation of the first *Division Légère Mécanique*, or D.L.M. The organisation of this formation had all the characteristics of the later armoured divisions but it differed considerably from the German panzer division, which it anteceded by about a year, in its intended method of employment. According to the official doctrine the primary mission of the D.L.M. was strategic reconnaissance and security for the benefit of the infantry formations, an important but hardly decisive role to which cavalry was reduced during the nineteenth century. Mobile offensive operations were not precluded but were definitely of secondary importance.

The first D.L.M. took part in the 1935 Army manoeuvres in Champagne and attracted a good deal of attention but if some of its potentialities were recognised even more attention was paid to the difficulties associated with the fuel consumption of such a formation. Its 2,000 vehicles and 1,500 motor-cycles consumed fuel at the unheard of rate of 320 gallons per mile. However, by 1938 a second D.L.M. had been created and their fighting power was increased by the arrival of new types of tanks, which supplemented the 2-man machine-gun-armed 5-ton A.M.R. Renault Model 1933, until then the cavalry's principal fully tracked armoured vehicles. In May 1940 there were 3 D.L.M.s, the third having been created in August 1939 by the transformation of a cavalry division, and the organisation of a fourth was beginning.

In the meantime the growing shadow of German rearmament and the recognition of the deplorable lack of modern equipment produced at long last funds for the provision of new tanks. The 1935 defence budget made possible the

9. British Medium Mark III, one of several multi-turreted tanks built during the twenties and early thirties. (*Imperial War Museum*).

10. Carden Loyd Mark VI, which during the late twenties set a fashion for two-man turretless tankettes. (*Vickers-Armstrongs Ltd.*).

11. Vickers-Armstrongs 6 ton tank, single turret model, one of the most sensible designs of the late twenties. (*Vickers-Armstrongs Ltd.*).

12. United States T3 medium tank, built by J. W. Christie in 1931, which represented a major step forward in speed and suspension. (*US Army*).

adoption for production of several new models and the programme of the following year, 14 per cent. of which was set for mechanisation, planned the production of 3,200 tanks. But even the provision of considerable sums of money can only produce results after a time, especially if industrial facilities are inadequate or largely inexistent. The highly specialised armaments industries, for years starved of long-term orders, such as those which kept naval shipyards going in peacetime, needed time to get ready. Industrial labour troubles and inadequate orders for certain types, which did not. allow up-to-date quantity production methods to be applied, added further difficulties to the usual problems of organisation, machine tools and raw materials. It is not surprising, there-fore, that in the summer of 1936 there were only 34 new tanks in service, excluding the cavalry's A.M.R., and that numbers increased slowly at first. But once production got under way numbers began to increase. By the time the Germans attacked Poland and the Second World War began the French had produced 2,200 tanks and in May 1940 this figure reached an impressive total of some 3,500 modern tanks, including about 800 medium and heavy tanks.

Compared with anything the French Army previously had, these new vehicles were a great step forward. The most numerous was the 10-ton Renault Model 1935, or R-35, whose development was initiated in 1933 and which replaced the original Renault F.T. in the infantry light tank battalions. Carrying a crew of 2, it had armour up to 40 mm. thick and was capable of a maximum speed of 13 m.p.h. A very similar but faster light tank, the Hotchkiss H-35, was supplied to the cavalry and later also to some infantry units. The cavalry also received a 20-ton S.O.M.U.A. S-35 medium tank, on the general lines of the D-1 and of the later 18.5-ton D-2, but capable of up to 28 m.p.h. and with a radius of action of about 125 miles. Finally the infantry units received the heavy 30-ton B-1 *bis* with a short hull-mounted 75 mm. gun and an APX turret, identical to that of the S-35 and D-2, mounting a coaxial 47 mm. gun and machine-gun.

In general, all the tanks were well armoured, the maximum thickness ranging from 40 mm. on the light tanks to 60 mm. on the type B-1 *bis*, when the Germans were only just beginning to introduce 30 mm. plates on their medium tanks. Extensive use was made of cast armour which the French pioneered. The infantry tanks were rather slow and the principal armament of the light tanks was a 37 mm. gun Model 1918, a short barrelled low-velocity weapon effective only against the lightest of armour. But the 47 mm. gun of the medium and heavy tanks was at the time of its introduction probably the best anti-tank weapon in any army. In addition, French tanks also had such advanced features as electric power traverse on the S-35 and regenerative controlled differential steering on the S-35 and B-1 tanks, in which they were several years ahead of the British Churchill and the German Tiger tank transmissions.

Progress in equipment was not, however, matched by any marked progress in the employment of tanks. With the exception of the cavalry's D.L.M., the bulk of the tank units continued to be mentally and physically tied to the speed of the foot soldier. Their employment followed the lines of the 1930 *Instruction on the employment of tanks*, which commenced with the definition that " the tank is an infantry-supporting weapon " and went on that tanks are nothing but supplementary means placed at the disposal of the infantry entirely subordinated to the infantry units to which they are attached. Thus, the light tank battalions were still intended only for an accompanying role, combined in the ratio of one infantry regiment to one tank battalion in a *groupement mixte*. The less numerous medium and heavy tank units, which started with the D-1, were similarly intended to operate for the benefit of the infantry, although on a higher level of division or corps. They were designated as *chars de manoeuvre d'ensemble* and their place was generally ahead of the infantry and the accompanying tanks, paving the way for them by destroying enemy guns and armour.

At various times views were expressed criticising this complete subordination of tank units to the infantry and pointing the wider potentialities of mechanised warfare. These among others, included General de Gaulle's *Vers l'Armée de Métier* published in 1934, which described the shortcomings of the system based on an " infantry army " and proposed the creation of a professional mechanised field army. Contrary to popular belief, this book did not exert any influence on the Germans and in France neither it nor other individual views were able to change official opinion which firmly believed in the doctrine of long continuous fronts and generally fighting *à la* 1918.

In the case of tanks the prevailing view, reinforced by some misguided lessons from the Spanish Civil War, was that they met more than a match in contemporary anti-tank guns. This was partly responsible for keeping tanks closely tied to the infantry and the slow artillery barrages and the lack of faith in the possibilities of their more independent employment. It seems to have been overlooked, however, that the intended method of employment was one best designed to expose tanks to the full effectiveness of anti-tank guns. In the words of the contemporary German *Truppenführung* manual, " if tanks are held in too close liaison with the infantry they lose the advantage of their mobility and are liable to be destroyed by the defence." The Germans did not mean this to preclude the co-operation of tanks with other arms, including the infantry, but they preached and practised that " in the zone of action of tanks, the action of other arms is to be based on that of tanks." No greater contrast with the French doctrine would have been possible.

Even the formation of the first French armoured division, the *Division Cuirassée*, did not mean as great a departure from hitherto accepted practice as might have been expected. The creation of armoured divisions was considered from 1935 onwards, but it was only when the Second World War broke out that one was hastily assembled on the basis of the 4 battalions of type B heavy tanks then in existence. By modifying the organisation to two B-1 and two light H-35 battalions per division 2 divisions were formed in January

1940, a third was added shortly afterwards and a fourth was in the process of organisation when active operations began.

The permanent grouping of a number of tank units was in itself a definite step forward and the *Division Cuirassée* had the making of a mechanised formation. In practice, however, it represented little more than a permanent grouping of the *chars de manoeuvre d'ensemble* and its role was to act as a kind of battering ram in breaking through strongly held lines and not to conduct mobile warfare, for which, in any case, its type B tanks were not very suitable. In theory, the extension of any breaks-through was to be left to the *Division Légère Mécanique* and motorised infantry divisions.

With such a background of doctrine and organisation, the disposition of French tank units on the day active operations began in May 1940, becomes more readily understood. A large part of the total tank strength was in the light battalions attached in groups of two to 7 battalions to each of the 8 French armies stretched from the Swiss frontier to the English Channel with about half the total actually behind the Maginot Line between the Rhine and the Ardennes. Of the 33 battalions thus deployed, the majority were equipped with R-35 tanks, but there were also 2 battalions of similar but diesel-engined F.C.M. light tanks, 7 battalions still equipped with the old Renault F.T. of 1918 and one battalion with 2C heavy tanks of the same vintage. The heavy type B tanks and the infantry's H-35 were all grouped in the armoured divisions, which were held in reserve. The rest of the infantry's tanks, mainly old F.T., were held in various training establishments all over the country and 8 battalions with about 320 modern tanks were in French overseas possessions.

Of the cavalry's tanks, which included all the S-35 and the greater part of the H-35 and similar H-39 tanks, the majority were in the three D.L.M., which formed part of the 1st Group of Armies facing the Belgian frontier. Altogether, the first line units of the infantry and cavalry had some 2,500 modern tanks and 700 *auto-mitrailleuses*, or " armoured cars " but half of which, the A.M.R. and A.M.C., were in fact fully tracked fighting vehicles. To be added to this total were another 500 tanks in units in the process of organisation.

Against this the Germans launched 2,570 tanks and about 600 armoured cars. But, if the total figures of French and German first line tanks did not differ, all the German tanks and the majority of the armoured cars were in the 10 panzer divisions, 9 of which were concentrated along the Belgian and Luxembourg frontier on a front of less than 100 miles—the remaining division being further north, on the Dutch front. These massed panzer divisions, very effectively supported by large-scale tactical attacks of the *Luftwaffe*, delivered the swift and crushing blows which shattered the French front along the Meuse. The drive to the Channel which followed and the subsequent elimination of the French, British and Belgian forces of the Northern Group of Armies virtually decided the issue of the campaign, which was sealed when the panzer divisions turned south, broke through the so-called Weygand Line, and outflanked the Maginot Line.

In contrast to this, the French armoured forces were committed to battle piecemeal, only to suffer heavy losses without being able to achieve anything. An unfortunate lack of concentration of effort and of sound methods of tank employment plagued the use of French armoured units at all levels of command. It led to such things as the annihilation of the 1st D.C.R., which, thrown in on the left flank of the ill-fated 9th Army, found itself alone facing the 39th Panzer Corps. Or to the piecemeal employment a few days later of the 2nd and 3rd D.C.R. in vain attempts to stop the drive of two other panzer corps, including Guderian's 19th. To a lesser extent it was responsible for the failure of the counter-attacks of General de Gaulle's hastily assembled 4th D.C.R. at Laon and Abbeville, which were repelled by German infantry and artillery. Even the units of the 2nd and 3rd D.L.M., which were organised into a mechanised cavalry corps, had a tendency to fight in small packets rather than in a co-ordinated body. Moving into Belgium in their textbook role of a strategic advance guard to the 1st French Army at the beginning of the campaign, they were badly mauled in turn by the 16th Panzer Corps.

If the employment of large mechanised formations lacked concentration and co-ordination, hardly better results could have been expected from the light tank battalions attached to the various armies. Used by companies and even platoons to bolster the morale of infantry units they were squandered without being able to achieve anything, for the benefit of the infantry or any other arm.

By refusing to concentrate a part at least of its scattered tank units, as General de Gaulle proposed in 1940 during the period of the Phoney War, and by squandering the few formations which it had concentrated in the reserve, the French High Command ensured that they were used in the least effective way. But there were also several other factors which further reduced their effectiveness.

With the exception of the mechanised cavalry, none of the tank units was really trained or equipped for the type of mobile operations in which they had to take part. Long marches imposed a heavy strain on the equipment and the shortcomings of the supply and repair services, with the consequent lack of spares, added to the difficulties of maintenance. Moreover, because they fought a retreating battle, the French had few opportunities to recover their tank casualties, whereas the Germans were able to repair and put back into service most of theirs. German air superiority, the crowds of refugees and the growing confusion in the rear areas added further difficulties to the movement of units and supplies. And although air attacks generally had little material effect on the tank units they seriously affected the morale of the troops.

Training of many units also left a good deal to be desired. This applied in particular to the 4 *Divisions Cuirassées*: none went into action fully organised or trained together. Some of their elements such as artillery, riflemen and signals, joined the divisions either on the eve of the departure for the front or even actually at the front, having never before had an opportunity to work with tanks. Such things hardly made up for efficiency or effective co-operation in battle.

At the same time, while some new units were very short of trained personnel, men and resources were used in keeping no less than eight first-line battalions of the obsolete Renault F.T., which were of very doubtful fighting value by then and which provided yet another example of the absence of economy of effort. The same applied to the one battalion of 6 ancient 2C heavy tanks, which impressed some newspaper reporters but whose proper place in 1940 was in a museum. Ironically, these 68-ton monsters were ultimately destroyed on their special railway carriages without ever going into action.

Lastly, the equipment itself had several shortcomings. They were largely the outcome of the specifications laid down by the High Command and of the prevailing doctrine, and none was as serious as the disastrous method of employment. Nevertheless, they contributed their share to the difficulties.

The infantry tanks were slow, underpowered and had limited radii of action, which meant frequent and laborious refuelling. None of this appeared serious in small-scale peacetime exercises but it soon made itself felt in battle. The Hotchkiss H-35 and H-39 tanks, which were originally ordered for the cavalry, were somewhat better and the S-35 designed by S.O.M.U.A. specifically for the cavalry was definitely above average. In fact, the S-35's performance, armour and armament, made many regard it as the best tank in the world at the time and its opponents, the Germans, certainly rated it highly.

The armament of the light tanks was not impressive and only a few later models, the H-39 and R-40 had longer-barrelled Model 1938 guns, instead of the Model 1918, but even this was below the average performance of contemporary 37 mm. guns. However, more than one-half of the German tanks were the light Pz.Kpfw.I and II. The first was armed with two rifle-calibre machine-guns only and the second with a 20 mm. cannon which, though superior to the French 37 mm. Model 1918, was not very effective against the 40 mm. armour of the French light tanks. As far as more powerful tanks were concerned, to oppose about 600 German Pz.Kpfw.III and IV the French had a somewhat greater number of type B, S-35 and D-2 heavy and medium tanks armed with 47 mm. guns which were comparable to the new German 5 cm. KwK L/42 and greatly superior to the 3.7 cm. KwK with which Pz.Kpfw. III were still armed.

Of several bad design features, such as cramped interiors, poor means of vision, further aggravated by hard springing, one is particularly worth noting : all French tanks, whether light, medium or heavy, had one-man turrets. This meant that in combat one man had to fire and load the turret armament, which included a manually loaded 37 or 47 mm. gun as well as a machine-gun, and at the same time he was expected to act as a commander of the vehicle and tactical leader. As a result, not only did the rate of fire suffer but it also becomes clear why French tanks could not and did not make better use of the ground and co-operate more effectively with each other, even if their crews had been as well trained in this as the Germans were. This feature alone was sufficient to hamper any type of joint manoeuvre, whether on a large or small scale.

Directly or indirectly the majority of the shortcomings and faults were due to one thing : the lack of understanding of the potentialities of mechanised warfare. This was in turn responsible for the lack of progress in employment of tanks, for the type of vehicles which were produced, and for the half-hearted way in which the armoured formations were organised and used. Few of the advantages of mechanised mobility were able to attract seriously the attention of the French High Command, which seemed incapable of lifting its eyes from the restricted lessons of 1918. Thus, the underlying tank philosophy remained almost entirely in terms of the limited benefits of armour protection and paid little heed to the wider benefits of mechanised mobility.

In the hour of test the French Army found facing it an enemy who was capable of looking beyond the limitations of fighting vehicles and of making full use of the strategic and tactical potentialities of mechanised forces. An enemy who had organised and trained his armoured forces to act together as a well-balanced team and who, instead of dissipating its efforts, made a principle of being as strong as possible at the decisive point. Neither the courage of individual tank units nor the heavy armour of the tanks nor the considerable material resources were able to redeem the mistakes which cost the French armoured forces and the whole French Army dear.

The defeat of 1940 swept away virtually all French armoured units. A few tanks remained in French North Africa where they fought in 1942, first against Allied troops and then—old D-1 tanks—against Axis forces in Tunisia. A few R-35 tanks also fought against British troops during the short 1941 Syrian campaign.

In 1943, however, French armoured forces began to be re-created in North Africa, on the basis of equipment supplied by the United States. A year later one armoured division, the 2nd *Division Blindée*, or D.B., landed with the Anglo-American forces in Normandy and in August 1944 the 1st D.B. landed with other Allied units in the south of France. Some months later another armoured division, the 5th D.B., entered into action as part of the 1st French Army.

All 3 armoured divisions were organised and equipped on American lines and American-built armoured vehicles formed the basis of the post-war French armoured forces. Even before the Second World War ended attempts were made to restart the development of armoured vehicles in France but, after several years of occupation and the loss of facilities, the process was slow and difficult. Nevertheless, starting in 1946, a development programme was put in hand based on 3 main types of vehicles : a " battle tank " of about 50 tons, a light air-transportable tank and a wheeled reconnaissance vehicle.

Of the 3, the battle tank, roughly the equivalent of the basic medium-type tanks of other armies, became the pre-occupation of the French Staff. In studying the problem the French made much use of captured German vehicles and on their basis decided that what was required was a tank as well armed as the Tiger II and as mobile as the Panther. From these premises the Atelier de Construction d'Issy-les-Moulineaux designed a new tank which became the AMX 50. In the meantime, as an interim measure, a small number of an indifferent 90 mm. gun ARL 44 tank, whose design was commenced during the war on the basis of the type B tank chassis, was completed and a battalion of captured German Panthers was put into service.

The AMX 50, prototypes of which were completed by 1951, was a promising vehicle : it had a high power to weight ratio thanks to its 1,000 b.h.p. petrol injection engine and it was well armed. It became even more so when the original 100 mm. gun was replaced by a 120 mm. capable of using the same ammunition as the American M103 (T43) 120 mm. heavy gun tank. However, it was an expensive tank and spending money on it was made all the more difficult by the availability of American M46 medium tanks. Moreover, by the early fifties the French military authorities began to feel that in the light of the new anti-tank weapons a heavily armoured tank of 50 tons had more drawbacks than virtues. The future was thought to lie more in the direction of lighter, more mobile vehicles with armour only thick enough against the most common types of projectiles, that is those of automatic weapons and shell splinters. In consequence, attention was transferred from the AMX 50, which was limited to a number of prototypes, to another product of the Atelier de Construction d'Issy-les-Moulineaux, the AMX 13.

This has been one of the most interesting designs to appear since the end of the Second World War. Conceived in 1946 as an air-transportable tank, it carries a high-velocity 75 mm. gun similar to that of the German Panther medium tank but weighs less than one-third—14.5 tons, in fact, fully laden with a crew of 3. This light weight combined with a 260 b.h.p. engine gives it a high power to weight ratio and a high average speed. In turn, its mobility and compactness fit in well with the latest operational ideas of mobile self-contained battle groups and it has proved itself in Israeli hands during their 1956 operations against the Egyptians.

The first prototype of the AMX 13 was completed in mid-1949 and its quantity production started in 1952, since when it has become increasingly widely used. In addition to Israel, AMX 13 tanks were also sold to Switzerland; and in the French Army, apart from their use in tank form, they have become the basis of a standardised series of vehicles consisting of a 105 mm. self-propelled howitzer, a 40 mm. self-propelled anti-aircraft gun and an armoured recovery vehicle.

The third of the post-Second World War armoured vehicles the Panhard *Engin Blindé de Reconnaissance*, or E.B.R., is no less interesting than the AMX 13. Derived directly from an experimental Panhard design of 1940, the AM 201, it is a 12.6-ton 8-wheeled vehicle armed with a 75 mm. gun and manned by a crew of 4, including 2 drivers—fore and aft—so that it can be driven equally well in either direction. Intended as the main equipment of far-ranging ground reconnaissance units, for which its high maximum speed and excellent cross-country mobility fit it well, it has been supplemented by a more powerful version equipped with the gun and FL 11 turret of the AMX 13 tank in place of its original FL 10 turret with a medium-velocity 75 mm. gun.

Noteworthy as it is, the E.B.R. does not exhaust the list of recent French developments. The Hotchkiss armoured personnel carriers and the SS 10 and SS 11 anti-tank guided missiles are but further examples of a series which shows not only intensive activity but also original ideas.

15

United States

THE application of motor vehicles to military purposes in the United States can be traced back to the earliest days of the American car. It was, in fact, as early as 1899 that a machine-gun car was built to the order of Major R. P. Davidson by Charles Duryea, who only a few years earlier built the first American petrol-engined vehicle.

This and several later experiments were, however, the work of one man—Davidson—and in the absence of favourable circumstances failed to attract general attention. Even after the First World War broke out in Europe next to no consideration was being given in the United States to the warlike use of motor vehicles, in spite of the fact that in 1914 the American automobile industry was already producing more than 500,000 cars a year. Similarly, in the absence of motivating military circumstances, the evolution of the tank from the basis of American-built tracked tractors was left to Britain and France.

It was only in mid-1917, after the United States entered the war and after the setting up of the headquarters of the American Expeditionary Force in France, that tanks, which were already in use with the British and French Armies, were looked into thoroughly for the first time. Their importance was acknowledged and it was recommended that British heavy and French Renault light tanks be obtained for use by American troops.

Neither of the Allies was, however, in a position to supply more than a few vehicles for experimental purposes. As a result, and to make use of American production facilities, it was decided that a modified version of the Renault F.T. light tank be produced in the United States. It was also agreed between the Allied authorities that the British Mark VIII heavy tank design be adopted for general use by the Allies, United States and Britain manufacturing components for it and France being responsible for the final assembly. The Mark VIII was actually the last of the British rhomboidal heavy tanks with overhead tracks and a main armament of two 57 mm. guns mounted in side sponsons.

However, the original tank programme proved to be over optimistic. In particular, as a result of chaotic conditions, the production of the light tank was considerably delayed and only about 10 tanks of this type reached France towards the end of 1918, too late to be of use in the field. The production of the Mark VIII was also considerably behind the original estimates and none was built up to the end of the war, except for prototypes. Large-scale production was also planned, on the basis of the facilities of the Ford Motor Company, of a small turretless 3-ton 2-man tank ; a larger Ford 3-man tank was also to be produced. Altogether, at the time of the Armistice of 1918, work was in progress in the United States on some 23,000 tanks of the above 4 types but of this impressive total only 952 Renault-type Six-Ton M1917, 100 Mark VIII and 15 Ford Three-Ton tanks were actually completed, the majority in 1919.

In the meantime, in mid-1918, when it became evident that no early deliveries of American-built tanks could be expected, sufficient French Renault F.T. light tanks were obtained to equip 2 battalions and enough British Mark V Star tanks for one heavy battalion. The first 2 went into action on September 12, 1918, at St. Mihiel and the heavy tank battalion, serving with the British Army, a few days later.

Further battalions were in training and the Tank Corps, created in January 1918, was to be expanded eventually to no less than 15 tank brigades, each of one heavy and 2 light tank battalions. However, shortly after the war the pendulum swung the other way and the Tank Corps was abolished altogether. Under the National Defense Act of 1920 tanks were assigned to the infantry and became its subsidiary. The organisation was fixed at 2 independent tank regiments and 7 divisional tank companies, equipped almost entirely with the Six-Ton M1917, although some Mark VIII were retained by the tank regiments up to 1932.

Under the infantry régime the role of the tank was officially defined in 1922 as that of " facilitating the uninterrupted advance of the riflemen in the attack." Two variants actually emerged on this theme, namely the infantry-accompanying light tank and the more powerful " leading tank " intended for more concentrated employment along the main line of effort of the supported large infantry unit. The two concepts and categories of tanks corresponded very closely to the French *chars d'accompagnement* and *chars de manoeuvre d'ensemble*.

Practice, however, differed somewhat from theory. The Caliber Board, constituted after the war to study future equipment policies, recommended the development of a single type of medium tank to replace both the Six Ton light tank and the Mark VIII heavy. The design of this tank was still dominated by the First World War requirements of crossing wide trenches and, in consequence, it turned out to be large and heavier by about 7 tons than the 14 tons (U.S. 15) originally stipulated. It was, nevertheless, quite a promising, well-laid-out tank. Its armament consisted of a coaxial 57 mm. gun and machine-gun in the main turret and of a second machine-gun in a small turret placed on top of the main one, a twin turret arrangement which was to be a feature of several American tanks during the following thirty years.

The construction of this first American medium tank, or Medium A, in 1921 was followed by that of two similar tanks, built in 1922 and 1925. In the mid-twenties, however, the infantry which had hitherto subscribed to the concentration of effort on a single medium type became interested in light tanks and interest in the medium tanks and the leading role to which they were assigned waned. The next model, the Medium T2 built in 1930, was designed strictly down to the 14-ton weight limit imposed by contemporary bridging equipment with the result that it was badly cramped and had the ungainly top-heavy appearance of the contemporary British Vickers Medium.

By comparison, light tanks made steady progress. The first T1 built in 1927 was the outcome of a specification calling for a dependable light tank of not more than 5 U.S. tons, which could thus be carried on standard 5-ton trucks. The T1 proved fairly rugged but as a fighting vehicle it was indifferent. Four more were built, embodying various improvements, but no major advance took place until 1931, when a Vickers-Armstrongs Six Ton Tank was brought over to the United States for a 30-day test and demonstrated its superiority. Several of its features were embodied in the next model, the T1E4, which—at last—had the engine placed at the rear instead of the front. In general, the T1E4 represented a marked advance on the earlier models of the light tank series, although it retained their armament of a 37 mm. gun and coaxial machine-gun and the same 6 to 16 mm. armour.

But at this stage the light tank development was completely overshadowed by the appearance of a far more advanced, almost revolutionary, type of vehicle designed by J. Walter Christie. Christie had already submitted a vehicle to the post-war medium tank specification, first in the 1919 turreted version with armament similar to that of the Medium A and then rebuilt into the 1921 turretless form. The vehicle was not adopted, although at first it excited a lot of interest, and for the next few years Christie devoted his attention to amphibious vehicles. But in 1928 he came out with a new design combining his earlier, 1919 idea of a convertible tank which could operate either on tracks or on wheels (when the tracks were removed) with a new and highly effective independent springing system. With a 338 b.h.p. Liberty engine in a 7.7-ton vehicle the 1928 Christie tank had an extremely high power to weight ratio and on test proved capable of a maximum speed of 70 m.p.h. on wheels and 42.5 m.p.h. on tracks—twice the maximum speed of the T1 light tank series and well in advance of any other tracked vehicle at the time.

As a result of the extraordinary performance of this vehicle the United States Army ordered 5 tanks from Christie in 1931 and Russia and Poland a further 2 each, the Polish order being subsequently taken over by the United States Army. Of the 7, 3 were given to the infantry as T3 medium tanks and 4 to the cavalry as T1 combat cars. To the cavalry, which had just begun to take an interest in tanks, they were particularly attractive because of their mobility. But the infantry was hardly less interested and in 1932 ordered 5 additional T3E2 tanks of the Christie type, though not from Christie, who had proved very difficult to deal with. When in 1933 the Ordnance Department developed a new T4 combat car of the Christie type and recommended its adoption by both the cavalry and the infantry, the infantry accepted it as the basis of its T4 medium of which 16 were built by 1936.

Except for its inadequate main armament of a .5 in. (12.7 mm.) machine-gun, the 11-ton 4-man T4 medium was a most promising tank. It suffered somewhat from the complication of the alternative wheel or track drive and steering and, in fact, the provision for operation on wheels might have been abandoned to advantage. Unfortunately, what happened was that its development was dropped altogether. At a time when funds were extremely limited the short-sighted could not see that the T4 was well worth the extra money it cost and that it was a far superior cross-country combat vehicle and a much better basis for further development than anything else in existence. Thus, in 1936, when Russia was already mass-producing them, the United States abandoned Christie-type tanks altogether.

Development went back—and backwards—on to the light tank series. The T1E4 was followed in 1934 by the 8-ton T2, and at about the same time a similar but twin-turret T5 combat car weighing 5.5 tons was built for the cavalry. From these two came the next model, which was accepted and standardised in 1936–37 as the M1A1 light tank and the M1 combat car. A little later the combat car designation, adopted to get round the legal difficulty of tanks being assigned by Act of Congress to the infantry, was abandoned and from the M2A1 light tank

13. Mark VI light tanks and scout carriers of a British mechanised cavalry regiment in 1940. (*Imperial War Museum*).

14. French H-35 light infantry tank of 1940. (*Imperial War Museum*).

15. German Pz.Kpfw.IV, the most powerful tank of the Panzer divisions in 1939-41. (*Imperial War Museum*).

16. Soviet T-34 medium tank of 1941. (*Imperial War Museum*).

onwards tank development concentrated on a single light tank series.

The concentration on a single stable design enabled the Ordnance Department to make the best use of its limited resources in developing satisfactory reliable components. In this way considerable progress was made during the thirties with the development of the Continental air-cooled radial engines, transmissions, volute spring suspensions and rubber-block tracks with rubber-bushed pins. The result of it all was mechanically sound, dependable vehicles and the accumulated engineering experience proved invaluable later.

Far less satisfactory was the armament position, due largely to the absence of a consistent policy on the part of the two user arms, the infantry and the cavalry, to whose general specifications the Ordnance Department had to work. The principal armament of the T1 series of light tanks and of the T3 medium consisted of a short 37 mm. gun mounted coaxially with a machine-gun, but the T4 medium and the T5 combat car had nothing more powerful than a .5 in. machine-gun, and this remained for some time the heaviest armament of the light tanks. What is more, not only was the armament weak but it was poorly mounted as well. For instance, the T5 combat car copied the twin-turret layout of the inferior of the 2 variants of the Vickers-Armstrongs Six Ton Tank. The cavalry quickly dropped this in favour of the single 2-man turret but the infantry took it over and 2 single-man turrets mounted side by side, one with a .3 in. and the other with a .5 in. machine-gun, were still used on the 1938 M2A3 light tank. However, even this layout could be described as excellent by comparison with what was done on the T4E1 medium. One of the T4s, normally a sleek turreted vehicle, was fitted with a " barbette " super-structure—a large square box with machine-guns poking out of its 4 sides and a striking example of what the infantry " mobile pill-box " concept could do even to a fast tank !

Nevertheless, in spite of the inadequate armament, progress was being made. That of the infantry was largely confined to the improved mechanical performance of its light tanks. But the cavalry made considerable progress both in the use of the new faster tanks and in evolving a new type of mobile unit—the mechanised cavalry.

The events leading up to the cavalry's development of its mechanised units date back to 1927, when the then Secretary of War, Dwight Davis, witnessed the trials of the first British Experimental Mechanised Force and on his return gave instructions that a similar force be organised in the United States. An Experimental Mechanised Force was duly set up in July 1928 at Fort Meade, Maryland, the location of the Tank School, but it was disbanded 3 months later. It was a mixed brigade-size force with a rather heterogeneous collection of elements whose old, M1917 and Mark VIII, tanks were not suited to the object of the experiment.

Interest in mechanised forces did not die out, however. Two years later, in 1930, a second Mechanised Force was assembled at Fort Eustis, Virginia. It amounted to a regiment and was thus smaller than the first Force but like the latter was also mixed. The appointment of General Douglas MacArthur as Chief of Staff gave further impetus to mechanisation and in 1931 the development of mobile mechanised forces was assigned to the cavalry, while the infantry retained tanks for its own use. Thus the cavalry, which had participated in the 2 experiments with some armoured cars, took over part of the Fort Eustis force, disbanded as such in 1931, and this became the nucleus of a mechanised cavalry unit organised in the same year at Fort Knox, Kentucky. In 1933 this nucleus was combined with the 1st Cavalry, hitherto a mounted regiment stationed in Texas, to form the 1st Cavalry Regiment, Mechanised.

From this there gradually grew the 7th Cavalry Brigade, Mechanised, a brigade which was nominally created in 1932 but which did not become a reality until after 1936. In that year a second cavalry regiment, the 13th, was transferred to Fort Knox and in that year the first production M1 combat cars appeared. By 1939 the full complement had arrived and thus when the Second World War broke out the brigade consisted of 2 mechanised cavalry regiments with a total of 112 combat cars, one motorised artillery regiment with sixteen 75 mm. howitzers and ordnance, quartermaster and medical detachments.

The role envisaged at the time for the 7th Cavalry Brigade was a mechanised form of the traditional cavalry role of exploitation, raids on enemy flanks and rear and so on. But under the impact of the successes scored by the German armoured divisions, particularly in France in 1940, ideas changed considerably. General A. R. Chaffee, who had been the mainspring of the cavalry's progress in mechanisation could now point to the decisive role played by the German armoured force and in this light the concept of a similar independent armoured force was adopted in the United States.

The new policy was put into effect on July 10, 1940. On that day the Armoured Force was created, combining all armoured units under one command and thereby putting an end to the previous division between infantry tank units and the mechanised cavalry. Its creation was a major advance on either of the two earlier lines of development and the founders of the Armoured Force clearly regarded it as the decisive and principal arm in ground warfare.

The original organisation of the Armoured Force consisted of one armoured corps with 2 armoured divisions and one G.H.Q. reserve tank battalion. Cadres for this were provided by the 7th Cavalry Brigade and 6 tank battalions into which the infantry's tanks had by then been reorganised, but a good many more men were required. As for tanks, not only were many more required but also of a more powerful type than those in existence.

On May 1, 1940, the army had 464 tanks, the sum total of the American tank production since 1935. The majority were of the light 9 to 11-ton type still armed with nothing more powerful than a .5 in. machine-gun. The Ordnance Department had evolved two new designs, both armed with a 37 mm. gun, the M2A4 light tank and the M2A1 medium, but only a few had been built. Moreover, by mid-1940, the M2A1 was no longer considered good enough for a medium tank. Its development began in 1938, under the T5 medium tank designation and on the basis of the well-tried M2 light tank components. At the time it was better armed than the light tanks but in 1940 the latter had caught up with it in just about everything except size and the number of machine-guns. What is more, the Germans were known to be using a 75 mm. gun in their Pz.Kpfw.IV medium tank. In consequence, in August 1940, a requirement was officially established for a new medium tank with thicker armour than the M2A1 and with a 75 mm. gun. Although a turret-mounted gun was preferred, it was recognised that a suitable turret for a 75 mm. gun would be larger than any previously built in the United States and would require some time to develop. In view of this and the need to have a more powerful medium tank quickly it was decided to adopt initially the easier hull mounting for which, moreover, a prototype fortuitously existed in the shape of the T5E2 medium which in 1938, on its own initiative, the Ordnance Department armed with a 75 mm. howitzer. From this came the M3 medium, a 27-ton tank with a 75 mm. gun mounted in the right front of the superstructure and still only with a 37 mm. gun in its small turret, a tank whose design was subsequently widely criticised.

The M3 was by no means perfect but it did provide a more powerful tank quickly. The pilot model was ready in January 1941 and quantity production started in July, much of the production engineering having been done while the design was still being worked out. Its design was closely followed by that of the T6 medium, which mounted the same 75 mm. gun as the M3, but in a turret. Like the M3, the T6 was based on the tried mechanical components of the earlier M2A1 but it had even thicker armour, of up to 75 mm. on the turret front, and it weighed 29.7 tons.

The prototype of the T6 was completed by September 1941 and quantity production began in July 1942. On passing from the experimental phase to a standard vehicle it dropped the T designation and became the Medium

Tank M4, the best-known American tank of the Second World War and also the one produced in largest quantity.

The quantities in which the M4 was produced were staggering. The major automobile companies together with several of the large railroad equipment manufacturers took a hand in this but, of course, production took time to get going. In 1940 the total American production of tanks amounted to a mere 331. But in 1941 it was already 4,052—already more than Germany's and only slightly below Britain's. And then, in 1942, it shot up to 24,997—almost twice that of Germany and Britain combined. The energy with which American production was organised is well illustrated by the story of the Detroit Arsenal, built and operated for the United States Army by the Chrysler Corporation: in August 1940 its site was still a field, in April 1941 it built its first tank and by April 1942 it had completed more than 2,000 M3 medium tanks.

In 1942, when the design work on the M4 medium was completed and its production was under way, the field was open for the design of a new medium tank. This was in fact started in May, resulting in the T20, a tank based on the mechanical components of the M4 but rearranged, with the drive placed for the first time since the T4 at the rear, giving a longer lower-silhouette vehicle. What was even more important, it had a more powerful 76 mm. gun in place of the medium-velocity 75 of the M4. Altogether it was a design which would have kept the United States in the forefront of medium tank development and which could and should have been introduced by the beginning of 1944. Unfortunately, this did not happen.

By 1943 the original concept of the Armoured Force had lost ground, its decisive role was played down and the official doctrine settled on the exploitation role. For this the M4 appeared quite adequate. It did well in the British offensive at El Alamein in October 1942, where it was used for the first time and it was generally well up to the contemporary standard in medium tanks. Earlier there had been some criticism by the British of the M3 on account of the mounting of its 75 mm. gun, though the gun itself was appreciated, and this was repeated when the 1st United States Armoured Division landed with it in North Africa in 1942. But the M4 was thought to put all this and other matters right.

Moreover, quite early in the broad planning of tank production there developed something of an obsession with numbers, based partly on the usual overestimates of enemy numerical strength. The introduction of a new model was, therefore, resisted as it would have caused some drop in the quantities produced, even though in 1942 medium tanks alone amounted to 14,000 and in 1943 their production accounted for 21,000 out of the peak annual total of 29,497 tanks. Altogether 57,027 medium tanks were produced, 49,234 of which were M4, out of a total of 88,000 tanks produced by the United States during the Second World War.

In addition, the new medium tank development handicapped itself when the earlier T20 and T22 models were succeeded by the T23, which had an electrical, instead of mechanical, transmission. All these factors, together with the absence during 1943 of large-scale armoured operations, such as those in Russia which spurred German and Soviet tank development, combined with the result that the production of the M4 was continued longer than it should have been. And as further result American armoured units which landed in Normandy in mid-1944 were still equipped with the 75 mm. gun M4, which by the standard of the Russian front and of the contemporary German Panther and Soviet T–34/85 medium tanks, was obsolete.

It was only in February 1944, only four months before the Normandy landings, that the need for a more powerfully armed medium tank than the 75 mm. gun M4 was acknowledged, and to try to put matters right the turret and 76 mm. gun of the T20 series were grafted on to the M4. A few of the resulting 76 mm. gun M4 were used in Normandy and its numbers grew thereafter, particularly in the final months of the war, in 1945. To some extent it redressed the balance as far as the quality of the American medium tanks went, but basically it was not as good a tank as the T20.

The T20 series did emerge eventually, but in a different guise. Having dropped the unfortunate electrical transmission and, under the influence of the German Tiger I, having acquired a 90 mm. gun it became a heavy tank, the 41-ton M26, or Pershing. The user arm, fixated in the exploitation role, had no part in it initially but the combined efforts of the Ordnance Department and of the General Staff brought it through and its production started at the beginning of 1944. Some were used in Europe, in the spring of 1945, too late to be able to exert any significant effect.

The attitude shown towards the M26 was not the only instance of a lack of appreciation of heavily armed tanks. It had already killed the M6 heavy tank, the first American heavy tank since the Mark VIII of the First World War. The design of this 56-ton model was started by the Ordnance Department in 1940 and the pilot model was ready in December 1941, when, thanks to its long 76 mm. gun, it was the most powerful tank in existence anywhere. But after some forty were produced it was abandoned, partly because of shipping considerations. Towards the end of the war the attitude changed somewhat for the better and, in addition to the M26, several other heavy tanks were under development: the 60-ton T29 with a 105 mm. gun, the T30 with a 155 mm. gun and the T30E1 and T34 with 120 mm. guns, all turret mounted. There was also the even heavier, 85-ton T28, a heavily armoured turretless vehicle with a 105 mm. gun, similar in conception to the contemporary British Tortoise turretless assault tank.

In the meantime, American armoured forces participated on a large scale in the fighting in France and, later, in Germany. Together with infantry divisions, armoured divisions played an important part in the break-out of the Normandy bridgehead in July 1944 and then, led by General G. Patton, exploited the success in the drive across France. Stopped at the German frontier, when they outran their logistical support, the armoured divisions fought hard through the winter in Lorraine and in the Ardennes, helping there to stop the last German offensive. Then, in the spring of 1945, they took part in the final drive into Germany. By then the total number of armoured divisions had risen to 16, and what they lacked in the gun power of their tanks they partly made up in the number and the reliability of the M4 medium, the two outstanding features of this tank.

The campaigns of 1944 and 1945 showed that the armoured divisions were as capable of winning a decision in battle as of the subsequent exploitation. And, on a few occasions when they were called upon, they proved equally successful on the defensive. Unfortunately, their versatility failed to be recognised and the impression persisted that their usefulness was confined to exploitation, in which they were certainly spectacular but which did not exhaust their potentialities.

Together with the impression that the usefulness of armoured forces was limited to exploitation there came, at the end of the Second World War, one of the periodic waves of decrying the value of tanks on account of new armour-piercing weapons. This time they were the American bazooka anti-tank rocket launcher, the German *Panzerfaust* and the recoilless guns. Thus, in the immediate post-war period, a reaction set against armoured forces as their further usefulness was considered to be very limited. The number of armoured divisions was drastically reduced, not only as part of the general over-hasty demobilisation of the American forces but also in relation to the much reduced post-war army. In contrast to the peak of 16 armoured divisions in a total of 89 divisions during the war, in 1947 there was only one among the 13 then in existence.

As a further result of the post-war attitude, tank units were scattered among the infantry divisions and it was the latter which now contained most of the available tank strength. Under the post-war organisation each infantry division received a divisional tank battalion and each infantry regiment 1 tank company. This amounted to each infantry division having the equivalent of 2 medium tank battalions, or 147 tanks, and the use of the great majority of tanks for infantry support, as before the Second World War.

Only when the Cold War between the West and the Soviet *bloc* grew in intensity, when the strength of the Soviet armoured forces was slowly realised and, above all, when four battalions of North Korean-manned Soviet tanks played havoc with American units in the opening phase of the Korean war, was there a re-awakening of interest in armoured forces and greater willingness to accord to them some of their former importance.

However, a few good things did come out of the immediate post-Second World War period. For instance, it was finally accepted that tanks must be able to fight enemy tanks and it was principally as powerful mobile anti-tank weapons that tanks were allotted to the infantry divisions. To be able to fight enemy tanks they had to be suitably armed, of course, and this put an end to some of the earlier theories of under-gunned mobility. It also put an end to the independent Tank Destroyer Command consisting of self-propelled anti-tank units half-way between artillery and tanks whose existence had unnecessarily complicated the development of armoured vehicles and helped to obscure the need for arming tanks with adequate guns. Then it was decided to concentrate the limited tank funds on the development of a new series of engines, transmissions and other basic components, a policy similar to that which was followed by the Ordnance Department in the thirties and which was fully vindicated by the mechanical performance of American tanks during the Second World War. Also from the same period came the specifications for 3 new types of tanks to replace the 3 which were in existence at the end of the war: the 17-ton M24 light tank armed with a medium-velocity 75 mm. gun, the 33-ton 76 mm. gun medium M4A3E8, and the 41-ton 90 mm. gun M26 heavy tank.

The 3 new tanks conceived around 1947 were to be the T41 light tank in the 20-ton class, the T42 medium in the 30-ton class and the T43 heavy tank and they were to be armed

with 76, 90 and 120 mm. guns, respectively. Development
of all three began in the late forties but in the meantime, in
view of the deteriorating world situation, it was decided
to rework some of the 2,000-odd M26 produced towards
the end of the war and since held in storage. Fitted with the
newly developed engines and transmissions, these became
the M46 Patton medium tanks, interim vehicles introduced
in 1948 while the new medium was still being designed.
Then, before the design of the T42 was completed, came
Korea and it was decided to use its new turret with range-
finder on the M46 chassis. The resulting hybrid became the
M47, first built in 1951. A year later came a further development of the Pershing-Patton family, the M48, a 44-ton medium
tank with characteristics similar to those of the M47 but with
a 1-piece cast ellipsoidal hull and a new rounded turret which
improved its ballistic properties, or, in other words, its resistance to anti-tank projectiles. And it was this tank, originally
known as the T48, and not the T42, which was adopted in the
early fifties as the new standard medium tank of the United
States Army.

Since its adoption the M48 has been developed further,
into the M48A2, which has a petrol injection engine and a
small machine-gun turret on top of the main turret, and
most recently into the M60, which uses the same chassis but
carries a new, ballistically improved turret with a British-
designed 105 mm. gun and is powered by a V–12 air-cooled
diesel engine.

Unlike the T42, the T43 heavy tank was finally adopted
as the M103 but only in small quantity and after a prolonged
struggle. It was a 53.5-ton vehicle evolved from the experimental T29–T30 heavy tanks which were built just after the
Second World War, similar to but larger than the Pershing-
Patton series and using the same 810 b.h.p. V–12 Ordnance-
Continental engine as that introduced in 1948 on the M46.
Like the M46 and M47, but unlike the M48, it had a 5-man
crew and, of course, a powerful 120 mm. gun. But, once
again, there was no unanimity of opinion that such a powerful

tank was essential and its weight told against it when compared with the more mobile medium tanks. Broadly speaking, it was only periodic reminders of the existence of the Soviet 122 mm. gun Stalin tank which kept the T43 alive.

In contrast, the T41 light tank was generally and quickly accepted. Essentially it was a bigger and more powerful version of the earlier M24 light tank. It weighed 22.8 tons and was armed with a 76 mm. gun similar to that used previously on the M4 medium tanks; it was adopted in 1950 as the M41 light tank and put into quantity production at a plant especially built in Cleveland. Yet it was the least successful of the 3-tank types conceived after the war. It was too large and not mobile enough for a good reconnaissance vehicle and not quite powerful enough in relation to its size for a combat role. And, what was even more serious, it was too heavy to be an airborne tank.

The failure of the M41 as an airborne tank meant that there was no vehicle with which armoured units could participate effectively in the important post-war development in airborne operations. A deplorable situation, both in view of the emphasis which the United States Army placed on airborne warfare and the fact that the development of airborne tanks started as early as 1941, when the T9 light tank was first considered. Unfortunately, the foresight shown in the development of the T9, or M22 as it later became, was not matched by the development, in time, of a suitable aircraft. Thus, when the opportunity for using the M22 came in 1944, the United States Army had no means of carrying it by air. The only aircraft which could carry this 7-ton tank was the British Hamilcar glider. Consequently it was the British 6th Airborne Division which finally used a few M22 at the crossing of the Rhine, in March 1944, having already air-landed 7 British Tetrarch light tanks on D-Day in Normandy in 1944.

After the war the M22 was successfully carried in the Fairchild C–82 Flying Boxcar, the standard twin-engined transport of the period, and, a little later, the M24 light tank was tried in the 4-engined Douglas C–124 Globemaster. By then, however, both the 37 mm. gun M22 and the 75 mm. gun M24 were obsolete and the 2 battalions of more modern, adequately armed tanks which were allotted to each airborne division were surface bound on account of their weight. It was only in 1957 that a lighter 76 mm. gun tank than the M41 finally appeared. This was the 16-ton T92, a vehicle rather on the lines of the earlier French AMX 13 air-transportable tank and a commendable departure from the " bigger and better " school in light tank design.

In contrast to the poor start in the important field of airborne warfare, the armoured forces did considerably better in the next and even more important field of nuclear warfare. Their inherent tactical mobility and equipment fitted them well for effective dispersed operation under the conditions imposed by the destructive power of nuclear weapons. At the same time the armour of the vehicles provided a measure of protection against the effect of nuclear explosions.

The potential value of tanks was indicated after the first nuclear explosion at Alamogordo, New Mexico, in July 1945, when a specially equipped M4 medium tank carried observers into the test area, and it was confirmed in later tests where armoured vehicles were exposed to the effects of nuclear explosions. However, before the continued importance of armoured forces under the new technological conditions was fully recognised, American tanks had to experience yet another dip in their fortunes. In 1954 the impetus given by the Korean war had largely spent itself and interest in tanks began to decline once more. As a result, tank production was cut by about 50 per cent. and funds for the development of new tanks were reduced even more drastically, with potentially far more serious consequences. But a brighter future for armoured vehicles was heralded a year later with an experiment staged in May 1955, in the Nevada desert, which has become something of a landmark in the development of American armoured forces.

The 1955 Nevada test was the culmination of the earlier smaller-scale experiments with armoured vehicles and in it, for the first time, manned vehicles were used in relative proximity to a nuclear explosion. Armoured units of Task Force Razor participating in the test consisted of a reinforced medium tank battalion which was deployed some 3,000 yards from the actual explosion and which, after the latter took place, moved rapidly into the blasted area in a simulated exploitation of a tactical nuclear weapon. Thus, the 1955 Nevada test clearly demonstrated the potential value of tanks under conditions of possible nuclear warfare and the continued value of armoured units in general.

16

Germany

IN contrast to their later achievements, the Germans were slow to take up armoured vehicles. So were the Austrians, their comrades in arms in the two World Wars, in spite of the fact that as early as 1904 the Austro-Daimler Company of Wiener-Neustadt constructed a very promising armoured car. The first German armoured car, the Ehrhardt, was built 2 years later but it was only in 1914, after the successful employment of armoured cars by its opponents, that the German Army ordered some for itself. And even then only 1 Daimler, 1 Büssing and 13 Ehrhardts were built by 1917.

The story repeated itself with tanks, with much more serious consequences. In 1911, almost 3 years before the outbreak of the First World War, an Austrian officer, G. Burstyn, submitted what was the first concrete design of a tracked armoured fighting vehicle. But, both in Austria and later in Germany, the proposal fell on deaf ears. It was only after the appearance of the first British tanks in 1916, that the Germans took up tank development. As a result, during the remaining 2 years of the war they found themselves completely outclassed in the field of mechanised warfare and could only reply with a few tanks of their own to the hundreds which the British and French Armies were launching against them.

The first German tank, the A7V, was designed in the early part of 1917 on the basis of a Holt tractor found in Austria. The chassis was ready in May and the first fully armoured vehicle completed in December 1917. A month later, in January 1918, the first detachment of 5 tanks was formed and on March 21, 1918, at St. Quentin, it received its baptism of fire.

The A7V was a 30-ton turretless vehicle with a forward-mounted 57 mm. gun and 6 machine-guns, manned by a crew of 18. It was manufactured in face of mounting industrial difficulties, and up to the end of the war only 20 were completed. In the meantime, however, the Germans managed to put into service a number of British Mark IV tanks captured at Cambrai and elsewhere and by October raised a total of three A7V and 6 captured tank detachments.

A considerable increase in tank strength was expected in the first part of 1919, when, it was hoped, the expansion programme launched in 1918 would begin to bear fruit. The formation of larger 15-tank heavy detachments was envisaged, as was that of three 100-tank light detachments equipped with new German 7-ton LK II light tanks. Besides the prototypes of the LK II and of the earlier LK I, the Germans also built the prototype of a new heavy, the A7V–U which was to succeed the A7V and which followed the general layout of the contemporary rhomboidal British heavy tanks. They were also building 2 super-heavy K tanks: each weighed 150 tons and was armed with four 77 mm. guns projecting out of the sides, and 7 machine-guns.

The Armistice of 1918 put an end to all this. Under the terms imposed by the Western Allies and embodied in paragraph 171 of the Versailles Treaty, Germany was forbidden to have tanks. The only armoured vehicles which the German Army was allowed to have were 15 unarmed armoured cars or wheeled armoured personnel carriers in each of its 7 motor transport battalions. In addition, German police were allowed a number of turreted armoured cars.

However, although the few existing tanks had to be destroyed and none was built for several years, design studies were resumed in secret. Even earlier studies began of the employment of motorised troops and armoured vehicles.

Paradoxically, the restrictions imposed upon Germany were, in at least one respect, favourable to the development of mechanised forces. Its small army, the 100,000-man *Reichswehr*, was compelled to think more in terms of quality and mobile warfare than it would have done had it remained a large and ponderous conscript army. The consequent emphasis on quick-moving, hard-hitting troops laid by its creator and chief during the 1920–26 period, General von Seeckt, made it more ready to explore the possibilities of mechanised warfare. In Seeckt's own plans armoured vehicles as such still played virtually no part but he was alive to the more general importance of technological developments and encouraged studies and experiments.

The development which actually led to the creation of German armoured forces was carried out by the supposedly non-combatant motor transport units and its driving force was General H. Guderian. He began, in 1922, by studying the employment of motorised troops and, gradually, from an analysis of British writings on mechanised warfare—particularly those of Fuller and Liddell Hart—and from his own small-scale experiments evolved the principles on which the evolution of the German armoured forces was based. In brief, Guderian visualised armoured forces formed into armoured divisions as the decisive element in ground warfare. The armoured divisions would be based on tanks but would also include infantry, artillery and other elements. Thus, he rejected both the theory of tanks working on their own, which prevailed in Britain, and the French doctrine of subordinating tanks to the infantry. To him the future of the tank lay in effective combination with other arms which, however, had to be brought up to the tank's standards of mobility.

So far as the practical side went, the motor transport troops had to make do with their old armoured cars and dummy " tanks "—first of canvas and then of sheet-metal—built on passenger car chassis. With these they took part in the first army manoeuvres in 1927 and did most of their work during the following 7 years, as they evolved into the first armoured units.

In the meantime the firms of Krupp, Daimler-Benz and Rheinmetall were commissioned to build new tanks. Two basic types were involved, a medium tank of some 20 tons with a short turret-mounted 75 mm. gun and a light tank of about 9 tons with a 37 mm. gun. They were designed in secret in about 1926 and completed in 1928, altogether about 10 vehicles being built. By then, as a result of military collaboration between the German and Soviet Armies, a tank centre had been set up at Kazan in Russia and some of the new German tanks were sent there for field trials.

As a result of the trials and further study a new medium tank called the Nb.Fz.—*Neubaufahrzeuge*, or " New Model Vehicle "—was designed. But it was only in the mid-thirties that 5 were completed by Rheinmetall and Krupp. They were 23-tonners armed, like their predecessors, with 75 mm. guns but in addition each also had a coaxially mounted 37 mm. gun and 2 small auxiliary machine-gun turrets, one at the front and one behind the main turret, for which the British Independent heavy tank set the fashion.

Partly because of the time taken by the development of the medium tanks, in 1931 and 1932 the German Command turned its attention to another type: the light machine-gun armed tank which the Vickers Carden Loyd designs popularised. Although of doubtful combat value, this type of tank had the attraction of cheap and quick production and could, therefore, provide at an early date tanks badly needed for training.

However questionable the policy of building such a lightly armed tank might have been, it was adopted, and in 1933 the Ordnance Office, or *Heereswaffenamt*, issued orders for its design. The orders were issued to Krupp, M.A.N., Henschel, Daimler-Benz and Rheinmetall under the camouflaged designation of " Agricultural Tractor," or La.S., and of the designs submitted the Krupp vehicle was accepted and its production ordered. The first tank of this type appeared early in 1934; by the end of the year its production was well under way and deliveries to troops had begun. Later called the Pz.Kpfw.I Model A, this first quantity produced German tank was a

5.3-ton machine with a crew of 2 and armed with 2 turret-mounted machine-guns; its armour varied between 15 and 8 mm. and it was capable of a maximum speed of 24 m.p.h. It was thus fairly representative of its type but it is doubtful whether its production, to the tune of some 1,500 vehicles built up to the outbreak of the Second World War, could really be justified.

The second light tank, designed in 1934, was more sensible. It was a larger, 3-man vehicle armed with a 20 mm. gun, as well as a machine-gun. Again more than one design was produced and after competitive trials the 7.5-ton M.A.N. model was accepted, becoming the Pz.Kpfw.II. This vehicle still possessed many of the advantages of a light tank but it carried more effective armament. In fact, at the time of its introduction, the 20 mm. gun could be regarded as effective even against medium tanks. But a few years later this was no longer the case. Nevertheless, the 20 mm. gun was retained even when, from 1937 onwards, better armoured 10-ton versions of this tank were produced and this in spite of the fact that in most other countries tanks of this weight were already being armed with 37 mm. guns.

Chronologically, the next vehicle for which orders were placed was the Pz.Kpfw.IV. This was a 75 mm. gun medium tank in the 20-ton class which was a continuation of the 1928 and the Nb.Fz. development and which, in its original Krupp-designed form, weighed 17.1 tons. Because of its low-velocity gun some British writers have wrongly compared it, in later years, with the British " close support " tanks, which were specialised vehicles armed with smoke or high-explosive-firing howitzers. In fact, however, the Pz.Kpfw.IV was conceived as the basic German medium tank and at the time its gun was adequate for both anti-tank and high-explosive fire.

Completing the quartet of German tanks was the Pz. Kpfw.III, which was ordered in 1936, a year after the Pz.Kpfw.IV. It was meant to be a 15-ton light tank with a 37 mm. gun and a companion vehicle to the 75 mm. gun medium tank. As produced, however, it differed little basically from the Pz.Kpfw.IV, except for its armament. It had the same general layout and appearance, the same 5-man crew, a similar engine and much the same weight, armour and performance. For a light tank it was a luxurious vehicle, large and expensive in relation to its fighting power although, admittedly, this was improved after 1939, when the original 37 mm. gun was replaced by the 5 cm. L /42.

Together these 4 tanks formed the equipment issued to the German armoured units between 1935 and the outbreak of the Second World War in 1939. The same period also saw the German armoured forces grow from the embryonic stage to a fully fledged fighting force.

The first year of the 1935–39 period was marked by four significant events. First, Adolf Hitler, who 2 years earlier had gained power and had already launched a programme of military expansion, denounced the Versailles Treaty, thus removing the last vestige of the restrictions on the development of the German armoured forces. Secondly, in the summer of 1935, the first armoured, or panzer, division was improvised from the units then available. Then came the creation of the Armoured Force, or *Panzertruppen*, as a distinct arm and, finally, in October, the formation of 3 panzer divisions on a permanent basis.

The following 2 years were spent in equipping and training the newly created units and establishing the position of the armoured forces in face of growing opposition to their ideas from the other branches of the German Army. In particular, they had to fight demands that part of the tank strength be diverted to infantry support instead of being concentrated in the panzer divisions. In 1936 crews and equipment were sent to help the Nationalists in the Spanish Civil War and eventually 4 German-Spanish tank battalions were formed, equipped with Pz.Kpfw.Is and Russian-built T–26s captured from the Communists. In 1938, the year of the *Anschluss* with Austria, there was a large-scale practical test in the march of the 2nd Panzer Division to Vienna. The shortcomings which became apparent during this 420-mile march, and others which were imagined, were seized upon by outside observers and together with erroneous conclusions drawn from the Spanish Civil War were widely used to condemn armoured forces in general. However, to the German armoured forces the march provided a useful lesson in logistics and maintenance, in which they later excelled, and the event did not prevent the formation of 2 more panzer divisions. And of a fourth light division, a cavalry-sponsored motorised formation with some tanks which became linked with the panzer divisions. In 1939, on the establishment of the " Protectorate " in Czechoslovakia, the Germans took over 469 tanks from the Czech Army and, what was more important, Czech tank manufacturing facilities. Later in the same year, shortly before the outbreak of the war, yet another panzer division was formed.

Thus, on September 1, 1939, the day Germany attacked Poland and the day the Second World War began, there were 6 regular panzer divisions, as well as one provisional improvised division, and 4 light divisions. On that day the total number of German tanks, excluding the recently acquired Czech vehicles, amounted to 3,195: 1,445 Pz.Kpfw.I, 1,226 Pz.Kpfw.II, 98 Pz.Kpfw.III, 211 Pz.Kpfw.IV and 215 command tanks. With these they outnumbered and outclassed the opposing Polish tank forces completely. Nevertheless, the Polish campaign represented a major effort for the German Army and the first battle test of its panzer divisions. The results proved the soundness of the ideas propounded by Guderian and established the effectiveness of the panzer divisions. They proved capable of striking decisive blows deep into enemy territory and henceforth occupied an increasingly important place in German planning as the mobile spearhead of the ground forces.

On the equipment side, any illusions which might have lingered about the combat value of the Pz.Kpfw.I were finally dispelled. Pz.Kpfw.II proved useful for reconnaissance but it was the Pz.Kpfw.IV which stood out as a really effective tank. There is no doubt that the original German policy, initiated in the mid-twenties, of developing a well-armed medium tank of the 20-ton 75 mm. gun type was right. And there is no doubt that this was the vehicle which the Germans should have emphasised consistently, developing it and gradually increasing the muzzle velocity of its gun, as the Russians were doing with their corresponding tank guns. Instead, in 1939 and 1940, production concentrated on the Pz.Kpfw.III, re-armed with the 5 cm. L/42. This was to prove useful in France and against the British forces in Libya. But, as the Germans found 2 years later, the Russians were already concentrating on 76.2 mm. gun tanks.

In April 1940, on the eve of their offensive in the West, the Germans had much the same total of tanks as they did at the outbreak of the war—3,379 to be precise. But the number of Pz.Kpfw.III had risen to 329 and that of the Pz.Kpfw.IV slightly to 280; there were also 381 Czech-built Pz.Kpfw.35t and 38t, which were armed with 37 mm. guns and which were issued to the new panzer divisions converted from the 4 light divisions.

Of the total, 2,574 were at the front. This was about as many tanks as the French had in their front line units, just as the total number of German tanks was roughly the same as that of modern French tanks. But while the French tanks were scattered over a wide front, in several different types of units, the German were all concentrated in the 10 panzer divisions. Moreover, 9 out of the 10 panzer divisions were massed on a narrow front of less than 100 miles. Organised into panzer corps, they were thus able to deliver a massive blow and after breaking through the French front they exploited their initial success by pushing rapidly to the Channel coast. The resulting elimination of the Northern Group of Allied Armies virtually decided the issue of the campaign, which was settled when the panzer divisions turned south and, in June 1940, broke through the so-called " Weygand Line."

The striking success of the panzer divisions in France confirmed their importance to Germany, and, what is more finally established armoured forces in the eyes of the rest of the world. If their success in Poland was noted, many, including the French, were inclined to dismiss it on account of the Polish weakness in modern armaments. But when the panzer divisions repeated their performance against large and well-armed armies there was no further doubt that the German method of concentrating their armoured strength in the panzer divisions was right and that the French practice of dispersing tanks among the infantry formations was wrong. As a result, after the 1940 French campaign, other armies followed the German example and turned their attention to armoured divisions as the decisive element in ground warfare.

In Germany, in consequence of the success in France and in preparation for the campaign against Russia, the number of panzer divisions was doubled. Unfortunately for them, tank production had not risen in proportion. In fact, the total number of tanks produced during 1940 amounted to only 1,460. In consequence, the expansion to 20 panzer divisions could only be achieved by reducing the number of tanks per division, a dilution of the tank strength which the panzer commanders deplored.

By June 1941, when they invaded Russia, the Germans had 5,264 tanks of all types but excluding captured French tanks which they later put to some use in occupied territories. Of this total only a portion was actually with front line units but they included the majority of the 1,440 Pz.Kpfw.III and of the 517 Pz.Kpfw.IV, in all about 3,350 tanks. Against them the Russians had an estimated total of 20,000 to 24,000 tanks of all types of which, of course, only a fraction was with front line units.

Yet, in spite of their numerical inferiority, the panzers defeated the opposing armoured forces and almost won the day. As in France, the whole tank strength was concentrated in the panzer divisions, which, in turn, were grouped into panzer corps and the corps into panzer armies. And as in France, the panzer divisions spearheaded the invasion, delivered the decisive blows and pushed deep into Russian territory. Only after 5 months of continuous fighting did the combined effects of depleted strength, over-extended supply lines and the Russian winter bring them to a halt. How success-ful they were until then is perhaps best shown by the fact that the Germans destroyed or captured about 17,000 Soviet tanks for the loss of 2,700 of their own.

The success is all the more remarkable in view of the fact that the Germans did not possess the qualitative superiority in tanks which at the outset of the campaign they thought they had. To be true, the Pz.Kpfw.III and IV were superior to the mass of the older Soviet tanks made up of the T–26 and B.T. But, within the first week of the campaign, the Germans found that the Russians had a new and powerful medium tank, the T–34.

The appearance of the T–34 made a deep impression on the Germans and made them reconsider hurriedly their own tank development programme. Until then, when one victory followed another, there were no immediate plans for the replacement of the Pz.Kpfw.IV by a more powerful vehicle. A heavier, 30-ton tank had been ordered as far back as 1937 and an even heavier, 65-ton tank was ordered in 1938, under the VK 6501 designation, but neither proceeded beyond prototypes. The former, known as the *Durchbruchswagen*, or " Break-through Tank," was merely succeeded by its improved version, the D.W.2, which was still being tested in 1941. Only after the opening of the Russian campaign was the inadequate pace of the development realised and new orders were issued calling for a 30-ton medium tank which would provide an answer to the Soviet T–34.

The orders for the new tank were issued simultaneously to four firms under the code name of VK 3001. However, in the case of two firms—Henschel and Porsche—the original specification was superseded by another, which was the result of Hitler's personal intervention. The new specification called for a more powerful 45-ton vehicle with an 88 mm. gun, the gun which in its anti-aircraft version had already acquired fame as an anti-tank weapon. Prototypes built by the two firms were completed in April 1942 and the Henschel design, which incorporated features of the earlier D.W.2, was adjudged superior. It became the Tiger I 56-ton heavy tank which first appeared from production in August 1942. Eventually a total of 1,350 was built but already in the autumn of the same year, after a few were tried on the Eastern Front, a redesign was ordered, leading to the more heavily armoured, 68-ton Tiger II armed with a more powerful version of the 88 mm. gun. As a matter of interest, 90 vehicles based on the unsuccessful Porsche design were also built in the form of the Ferdinand (or Elephant) self-propelled 88 mm. gun.

In the meantime, the remaining two firms of the VK 3001 order, Daimler-Benz and M.A.N., went on with their design, which incorporated sloping armour of the T–34 type and a 7.5 cm. L /48, a gun with a barrel twice as long as that of the 7.5 cm. L /24 of the contemporary Pz.Kpfw.IV. Prototypes were ready in March 1942 and after some vacillation the M.A.N. version was adopted, the armament being changed by Hitler to the even more powerful 7.5 cm. L /70, and its weight having exceeded the original target of 30 tons by as much as 15 tons. The first production vehicles were completed in November 1942 and it became the Panther medium tank.

When the Tigers and Panthers appeared in quantity in 1943, the Germans were able to establish qualitative superiority over the Russians and to maintain it during the following year not only on the Eastern Front but also in the West against American and British tanks. But in 1941, when the development of these new tanks had barely begun, they still had a long way to go. The situation on the Eastern Front was improved somewhat by the appearance in the early part of 1942 of an improved Pz.Kpfw.III with the long-barrelled 5 cm. L /60 in place of the earlier and less powerful 5 cm. L /42. At about the same time came an improved Pz.Kpfw.IV, armed with a 7.5 cm. L /46 in place of the original short-barrelled L /24, which was adopted as an interim measure while the production of the Panther was getting under way. A gun of the type introduced on the improved Pz.Kpfw.IV was experimented with in a Rheinmetall turreted half-track as early as February 1940, but at the time there seemed little need for it in tanks. When it was finally introduced in 1942, it gave the Pz.Kpfw.IV a measure of superiority over the contemporary T–34, as well as over the American M4 medium, which was introduced shortly after it. The mobility of the Pz.Kpfw.IV was inferior to that of either of the 2 opposing tanks but it proved, nevertheless, a useful vehicle and its production continued into 1945. By then over 8,000 of this long-lived model were built.

In this way, in 1942, the Germans were solving the problem of battle-worthiness of their tanks. The problem which was much further from a solution was that of quantity. It was particularly so when the successful resumption of offensive operations in 1942 was followed by the disaster at Stalingrad in the winter of 1942–43 and the defeats at El Alamein and in Tunisia. During this period the German armoured forces suffered their heaviest losses and the need for more tanks became more urgent than ever, to replace those lost in battle and to balance the increasing numbers of Soviet tanks.

A considerable increase in tank production was ordered but, inevitably, took time to become effective. An increase had already taken place on the totally unrealistic level of 1940, and in 1941 production amounted to 3,256 tanks. In 1942 it rose to 4,278 but it was only in 1943 that it reached something like double the 1941 rate with a total of 5,966. By then the turretless but tank-like *Sturmgeschütz* and *Jagdpanzer*, intended for infantry support and anti-tank roles, also entered production in quantity. In 1942 only 778 were produced but in 1943 the number jumped to 3,406 and in 1944, with a total of 8,682, their production almost equalled that of tanks, which was 9,161. This further increase was no mean effort in the face of the intensified Anglo-American bombing of Germany and it enabled the German

Army to build up the total number of battle-worthy tanks to a peak of about 5,500 in mid-1944 and to maintain it at roughly that level into the early part of 1945.

Nevertheless, all these production figures were puny by comparison with the combined tank production of the Soviet Union, the United States and Britain. As it mounted, the initiative was wrested from the Germans and their armoured forces were forced on to the defensive. They managed to stage one more large-scale offensive come-back, at Kursk, in July 1943. But this resulted only in heavy losses, including that of Tigers, Elephants and Panthers which were committed in quantity for the first time. Thereafter the role of the German armoured forces became that of mobile defence and local counter-offensives, roles in which they had already distinguished themselves, stemming the Soviet tide after Stalingrad.

On the defensive the German armoured forces inflicted heavy losses on the Russians and baulked more than one offensive attempt by Soviet armoured forces, in spite of the latter's continuously growing numerical superiority. In the West, too, after the Allied landings in Normandy, they took a heavy toll of British and American tanks and, but for Hitler's operational mishandling, might have been more damaging still. In the end, however, they too succumbed before the combined pressure of Allied land and air forces.

The impressive performance of the German armoured forces during the defensive phase of the war was due to the continued concentration of practically all the tanks in the panzer divisions, their tactical handling and, in part, the quality of the tanks or, more specifically, the tanks' gunpower. Having been caught napping by the Russians in 1941, the Germans more than redressed the balance in the latter part of the war. Even when the Stalin heavy tank appeared the Germans were able to counter it, qualitatively, with the Tiger II and then retaliate with an even more powerful vehicle, the 128 mm. gun Jagdtiger. Like the 68-ton Tiger II, the 70-ton Jagdtiger compared unfavourably with the Stalin on account of its weight but it was, none the less, the most powerful armoured vehicle used during the Second World War.

In part, the progress made in tank armament during the latter part of the war was due to Hitler who backed the very sound armament-mobility-protection order of priorities established by the experts, as earlier he supported the creation of the armoured forces. In the case of the Tiger and the Panther he even went beyond the recommendations of the experts. However, his judgment was erratic and his interference in tank development, as in strategic matters, was often unfortunate. It was responsible, for instance, for some of the dispersion of design and production effort and such useless projects as the 180-ton Maus heavy tank which was designed in 1942 by Porsche and whose limited production was actually started.

Into the same category of wasteful projects must be put the 123-ton 600 mm. Karl self-propelled siege howitzer, the 380 mm. mortar on Tiger I chassis and the Goliath remote-controlled demolition vehicle. They all drew resources away from the development and production of the basic tank designs, while the multiplicity of types and modifications hampered employment in the field. In fact, the failure to concentrate on one or two satisfactory designs, like the Russians did with their T–34, was one of the German failings and a major lesson of their tank development.

Of course, some of the multiplicity of types was simply due to emergency measures, which had to be taken several times. This applied in particular to the lightly armed self-propelled anti-tank guns which appeared in quantity during 1942. Introduced as a result of the urgent demands of the Eastern Front for more effective anti-tank weapons and in order to make up some of the deficiencies in tanks, these vehicles simply made use of various German, Czech and French obsolescent tank chassis which happened to be at hand.

However, even in the latter part of the war the Germans were developing simultaneously as many as 6 different types of tanks, ranging from the light 5-ton E.5, through the E.10, E.25, E.50 and E.75, to the E.100 of 140 tons. Work on them began in 1942 and they were intended for introduction in 1945 or 1946, though by then circumstances would, no doubt, have forced a reduction in the number of types and a more rational programme.

By 1945 too, enthusiasm for the super-heavy tanks of the E.100 and Maus type had definitely waned. On the other hand, the Tiger II heavy tank was at the time considered satisfactory. Even greater general satisfaction was felt, however, with the Panther as the basic medium tank. Further development of it was intended, the main improvements being a new turret with a range finder and the 88 mm. gun used hitherto on the Tiger II. None of this was put into practice when the war ended but the proposed Panther development clearly foreshadowed the heavily armed 45-50-ton medium tanks which came to be represented after the Second World War by the British Centurion III, the American M46–M48 and the French AMX 50.

In the final German production programme planned for the second half of 1945, Panther and Tiger II were still the two main types of medium and heavy tank respectively. They were, also, the only two turreted vehicles in the programme. The rest consisted of limited traverse types. It included a number of Jagdtigers and Jagdpanthers, as well as 8-wheeled armoured cars, but the bulk of the programme consisted of the light turretless Jagdpanzer 38t and 38d, which were to represent about 60 per cent. of all the armoured vehicles produced.

The production programme was, of course, never realised. But it illustrates clearly the position in the closing stages of the war and the trend towards lighter vehicles. The Jagdpanzer 38, in either of its two forms, was a compact 16-ton vehicle, with a limited traverse 75 mm. gun, based on the very successful pre-war Czech L.T.H. light tank chassis which, in various forms, saw extensive service in the German Army. It was economical of material and production man-hours and this, combined with the contemporary need for a maximum number of highly mobile anti-tank weapons, accounted for its growing importance in the final stages of the German war effort.

The surrender of Germany in May 1945 and the occupation by Allied and Soviet Armies brought to an end the existence of German armoured forces and stopped further armoured vehicle development. It was only several years after the end of the Second World War, after the final breakdown of the unnatural alliance between the Western Powers and Soviet Russia, that the Federal German Republic was freed from the restrictions forced upon it, which, this time, denied Germany any armed forces.

But as soon as it became possible to think about re-creating the German Army, armoured forces came to the fore again. In view of their past performance and continued importance 6 panzer divisions were again planned and the development of armoured vehicles restarted. However, the first equipment came from the United States, under the Military Aid Programme, in the shape of M47 medium tanks. This was followed by an order for American-built M48 tanks, which were chosen after competitive trials with the British Centurion. Earlier orders were also placed for French-designed Hotchkiss and for Hispano-Suiza armoured personnel carriers for the new Panzer Grenadier units.

Thus, by 1957, German armoured forces were reborn and resumed their place as an important element of the German armed forces.

17

Soviet Union

SOVIET importance in the field of armoured vehicles dates from a large-scale programme of tank development and production initiated in the late twenties. This does not mean, however, that the Russians showed no earlier interest in armoured vehicles. On the contrary, as early as 1900 a steam-engined armoured car was built under the supervision of the Imperial Artillery Committee, and the Tsarist Army was the first to place an order with the French firm of Charron-Girardot et Voigt 3 years after the latter exhibited its first armoured car at the 1902 Salon de l'Automobile.

The opening years of the First World War saw experiments with a large wheeled vehicle designed by Lebedenko and of a smaller tracked model by Porokhovshchikov, which in recent years has prompted exaggerated Soviet claims to the Russian invention of the tank. During the same period a number of armoured cars was built on imported chassis and used to some effect. Many of these Tsarist armoured cars were later taken over by Soviet forces, to whom they proved valuable in the fluid conditions of the Civil War, as did armoured trains whose employment was not all that different from that of the contemporary road-bound armoured cars.

During the Civil War Soviet forces also acquired their first tanks by capture from the White Armies of the large rhomboidal British Mark V and the small French Renault F.T. In the final stages of the Civil War the Russians also claim to have built 16 copies of the Renault F.T. But even they agree that the development of Soviet tanks and mechanised forces did not begin in earnest until the late twenties, when the Red Army emerged from the post-war and post-revolutionary doldrums and set about the task of reorganisation and modernisation.

The conditions of the period were, in a sense, favourable to tank development. The contemporary Red Army was relatively free from the bonds of traditional concepts and receptive to novel ideas, such as those on tank warfare demonstrated in its embryonic form by the British and French tanks during the First World War and preached after the war by a handful of enthusiasts. Much closer, the Red Army had the stimulus of German interest in the subject. As part of the military rapprochement which followed the 1922 Rapallo Agreement, a German tank centre was established at Kazan on the Volga and there the Germans proceeded to try some of their ideas and vehicles, denied them in their own country by the terms of the Versailles Treaty. In addition to, and as important as, any military considerations, there was the desire of the Soviet leaders to catch up with and overtake the bourgeois West in the field of technology, which found a particularly attractive outlet in tanks and aircraft.

However, before any large-scale tank production could be contemplated, a suitable industrial base had to be established first. It was not until 1924 that the first trucks were built on Russian soil and 4 more years had to pass before the basic industries—coal, iron and transport—recovered their pre-1914 production levels. But with the beginning of the first Five Year Plan industrialisation was pushed forward with all the ruthlessness of the Soviet regime and, in spite of all the attendant wastefulness, at the conclusion of the first Plan in 1932 the elements of heavy industries necessary for the production of armaments were created. Foreign technical help was welcomed and for years British, American and German companies contributed, in their shortsightedness, to the creation of powerful Communist war industries.

Simultaneously with the development of industries came the first Russian-designed tanks. The most important of these was the MS–I, or T–18, a more up-to-date version of the popular French Renault F.T. infantry-accompanying light tank. However, neither the T–18 nor the less numerous T–24 medium tank, nor any of the other vehicles of the

1927–28 period were entirely satisfactory, or sufficiently advanced on the tanks of the First World War. In consequence, when at the time of the first Five Year Plan greatly superior types of vehicles appeared in Britain and in the United States, the Russians turned to them for ideas and designs. This was all the easier because in many instances they could buy sample vehicles and then use them as prototypes for their own development and production.

Several of the ideas and vehicles came from the British firm of Vickers-Armstrongs, the leading tank builder during the twenties. Among the vehicles which it sold to Russia between 1930 and 1932 were 15 Vickers Mediums, 15 Six Ton Tanks and several Vickers Carden Loyd light vehicles. The first named were by then already obsolescent and they had no issue in Russia. But the Six Ton light tanks and the Carden Loyd Mark VI, which were among the outstanding vehicles of the period, were copied on a large scale. The latter was the most successful of several attempts during the first post-war decade at producing a small and inexpensive armoured vehicle and it became a model for a whole host of similar vehicles, such as the Italian L.3, the French Chenillette Model 1931–R, Polish TK, Czech MU4/T1 and the Soviet T–27. Like the other vehicles, the T–27 was a 2-man turretless tankette and was much in evidence during the early thirties. Its fighting value was extremely limited but at least it served a useful purpose in training and as an easy introduction to the problem of quantity production of armoured vehicles.

The Vickers-Armstrongs Six Ton Tank failed to interest the British Army but it was, nevertheless, one of the outstanding vehicles of the period and was better assessed elsewhere, including Russia. Among others, it influenced the development of the American T1 light tank series and in Russia it was adopted as the prototype of the T–26 tank series.

As with the Vickers-Armstrongs original, there were two distinct versions, the earlier T–26A which had two turrets each with 1 machine-gun and the T–26B and C with a single turret and coaxial 45 mm. gun and machine-gun. By the mid-thirties the former was definitely superseded by the more sensible single turret models which became the most common Soviet tanks in the years preceding the Second World War. They formed the equipment of the divisional tank battalions, which regular Soviet infantry divisions possessed, and of the light tank brigades which provided infantry support at the higher level of corps or army. On the whole, they were on a par with other contemporary " light-medium " tanks: they were less well protected than average perhaps but better armed. Their 45 mm. guns were definitely above average in tank guns and ensured their superiority over the all-too-popular breed of lighter machine-gun-armed tanks of the period, a fact demonstrated in the Spanish Civil War where the T–26B saw action in the hands of the Communist troops.

The Russians adopted light machine-gun tanks also but, more adroitly, as amphibious reconnaissance vehicles in the shape of the T–37 and T–38. These too owed their origin to a Vickers-Armstrongs model, the Vickers Carden Loyd amphibian, which was tried by the British Army under the experimental designation of A.4 E.11 and of which the Russians subsequently purchased 8. Apart from being amphibious, the T–37 and T–38 did not differ much from their contemporaries but the T–38 had the distinction of being the first tank carried by air, slung under the bellies of 4-engined Soviet bomber-transports, during peacetime manoeuvres in the mid-thirties.

Second only in numerical importance to the T–26, and more so from many other points of view, was the B.T., or *Bystrokhodnii Tank*, series based on the American Christie tanks two of which were purchased in 1931, after Christie delivered a number of similar vehicles to the United States Army.

Christie vehicles had several noteworthy and, for their time, very advanced features such as independent suspension with large bogie wheels, ability to move on wheels or tracks,

H.A.

a very high power to weight ratio, all of which contributed to a very high degree of tactical and strategic mobility. The power to weight ratio was actually higher than could be efficiently used but the Russians copied it all and confined their development largely to armament, which increased from a 37 mm. gun on the original models of 1931–32, to 45 mm. guns on the B.T.5 of 1935 and eventually to short 76.2 mm. guns on some of the final models of the series.

Like the T–26, B.T.s were standard equipment until the end of 1941 and enjoyed the same advantage of good armament. In addition they had the high degree of mobility, a feature particularly desirable from the point of view of their " long range " role in the ranks of the mechanised brigades.

Apart from the T–26, the fast B.T. and the light amphibians, the Russians developed 2 more major types of tanks: the 29-ton T–28 medium and the large 45-ton T–35 heavy tank. Unlike the others, both were designed without the benefit of foreign prototypes showing growing Soviet independence in tank design. Nevertheless, the layout of the T–28 resembled that of the British Sixteen Ton medium tank of the 1928–30 period. Like the latter, the T–28 had three turrets, a main one with a short 76.2 mm. gun and machine-gun and two smaller turrets, one on either side of the driver and each with 1 machine-gun. The heavy T–35 carried the multi-turret idea to the extreme, already demonstrated by the Vickers " Independent," or A.1, experimental heavy tank of the mid-twenties. It had no less than 5 turrets, the main one with the same armament as that of the T–28, 2 smaller ones with 45 mm. guns and 2 others with machine-guns only. The original idea behind this multiplicity of turrets was that these tanks would operate on their own and should, therefore, be able to engage targets all round. Eventually, however, their method of operation did not differ much from those of the French *chars de manoeuvre d'ensemble*, that is they were intended to deliver massive blows in support of the main effort of the infantry formations with which they co-operated.

Apart from their size and the fact that the Red Army was able to afford numbers of them in peacetime, the main point of note about the T–28 and T–35 was their armament. In this they differed markedly from their British forerunners. The principal armament of the British " Independent " and the Sixteen Tonner was only a 47 mm. gun but that of the T–28 and T–35 was a 76.2 mm., and the T–35 had two 45 mm. guns as well, for good measure. The example of the secret German experimental tanks of the late twenties, which had short turret-mounted 75 mm. guns, and the general Russian respect for the power of high explosive have no doubt been contributory factors, but whatever the precise cause it showed that the Russians were well ahead in tank armament. This was further illustrated by the early move to 45 mm. guns on the lighter vehicles, when other armies were still thinking in terms of 37 mm. guns.

Other features remained essentially unaltered, as well they might, for the Russians were wise in their initial choice of designs. Having picked the best, they could afford to leave them alone for some time and to concentrate instead on quantity production. This they certainly did, numbers becoming almost an obsession. Already by the mid-thirties, on manoeuvres and parades, they were able to show hundreds of tanks. By 1941, the total strength of the Soviet tank forces was in the region of 21,000 to 24,000 tanks, or about 4 times as many as the Germans had and more than all the other tank forces of the world put together.

But the concentration on mass production and on the numerical expansion of the tank forces had its negative side also, especially in its effect on new tank designs. Inevitably it delayed the introduction of new models while the production of the older ones was continued longer than was strictly justified. As a result, when the Germans attacked, in June 1941, the majority of Soviet tanks were obsolescent and inferior to the main types of German tanks.

The position was aggravated further by inept operational methods and changes in policy and organisation. In contrast to the mid-thirties, when the Soviet Army attached considerable importance to its mechanised brigades and corps, on the eve of the Second World War its emphasis shifted to small tank units and infantry support. In other words, the effectiveness of large bodies of tanks and their more independent employment were no longer believed in. Shortly afterwards, however, under the impact of the successes of the German armoured forces in Poland and France, the Soviet command recognised its error and set about reorganising its armoured forces on more effective lines. But the German attack caught the Soviet armoured forces in the throes of this reorganisation and their employment was still largely governed by the inferior piecemeal infantry-support methods.

Fortunately for them, the development of new tanks was not affected by the policy changes with respect to the employment of the armoured forces. In fact, when the Germans attacked, new and greatly improved tanks were already in service in quantity. They provided a complete and unpleasant surprise for the Germans who came up against them in the first few days of the campaign—and not later, at the gates of Moscow, as has often been claimed. They were a considerable advance on the mass of the earlier tanks and the impression which they made on the Germans did much to establish the reputation of Soviet tank designers since then.

The most important of this new generation of Soviet tanks was the T–34 medium tank. Mechanically it was a direct descendant, via the T–29 and T–32 experimental tanks, of the B.T. series from which it inherited several features. In relation to contemporary medium tank designs it represented an advance both in armament and in armour and was superior not only to the German light-medium Pz.Kpfw.III, but also to the most powerful German tank of the time, the medium Pz.Kpfw.IV.

As with the earlier T–28 and T–35, the most notable feature of the T–34 was its main armament in the shape of the 76.2 mm. gun Model 1939, 30.5 calibres long, which placed it well ahead in the armament race. Yet the move to this gun was quite gradual. Having started with 76.2 mm. guns 16.5 calibres long on the T–35 and the early T–28, already some time before the war the Russians increased its barrel length, and hence performance, to 26 calibres on the later T–28s, 2 calibres longer than the 75 mm. gun of the contemporary German Pz.Kpfw.IV. The next step, to 30.5 calibres, that is, the level of the average 75 mm. field-gun and of the gun in the French St. Chamond tank of 1916, was only natural.

Similar comments apply to the armament of the second main Soviet model, the 43-ton KV heavy tank. Like the T–34, it started with the 76.2 mm. gun of 30.5 calibres and like the other was then rearmed with the more powerful 41.5 calibres Model 1940. The KV was actually an earlier design than the T–34 and was preceded by some more multi-turreted experimental heavy tanks of the T–35 variety. The decision for finally abandoning these and adopting the much more sound single gun and single turret was, as was usual in such matters, attributed to Stalin. Be that as it may, KV tanks were already coming into service at the time of the Russo-Finnish War of the winter of 1939–40, as was the KV–II, a heavier version with a huge slab-sided turret and a 152 mm. howitzer, possibly inspired by the example of the one French 2C *bis* heavy tank which was rearmed with a 155 mm. howitzer in the late twenties.

As regards the thickness of armour, the 45 mm. of the T–34 and the 75 mm. of the KV were less spectacular than their armament. German tanks at the time had 30 mm. armour, in some cases increased to 50 mm. by means of extra plates. But the much earlier French S–35 (Somua) medium tank had armour up to 55 mm. thick and the even earlier light tanks had up to 40 mm. As for heavy tanks, as early as 1931 the French specified 75 mm. armour for heavy tanks, and the British Matilda infantry tank, which saw action before the KV did, had up to 78 mm.

In other respects the two new Soviet tanks were simple and robust, if a little primitive, as in the use of clutch and brake steering. Both were powered by the same 12-cylinder water-cooled diesel engine, a successful diesel adaptation of contemporary aero engine designs, which developed 500 b.h.p. on the T–34 and 550 to 600 on the KV.

The design of the T–34 has been particularly praised and with some justification. It must be remembered, however, that it owed several of its good points to its predecessor, the Christie-type B.T., whose type of suspension, drive, tracks and high power to weight ratio it inherited. A feature which has probably received most attention was its well-sloped frontal armour. For this the Soviet designers deserve full credit, yet lest it be thought that they invented it, it must be pointed out that several original Christie designs had sloping frontal armour of one form or another and that the Dutch Van Doorne (D.A.F.) armoured car of 1938 had well-sloped armour all round, just like that which was later admired on the T–34.

The general layout of the KV followed the lines which had been established earlier by German medium tanks. Its most noteworthy mechanical features were the use of independent torsion bar suspension and of steel-tyred resilient bogie wheels. The latter were a Soviet novelty but the former, for which the Russians also like to take credit, was not. Torsion bar springing was pioneered in Germany and was used on several German vehicles before the Second World War, including the Pz.Kpfw.III and the half-track carriers.

Points such as these must be borne in mind, not to belittle the work of the Soviet tank designers but to place Soviet tank design in its true perspective. Exaggerated opinions about Soviet tank designs are as unjustified and dangerous as belittling them.

When all the facts are considered, it is clear that the Soviet tanks encountered by the Germans in 1941 were not born out of some unique Marxist genius but were the product of several factors: the attention paid to armament and its gradual development; the availability of resources for the development of a satisfactory tank engine, a thing denied to Western tank designers until the Second World War; the existence of a good basic design on which the T–34 was based; and the choice of a good, but by no means original, layout for the KV. To this must be added the strong influence of local Russian conditions, such as snow and mud, which made broad tracks imperative.

Against the good points of these 2 tanks must also be set off a number of bad ones: the use of very cramped 2-man turrets on the T–34, poor vision, transmission failures, short track life, the inefficient use of uniformly thick armour on the KV and so on. Vehicles other than the KV and the T–34, the T–50, T–60 and T–70 light tanks and the T–40 amphibian were by no means outstanding and the huge KV–II proved a clumsy failure. They all faded quickly out of the picture and production concentrated on the T–34 and the KV.

Producing enough of the T–34 and KV was the main concern of the early war years and the Russians concentrated once more on quantity production. Production effort was spurred by the staggering losses of the 1941 campaign, which cost the Soviet Army some 17,000 tanks, and the wrongly supposed German numerical superiority. Working against it was the loss of the Western industrial regions and the dislocation of part of the Soviet tank industry, which was evacuated to the Urals to join plants already in existence there, as at Chelyabinsk. Added to this were various shortages of materials and skilled labour and transport difficulties.

However, in spite of all the difficulties, the Russians managed to produce large quantities of armoured vehicles. In the last 3 years of the Second World War, according to Soviet statements, the annual rate of production was 30,000 tanks, assault guns and armoured cars. This compares well with the peak German production of 19,000 tanks, assault guns and self-propelled guns in 1944, and the peak British and American annual production of tanks, self-propelled guns, armoured cars and armoured carriers of 30,000 and 90,000 respectively, the latter figure including some 29,000 tanks. During the course of the war the Russians also received 5,258 tanks from the United States, 4,260 from Britain and 1,220 from Canada. They preferred their own, however, and these tanks were far less valuable to them in building up their mechanised forces than the 430,000 American trucks and other motor-vehicles which were supplied under the Lend-Lease programme.

Of the two main types of Soviet tanks the T-34 was not only the more numerous but also the basic type, used alike for infantry support and in mechanised formations. For the greater part of the war it was armed with the 76.2 mm. Model 1940, instead of the original and less powerful Model 1939, which put it roughly on a par with the later German Pz.Kpfw.IV with the long 75 mm. gun and the American Medium M4, or Sherman. From the winter of 1943–44 it began to be replaced by a further development of the series, the T-34/85. As in the case of other new tanks it was first issued to the élite Guards armoured units but after the Second World War it replaced the earlier T-34 in all Soviet and satellite tank units.

The main feature of the T-34/85 was a long-barrelled 85 mm. gun, a tank adaptation of the pre-war Model 1939 anti-aircraft gun and roughly similar in performance to the famous German " eighty-eight " used in the Tiger I. It also had a larger, 3-man turret which corrected the weakness in this respect of the original T-34 design. On the whole the T-34/85 was not as formidable a tank as the German Panther but it was superior to the contemporary tanks of the Western Allies which were a product of the mistaken faith in under-gunned mobility.

The same type of turret and armament as on the T-34/85 had appeared earlier on a development of the KV series, the KV-85. This first appeared in action in the winter of 1942–43, in time to counter the German Tiger I, but it occupied a relatively insignificant position for a year later it was replaced by a much more powerful version, the Stalin heavy tank. This, or, to give it its proper Soviet designation, the JS heavy tank was also based on the KV chassis. But it had a better shaped hull front and a larger turret, based on that of the

KV-85, with a 122 mm. gun. The latter was an adaptation of an artillery piece and the Russians managed to achieve with it roughly what the Germans did in their Tiger II. But, characteristically enough, they did it by sheer weight of the projectile rather than its quality and high velocity.

They also managed to do it within the relatively low weight of 46 tons and modest overall dimensions, one of the noteworthy features of the JS being its small height. But, as usual in such matters, something had to be sacrificed for it and in this case it was the crew space and the amount of ammunition carried. Nevertheless, within its limits, the JS has been a formidable vehicle and represents a clever use of the KV further enhanced on the later model, the JS-III, by the well-angled frontal armour.

In addition to the turreted models, the KV and T-34 chassis were also used for a series of turretless vehicle which the Russians introduced under the designation of S.U., or *Samokhodnaya Ustanovka*, a self-propelled gun. Influenced, no doubt, by the earlier German *Sturmgeschütz*, the SUs were " turretless tanks " as much as anything else and represented a much more direct employment of artillery fire power than the more conventional self-propelled guns. About the only example of the latter category to be found in the Soviet Army was the SU-76, a 76.2 mm. field gun mounted on a modified T-70 light tank chassis, introduced in 1943 and subsequently relegated to use by infantry formations, while the mobile heavy gun support of the armoured formations has relied exclusively on other types well armoured all round.

Technically, at the expense of traverse, the SU type offers the possibility of mounting a more powerful weapon on a given chassis than a turreted version. Thus, while the standard T-34 was armed with a 76.2 mm. gun its companion, the SU-85, was armed with an 85 mm. gun. Later, when the T-34 itself was armed with an 85 mm. gun, the SU-85 gave way to the SU-100. The latter also consists of the T-34 chassis and is similar to the earlier SU-85 but it mounts a long-barrelled 100 mm. gun. Introduced in 1945, about 2 years later than the SU-85, the SU-100 corresponded roughly to the heavier German *Jagdpanzer*, and after the Second World War it became the principal Soviet anti-tank vehicle.

At first the T-34 chassis was also used for the 122 mm. howitzer, the resulting vehicle being known as the SU-122. The same designation was also used for the 122 mm. gun on the KV chassis, the companion vehicle of the much more numerous SU-152, a 152 mm. gun-howitzer on the KV chassis. After the war both were replaced by the very similar JSU-122 and JSU-152, based on the JS instead of KV chassis.

The JSU-152 has been particularly well represented in the post-Second World War armoured formations. As in the case of the Stalin heavy tank, its main characteristic is its heavy armament which enables it to perform the functions of a heavy assault gun, self-propelled howitzer or of a heavy anti-tank vehicle. Powerful armament is also the principal characteristic of the post-war medium tank, the T-54. Developed from the T-34/85, which it began to replace in the early fifties, the T-54 is only slightly heavier and yet carries a long 100 mm. gun. Like the Stalin and the JSU-152, the T-54 underlines the continued Soviet emphasis on the most important characteristic of all armoured fighting vehicles, their armament. Whatever their other points, Soviet tanks have never been under-gunned, which is more than can be said of tanks in other armies where mobility and armour protection have at various times been given precedence over armament.

The way in which Soviet tanks designs have achieved their good armament may, at times, have lacked refinement. Often the nearest available gun was adapted instead of a special one being developed. Obviously the Russians were not striving after costly perfection but were after acceptable designs which could be simply and quickly produced. With similar considerations in mind they eschewed other refinements and concentrated on essentials. The dividing line between the two is, of course, difficult to draw and from the mechanical point of view Soviet tanks could at times be regarded as backward. To look at, too, Soviet equipment has appeared rough and poor but, on closer examination, important functional parts prove to be finished to accepted engineering standards. One might say that the whole philosophy behind Soviet tank design has been that the ideal design is one which is just good enough and that anything better than that is a waste of effort. A truism recognised elsewhere but nowhere so consistently practised.

The Russians have also kept to a minimum the number of changes and modifications, not only when the calls for quantity production were most urgent but logically pursued this policy when their situation improved. Partly, of course, the virtue was a necessity. With their shortages of skilled men and a rigid over-centralised system they found it difficult to introduce major changes at the best of times. But the long production runs helped the use in the field and the production of the large quantities of tanks which throughout has been an important feature of Soviet tank development.

By themselves, the large quantities of Soviet tanks could and did make up for many deficiencies in other respects. Combined with the good points of tank design and a general improvement in quality they made Soviet armoured forces into a very formidable instrument.

The rise in the general quality and performance of the Soviet armoured forces from the depths to which they sunk during 1941 and 1942 began well before the end of the Second World War and they became an arm of quality within the mass of the Soviet Army. Their strength and importance grew in parallel : the tank brigades of 1941 were followed by tank corps and the tank corps by tank armies ; their employment progressed from inept piecemeal infantry-support methods to effective use, in the final stages of the war, as the spearhead of the Soviet Army.

After the Second World War, in striking contrast to the armoured forces of the United States and Britain, the Soviet forces not only retained their leading position but grew further in strength in relation to the rest of the ground forces. So much so that by the early fifties tank and mechanised formations formed about one-third of the Soviet field forces. They also further improved in quality, through more thorough training possible in peacetime, by making up various earlier deficiencies, such as those of radio equipment and armoured personnel carriers, and by an improved post-war organisation. These and other improvements added to the quantities of well-armed tanks have made Soviet armoured forces a factor to be reckoned with, in the light of tactical nuclear weapons as under conditions of conventional warfare, and a major asset for the Soviet *bloc*.

18

Italy

ITALY's contribution to the development of armoured vehicles has been sporadic and the fortunes of her armoured forces have fluctuated widely. To her, nevertheless, belongs the distinction of being the first to use motor-vehicles in warfare. This historic event took place during the 1912 Italo-Turkish campaign in Tripolitania, at the battle of Zanzur, where the employment of units carried in Fiat trucks foreshadowed something of the later rapid movement of mechanised forces.

A Fiat truck also served as the basis of the first Italian armoured car built in 1912 at the artillery arsenal in Turin and later sent to Libya together with a second, Bianchi armoured car. The usefulness of the two vehicles proved rather limited, however, and it was only in 1915 that the development of armoured cars was undertaken seriously with the construction of the Lancia I.Z. model. Shortly afterwards the first armoured car unit was formed and, on Italy's entry into the war on the Allied side, was sent into action against the Austrians. As on other fronts of the First World War, their use was limited to favourable circumstances but by the end of the war the total number of armoured cars rose to 120, all of the Lancia type.

In the meantime, the Italian High Command became aware of the existence of British and French tanks and, in 1917, managed to obtain from France one Schneider model. Experiments with it proved encouraging but attempts to obtain further vehicles were unsuccessful. The same thing happened a little later with the Renault F.T., except that the Italians managed to obtain more than one sample. However, on its own initiative, the Fiat motor company had already begun design work on a heavy tank and in 1918 it was decided that Fiat should also undertake production of the Renault light tank.

Of the heavy Fiat 2000 type only 2 were built. It was a large 40-ton vehicle with a turret-mounted 65 mm. gun and 7 machine-guns and, as might have been expected from a first attempt, not altogether successful. On the other hand, production of the Italian version of the Renault, the Fiat 3000, was not very advanced when the war ended. Eventually 100 were completed and delivered in 1921.

Thus, the first Italian tank unit formed in December 1918, under the title of *batteria autonoma carri d'assalto* was only equipped with the 2 Fiat 2000 and 6 French-built Renault F.T. After 1921 this unit was re-christened an independent tank company and re-equipped with the Fiat 3000 but no further material progress took place until the late twenties.

It was in 1926, the fourth year of Mussolini's régime, that tanks began to be taken up again seriously. Tank units ceased to form an integral part of the infantry and became a specialised arm. A tank centre was created in Rome and a year later transformed into a regiment with a nominal strength of 5 battalions.

The equipment at the time still consisted of the Fiat 3000, officially designated the *carro armato modello* 1921, which was armed with twin machine-guns and weighed 5.5 tons. However, at about this time the Italian Army became interested in the new British Carden Loyd tankettes, which were considered particularly attractive for the mountainous Italian terrain. In consequence, in 1929, first 4 and then a further 21 Carden Loyd Mark VI were purchased in Britain and issued to the tank regiment as the *carro veloce* 29. By 1930 there was also a modified, improved version of the Fiat 3000, the 3000 B or model 30, armed with a long-barrelled 37 mm. gun, one of several attempts at improving the long-lived Renault-type light tanks of the First World War. However, by then interest definitely centred on the Carden Loyd and as a result its development and production were undertaken in Italy by the Ansaldo organisation of Genoa.

The first Ansaldo vehicle was approved in 1933 and became the *carro veloce* 33. It was a small turretless vehicle with a crew of two and an armament of a single machine-gun ; it weighed only 3.2 tons but was capable of a maximum speed of 28 m.p.h. Together with the improved twin machine-gun model introduced in 1935, it was produced in quantity, so much that in 1936 there were about 1,000 of the two, later collectively called the L/3. In addition to the standard version, flame-thrower and bridging models were also built and a number was sold to Austria, Hungary, Bulgaria and Brazil.

In the meantime, in 1935, in the invasion of Ethiopia, the L/3 received its first test. It proved useful, being able to accompany the infantry almost anywhere, and though the opposing forces lacked armour piercing weapons overcoming difficulties of the terrain was, in itself, an accomplishment. Like Korea before the invasion of 1950, Ethiopia was definitely not considered suitable for the use of tanks and it was, in fact, the first time that tanks were used on any scale in mountainous country.

The numbers of tanks actually used are of some interest : from a total of 82 in the whole of the Italian East Africa at the beginning of 1935, they rose to 45 in Somaliland and 112 in Eritrea in October 1935, when the invasion began, and in the following April, in the closing stages of the campaign, the total reached 498 tanks.

While the Abyssinian campaign provided a valid technical test it could not provide significant combat lessons, although the handicap of the limited traverse on the L/3 appears to have been noted. A much more comprehensive test came a year after the Abyssinian campaign, when an Italian corps, known officially as the *Commando Truppe Volontarie*, or C.T.V., was sent to take part in the Spanish Civil War of 1936 to 1939.

There the light Italian tanks proved vulnerable even to light anti-tank guns and were completely outclassed by such tanks as the Soviet T-26, which was used by the Communist troops and which was armed with a 45 mm. gun. And not only the equipment but Italian mechanised forces as a whole came under severe criticism from many quarters as a result of the fighting in Spain and the unfavourable conclusions were often extended to armoured forces in general.

The main basis for this was the widely publicised failure of an Italian offensive in the Guadalajara sector in March 1937. This, the second action of the C.T.V., began with a successful penetration of the enemy lines but after 2 days the attack bogged down amidst heavy rains which, among other things, kept the supporting Italian aircraft on the ground. A number of Communist International Brigades and Spanish Republican formations, hastily brought from other parts of the front, then counter-attacked with air and tank support, and the Italians, already fully committed, were thrown back in disorder. The significance of this battle lies not in its course, however, but in the fact that it was widely believed to have been conducted on the Italian side by mechanised forces.

In actual fact the divisions of the C.T.V. were ordinary infantry divisions with only some motor transport columns. As for Italian tanks, the total at the time consisted of one battalion with 4 companies of L/3 tanks and one company of armoured cars. Any talk of a mechanised force was, therefore, a wild exaggeration. Yet the idea was generally accepted at the time and from the battle of Guadalajara sprang many conclusions to the detriment of mechanised forces in general.

This battle also largely obscured the lessons of the later operations in Aragon and Catalonia, where small mechanised forces were actually used. They were generally successful in exploiting the initial breaks-through and on one occasion, in the Ebro sector, an Italian tank-infantry column covered more than 100 miles in a day. By the autumn of 1938 the reorganised C.T.V. had a tank group consisting of two L/3 light tank battalions, one motorised infantry battalion and one support battalion of machine-guns, flame-throwers and anti-tank guns and a troop of 65 mm. howitzers.

As far as the Italian forces were concerned, the most important lesson to emerge from the Spanish Civil War was the need for a more powerful vehicle than the L/3. The development of a new and more heavily armed tank had begun in 1935, originally intended as a replacement for the Fiat models 21 and 30. The first design was not accepted, which is hardly surprising considering the characteristics of the prototype : an 8-ton turretless vehicle armed with a short-barrelled 37 mm. gun. The prototype of the second version was ready in 1937 and it was approved at the beginning of 1939, becoming the M/11 medium tank. Close behind the medium came a new light tank design which was derived from the L/3 and eventually evolved into the L/6, a 2-man 6.8-ton vehicle with a turret-mounted 20 mm. gun and machine-gun adopted in 1940. There was also a very promising new armoured car, the *autoblinda* 40, originally armed only with machine-guns but later, in its 41 form, fitted with the turret and armament of the L/6.

At the time of its introduction the M/11 was regarded as an assault tank and suitable for break-through roles. In fact it was a 3-man 11-ton vehicle armed with a 37 mm. gun and 2 machine-guns ; its armour varied between 30 and 10 mm., and with a 105 (later 125) b.h.p. diesel engine it was capable of a maximum speed of 20 m.p.h. and had a 125-mile radius of action. In all this and other respects the M/11 was comparable to other contemporary light-medium tanks. But the lay-out of its armament, with only the machine-guns in the turret and the gun mounted in the hull with limited traverse, nullified most of its potential value. In general it was inferior, therefore, to the Soviet T-26 used in Spain and to the L.T.H.-type tanks which the Czechs were selling at the time to the Swiss and the Persians. It was, in fact, about the worst design of the period.

Better progress than in the construction of equipment was made during that period in developing tactics and organisation. Through the thirties Italian tanks were still regarded chiefly as an auxiliary to the infantry and their employment was in terms of close support of the latter. The subordinate role was emphasised in September 1936, when the independent tank regiment was replaced by 4 *Reggimento fanteria carrista*, or infantry tank regiments.

But the occupation of Albania, in April 1939, in which some 200 tanks were used, saw something of a continuation of the mechanised warfare experiments carried out in Spain. The main feature of this operation was the advance of a mechanised column on the Albanian capital, Tirana, which was reinforced by air-landed infantry within three-quarters of an hour of its vanguard reaching the objective. An interesting model of air–ground co-operation, in keeping with the supply of advance columns by parachute which the Italians pioneered in Ethiopia, but, of course, carried out in the absence of opposition.

Another demonstration of the new methods took place 4 months later, during manoeuvres in Northern Italy. Called the *guerra di rapido corso* by Mussolini, these were meant to be the Italian equivalent of what later became known as the *Blitzkrieg* in which mechanised and air forces played a prominent part. The latter included special " assault " squadrons for tactical roles which General Meccozi of the Italian air force advanced against the strategic air power concepts of that other Italian general, Giulio Douhet. The most interesting feature of the manoeuvres, however, was the first appearance of an Italian armoured division.

The history of this and other Italian armoured divisions actually dates back to June 1936, when the 1st *Brigata Motomeccanizzata*, or Mechanised Brigade, was formed in Siena. It consisted of a light tank battalion, a Bersaglieri light infantry regiment with 2 battalions, a motorised artillery battery and an engineer platoon. A year later it was renamed *Brigata Corazzata*, or Armoured Brigade, and expanded considerably. In particular, the light tank battalion was replaced by the newly created 31st Tank Regiment, actually the fifth Italian tank regiment to be created. Other elements of the brigade consisted of the motorised Bersaglieri regiment, 2 companies of 47 mm. anti-tank guns, a battery of 20 mm. anti-aircraft guns and an engineer company.

The nominal strength of the Armoured Brigade was more

like that of a division but no corresponding change in designation took place until 1939. By that time a second brigade
had been created and it was this which, in February 1939, was
transformed into the first *Divisione Corazzata*, the 132nd
Ariete Armoured Division. The 1st Armoured Brigade
followed in April 1939, when it was transformed into the 131st
Centauro Armoured Division. Yet a third armoured division,
the 133rd *Littorio*, was created in the same year by the transformation of a cadre infantry division of the same name.

On their creation the organisation of the armoured divisions
followed closely that introduced with the 1937 armoured
brigade. Each had a tank regiment, a Bersaglieri rifle regiment
with one motor-cycle battalion and one truck-borne battalion,
a motorised artillery regiment with two 75 mm. batteries and
a troop of 20 mm. anti-aircraft guns, and one engineer company.
The tank regiment itself had a nominal strength of 4 battalions
but in practice it usually consisted of only 2—one light and one
medium—and the tank battalions had only 2 companies.
Heavy tanks and a fifth tank battalion were talked about but
neither ever materialised.

In theory the Italian armoured divisions of the 1939 period
were well-balanced mechanised formations. In practice,
however, they were very weak in effective tanks and this
problem continued to plague all the Italian armoured formations throughout the Second World War.

At the time it was proposed that two armoured divisions
should be combined with two motorised infantry divisions to
form an armoured corps, the *corpo d'armata corazzata*. The
two motorised divisions, the 101st Trieste and the 102nd
Trento, were larger by one battalion than the contemporary
6-battalion Italian infantry divisions but otherwise the main
difference was in the number of motor-vehicles. Neither type
of infantry division had any tanks : only the regular infantry
divisions stationed in Libya had an organic tank battalion ;
other infantry tank battalions were held at corps level.

As regards ideas on the employment of armoured formations, the original armoured brigade was regarded as an assault

unit but by the time the first armoured division was created ideas advanced considerably. Operational mobility as well as striking power were stressed and the task of breaking through organised fronts was now considered an exception, only to be carried out with the full co-operation of infantry divisions. The *Divisione Corazzata* was still, however, not as versatile as the panzer division and for strategic exploitation, for instance, another type of formation was envisaged.

How this other type, the *Divisione Celere*, could be considered suitable for a strategic role is now difficult to understand. It was only a cavalry division in the transitional stage of its evolution from horses to motor-vehicles, and a fairly early stage at that, as its composition shows. In 1939 it consisted of 2 horse cavalry and one Bersaglieri bicycle regiment, a tank group of about 50 L/3 and partly motorised artillery and divisional troops and services.

Comparing this with the evolution of the French cavalry division, it was a stage which the French had already reached in the late twenties. Nevertheless, there was an interesting similarity of ideas between the two armies as shown by the existence of the two types of divisions. The French had the *Division Légère Mécanique* to be used in the traditional cavalry manner and the infantry *Division Cuirassée* intended at first for breakthrough roles. The Italians had the *Divisione Celere*, which corresponded roughly to the former though it was well behind in mechanisation, and the *Divisione Corazzata*, which resembled the latter both in its infantry origin and initial conception, although it lacked the French division's powerful tanks.

In September 1939 practically all of the 1,500 or so Italian tanks then in existence were still of the L/3 type. The only more powerful tank was the indifferent M/11 of which, moreover, only 70 had been built. The equipment situation was, therefore, well-nigh catastrophic.

The following year brought little material change, and the Italian armoured forces were still not capable of effective mobile operations. It is not surprising, therefore, that the armoured divisions were held back and took no part either in the short Italian intervention in the closing stages of the 1940 French campaign or in the disastrous Libyan campaign during the winter of 1940–41.

In the latter, and in East Africa, Italian tanks were used in driblets, parcelled out among the infantry. Such methods were a far cry from the *guerra di rapido corso* and like the L/3 and M/11 tanks, which were used, proved a failure. Only in the final battle of the first Libyan campaign, at Beda Fomm, in February 1941 did better tanks appear, the M/13. Mechanically the M/13 was similar to the M/11 but it was armed with a 47 mm. gun mounted in a 2-man turret, instead of the hull-mounted 37 mm., and it had one coaxial and twin hull machine-guns, as well as a larger 4-man crew. In general, the M/13 represented a considerable advance on earlier Italian tank designs but its appearance failed to have any effect on the outcome of the campaign which, altogether, cost the Italian Army some 400 tanks.

Only when the campaign was drawing to a close did the elements of the first Italian armoured division sail for North Africa. This was the *Ariete*, which left for Tripolitania in January 1941, only just ahead of the German 5th Light Division. It took part in Rommel's first highly successful counter-offensive and from then right on to El Alamein, where it was destroyed, it shared the fortunes of the German *Afrika Korps*.

The *Littorio* was the next to go. Withdrawn from Dalmatia, it began to be shipped from Italy in January 1942 and its first units went into action around Tobruk in June. It took part in the advance into Egypt and like the *Ariete* was destroyed at El Alamein. The *Centauro* was sent to Albania in 1939 and like the *Littorio* took a small part in the 1941 Yugoslav campaign. It returned to Italy in mid-1942 and in November was sent to Tripolitania. It went into action during the Axis withdrawal into Tunisia and its remnants surrendered there in April 1943.

During the whole of this period, all three armoured divisions retained in principle their pre-war organisation. That is, each had a tank regiment, a Bersaglieri regiment and an artillery regiment, although, for a time, in 1941, both the *Littorio* and the *Centauro* had two tank regiments each. However, in the field, in Africa, their effective strength varied considerably. As a rule they were considerably under-strength but their artillery acquired additional units, up to a maximum of 6 groups per division.

Throughout their service in Africa the principal tank of the Italian armoured divisions remained the M/13 or its slightly improved version, the M/42. This was a serviceable enough tank when first used, but it rapidly lost its relative effectiveness during 1942. At El Alamein it was in about the same hopeless position relative to the American-built Shermans of the British armoured forces as the L/3 was to the British cruiser tanks in 1940.

The only new armoured vehicles to reach Italian forces in Africa were self-propelled 75 mm. howitzers and 47 mm. anti-tank guns. The former, based on the M/13 chassis, looked like an Italian version of the German assault guns but were used chiefly as self-propelled artillery. There was also a larger 105 mm. gun version of the same type of vehicle and 2 partly armoured 90 mm. and 149 mm. self-propelled guns, also on M/13 type chassis, but all 3 were produced too late to be used in the field.

The same applied to the P/40, a 25-ton 4-man tank with a turret-mounted medium-velocity 75 mm. gun (75/32) and powered by a 330 b.h.p. V-12 diesel. Its prototype was actually built in 1939 but it was only in 1943 that the first few production vehicles appeared. Classed by the Italians as a heavy tank, it was by contemporary standards a medium, and although potentially useful it was not quite as good as the American M4 or the German Pz.Kpfw.IV Model G, both of which were already in service in 1943.

A good many of the shortcomings of the Italian equipment go back to the pre-Second World War expansion which gave an army strong in the number of bayonets but poorly equipped with effective weapons. In the particular case of tanks, too little attention was given to quality, to building well-armed battle-worthy tanks and not merely numbers. The L/3 may have been a good start, as a training machine and for colonial warfare, but its continued production was a very doubtful investment. Smaller and technologically less advanced countries were developing or buying light-medium tanks armed with 37 mm. guns while the Italian Army still had made no progress beyond the machine-gun-armed tankette. Yet, at the time, one 10-ton tank with a 37 mm. gun was worth much more than any three L/3 which were its financial equivalent.

When the Italians finally produced their 37 mm. gun tank, the M/11, it was not only overdue but proved to be a poor design as well. Its successor, the M/13, was better, although it inherited the indifferent suspension and low power to weight ratio of the M/11. However, it was still only just up to the average standard of contemporary medium tanks and in 1942 it should have been supplemented and later replaced by a more powerful vehicle. The Italians were on the right track towards such a tank in 1939 with the 75 mm. gun P/40 but they took far too long putting it into production and service.

Industrial and supply difficulties were also partly responsible for the unsatisfactory equipment situation. Even before the Second World War, Italy was beset by shortages of various raw materials and her productive capacity was limited. Steel production, the sinews of munition making, was only a quarter of Britain's and an eighth of Germany's. However, the total expenditure of effort on tanks was not inconsiderable. In 1941, for instance, Italy produced 1,222 medium tanks which, all things considered, does not compare badly with the contemporary German, British or American production. True, this effort could not be kept up and in 1942 production was down by about a half. But the chief trouble was not the quantity but the fact that the tanks which were produced were obsolescent or downright obsolete by the time they reached the troops.

The last actions of the Italian tank units during the Second World War, in Sicily, were also a climax to their misfortunes. There were 3 battalions there in July 1943, split up among the defences of various airfields : one was equipped with L /6 and L /3 light tanks and the other 2 with French-built R-35 infantry tanks ceded to Italy after 1940. This obsolete equipment made their case hopeless.

The Armistice of 1943 saw the end of other Italian armoured units. At the time the *Ariete* was being re-created as the 135th Armoured Cavalry Division, the 134th Armoured Division designation having been carried for a few months of 1942 by the 2nd *Divisione Celere*. In mid-1943 there was also the Blackshirt Division M, hastily equipped with various armoured vehicles which happened to be at hand, which carried the name of the Centauro Legionary Armoured Division. But all these formations disappeared when the Germans took over control of the major part of Italy.

After the Second World War Italian armoured forces were restricted for a time to a few old M /13 and *Semovente* 75 /18, augmented later by Staghound (T17E1) armoured cars and other wartime American-built vehicles, such as the M5 light tank, M10 tank destroyer and then M4 medium tanks. The peace treaty imposed on Italy limited the total number of medium and heavy tanks which her Army could possess to 200 and it was only in 1951–52 that the restrictions were lifted.

Three years earlier, in 1948, the year of the ratification of the peace treaty, the Italian Army once more called into being the *Ariete* armoured brigade. This became effective in the following year, when 2 more armoured brigades were planned. The second, the *Centauro*, was, however, only formed in 1951. Equipment was a major obstacle to progress and no substantial improvement took place until 1952 when some 800 tanks were received from the United States. Among them were 90 mm. gun M46 medium tanks which at last replaced the obsolete Second World War 75 mm. gun M4 tanks, until then the principal equipment of the Italian tank units.

By this time the *Ariete* had grown into a large formation.

Its principal component consisted of a tank regiment with 2 battalions and a total of 135 tanks, a Bersaglieri regiment with 2 rifle battalions, an artillery regiment with 3 battalions of self-propelled American-built M7 105 mm. howitzers, one of M10 tank destroyers and one of 40 mm. anti-aircraft guns. From this basis it was relatively easy to expand it into a division which took place towards the end of 1952. The organisation of the division was similar to that of the brigade in that it was based on a regiment each of medium tanks, Bersaglieri and 105 mm. self-propelled howitzers, but each regiment now had 3 battalions.

The *Centauro* brigade was transformed into a division at the same time as the *Ariete* and in the following year a third division, *Pozzuolo del Friuli*, was created. Thus, the Italian Army once more came to possess 3 armoured divisions, which formed about one-fifth of the Italian ground forces and as large an armoured force as any west of the Iron Curtain.

19

Japan

OF all the major armoured forces of the Second World War, the Japanese were by far the least known. What little was said about them at the time barely touched the facts, and the obscurity in which they remained gives added interest to their development and performance as they emerge in the light of more complete and accurate information. Japanese armoured forces and their equipment are also of interest for having been out of the main stream of developments and thus evolving along more independent lines, as well as a number of features peculiar to them.

In a broad sense the development of the Japanese armoured forces started in 1918, when some Mark V heavy tanks were delivered from Britain. Soon afterwards this was followed by the acquisition of a few British Medium A and French Renault F.T. light tanks, but beyond this little was accomplished in the tank field in the early twenties, particularly as the period coincided with a general reduction of the Japanese Army.

It was in 1925 that the Japanese first took up tanks really seriously. In that year the first 2 tank companies were established, the second being an experimental unit at the Infantry School at Chiba, near Tokyo, where the study of tank tactics was undertaken at the same time. In 1925 also, the Japanese began the design of their first tank, which was completed in March 1927 at the Osaka Arsenal.

The first Japanese tank was a vehicle of some 22 tons armed with a short 70 mm. gun in the main turret. In addition, it had 2 smaller machine-gun turrets, one at the front and the other at the very rear, behind the engine compartment, a feature peculiar to Japanese tank design ; it also had another distinguishing feature in the shape of the large number of 17 bogie wheels per side.

As well as starting their own development, between 1926 and 1932, the Japanese also purchased further tanks from Britain and France. The French tanks were the Renault NC, an improved 8-ton version of the wartime F.T., which the French Army had developed by 1926 but did not adopt. British vehicles included one Vickers Light Tank Type C, a commercial version of the standard Vickers Medium, and 9 Vickers Carden Loyd Mark VI. These purchases from abroad provided samples of modern equipment for experiments and material for study and design development.

The Vickers Type C did, in fact, become the model for the second Japanese tank which was completed in the spring of 1929, again at the Osaka Arsenal. An 8-ton 4-man vehicle armed with a short 57 mm. gun and 2 machine-guns it was originally classed as a light tank. But when after modifications it was decided to produce it and its weight exceeded 11 tons it was called the Type 89A Medium, the " 89 " representing the last two digits of the year 2589, or 1929 in our chronology.

Production of this model, and of Japanese tanks in general, began in 1931, when the first 10 were manufactured, and the following year saw the completion of a further 20. During 1931 and 1932, also, the " incidents " in Manchuria and China, in which the Japanese became involved, provided an opportunity for trying some of the tanks in action. Both the Renault NC and the Type 89A were used, the former in Shanghai, but without any startling results.

In the meantime further development of the original 1927 70 mm. gun tank continued, a modified version being built in 1930, and in 1932 Osaka Arsenal completed a very similar Type 91 Heavy Tank which differed from the original mainly in having its maximum armour thickness increased from 15 to 35 mm. and its weight to about 29 tons. Yet another heavy tank, the Type 95, of the same general layout and with the same skirted suspension but distinguished from the earlier designs by having only 9 bogie wheels per side, was built in June 1934. Its weight increased further to 35 tons and its armament was augmented by the mounting of a 37 mm. gun in the forward auxiliary turret but, like the earlier designs, it was not accepted for production.

On the other hand a new light tank design, adopted as the Type 92 Heavy Tankette, was produced in limited quantity. This was a 3-man vehicle of less than 4 tons armed with one machine-gun in the turret and another beside the driver, which was later replaced by a Hotchkiss-type 13 mm. heavy machine-gun. The next design was an even lighter 2.65-ton 2-man model armed with a single machine-gun, the Type 94 Tankette, commonly and erroneously known outside Japan as the " Type 92." First built in 1933, the Type 94 was essentially a turreted development of the Vickers Carden Loyd Mark VI, with most of the economic attractions and combat shortcomings which this implied. In particular, its offensive power was extremely limited but it was mobile and inexpensive : its Type 94 four-cylinder air-cooled petrol engine gave it a maximum speed of 25 m.p.h. and being cheap it was produced in quantity.

A more useful light tank design was completed in 1934 and standardised in the following year as the Type 95 Light Tank, a 6.5-ton 3-man vehicle as fast as the Type 94 Tankette but armed with a 37 mm. gun and 2 machine-guns. One of its noteworthy design features was the suspension, derived from that of the Type 94 Tankette and used also on the later Type 92 Heavy Tankettes. It consisted of paired bogie wheels, 2 pairs on each side being connected by a single coil spring mounted horizontally outside the hull—an interdependent type of suspension which was used on almost all Japanese tanks of the following 10 years. Another, and perhaps even more important, feature was the use of a 6-cylinder air-cooled diesel of 115 b.h.p. which had just been developed. The same engine was also installed in a modified version of the Type 89 Medium, usually and erroneously called the " Type 94," in place of the original 105 b.h.p. water-cooled petrol engine. The weight of this modified Type 89B crept up to 13 tons but it could reach a maximum speed of 16 m.p.h.

By this stage, in 1935, Japanese tank production rose to 400 per annum and the tank forces were expanding. In 1933 the first 3 tank regiments were formed, each of two 10-tank companies, 2 of the regiments being stationed in Japan and the third at Kungchulung in Manchuria. A year later Kungchulung also saw the formation of the first tank brigade, which consisted of the 4th Tank Regiment with 3 companies, a motorised infantry regiment, a motorised 75 mm. gun artillery regiment and a motorised pioneer company.

Thus, by 1937, when they became involved in a full-scale conflict with China, the Japanese had the makings of a strong armoured force. They had built 1,060 tanks and were manufacturing more at the rate of about 300 per annum. The two principal vehicles in use were the Type 89B Medium and the Type 94 Tankette. Of the two, the former was already obsolete by European standards, although the British Army was still using the Vickers Mediums from which it was indirectly derived. As for the Type 94 Tankette, the Spanish Civil War was about to demonstrate the low value of similar lightly armed vehicles. But in China the Japanese were faced with an enemy lacking both tanks and anti-tank weapons and the shortcomings of their tanks were not, for the moment, serious.

Like the French, and indeed most people before 1939, the Japanese regarded their tanks mainly as infantry support weapons and employed them accordingly. In theory the employment was based on the attachment of a tank regiment to an infantry division and the use of tanks by companies as a spearhead or an integral part of infantry attacks. The only major departure from such methods was the employment of tankettes for reconnaissance, and in 1935 each regular infantry division acquired an organic tankette company.

Against the poorly equipped Chinese the Japanese tank-infantry tactics were quite successful. Preoccupied with this conflict the Japanese made little progress for a time towards a more mobile and effective employment of their tanks. However, the full-scale battles with well-equipped and partly mechanised Soviet forces on the Manchurian border in 1938 and 1939 and the early successes of the German panzer forces in Europe spurred further development. As a result, in 1940, 2 tank, or armoured, divisions were organised at Tungning and Tubgang in Manchuria, followed shortly afterwards by the formation of a third tank division. At the same time each infantry division received 2 light tank companies for reconnaissance work.

Progress was also made with equipment. In addition to the Type 95 *Kyu-go* Light Tank, whose production began in 1935, the Japanese also began to replace the Type 94 Tankette with the Type 97 *Te-ke*. This was essentially an enlarged version of the earlier tankette, still manned by a crew of 2, but armed with a 37 mm. gun as well as a machine-gun and, in keeping with the contemporary Japanese trends, powered by a 4-cylinder air-cooled 60 b.h.p. diesel instead of the Type 94 petrol engine.

What was far more important, however, was the introduction of a new medium tank, the Type 97 *Chi-ha*. Its general arrangement followed that of the Type 95 Light Tank but it was larger, with a 2-man turret and 6, instead of 4, bogie wheels per side. It had armour up to 25 mm. thick and weighed 15.3 tons but, being powered by the Type 97 V-12 air-cooled diesel of 170 b.h.p., it was capable of the same 25 m.p.h. maximum speed as the lighter tanks. Its one great weakness was its principal armament of a short Type 97 57 mm. gun, a low-velocity weapon virtually the same as the Type 90 used on the earlier medium tanks; it also had 2 machine-guns, one at the back of the turret and one next to the driver, and it was manned by a crew of 4.

In 1937, when the Type 97 *Chi-ha* was designed, the Japanese also built the prototype of a smaller, 3-man medium tank, the *Chi-ni*. Like the *Chi-ha*, it had armour up to 25 mm. thick and was armed with a low-velocity 57 mm. gun and one machine-gun. But it weighed only 9.8 tons and considerable attention was given in its design to low production costs. However, in spite of these advantages, the Japanese wisely preferred the *Chi-ha*, which was more roomy and had far greater development potential.

In general, except for the armament of the medium model, the 3 types of Japanese tanks developed during the mid-thirties compared favourably with contemporary European designs. There were weaknesses in detail design but the main components, such as engine and transmissions, were sound and the vehicle performance satisfactory. Thus, by the outbreak of the Second World War the Japanese were in a reasonably good position, both qualitatively and quantitatively. As far as numbers went, the total of tanks produced during the thirties was actually the fourth highest, inferior only to the Soviet, German and French. Up to the end of 1939, the Japanese had, in fact, produced 2,030 tanks, which was close to the total French production since the First World War.

But once the Second World War began in Europe the Japanese rapidly lost their position. They could hardly conceive of the pace that would be set in the development and production and, out of touch for a time with the latest developments of other countries, they lacked both the urge and the resources to keep abreast in the tank field. When they did realise the need for quantities of more powerful tanks it was too late to catch up with developments elsewhere, both because of the time lost and of the production situation.

At the end of 1941, when they entered the war in the Pacific and South-East Asia, the Japanese forces were still in a relatively strong position with respect to their opponents and, in terms of their strategic plans, the stock of military supplies was deemed sufficient. Tanks were not called upon to play a major role in the Japanese offensives but elements of the 3rd Tank Division participated effectively in the lightning campaign down the Malay Peninsula and two tank regiments took part in the fighting on Bataan in the Philippines. Elsewhere they were generally used in small packets, without significant results. Of the vehicles used Type 95 Light Tanks were the most common but there were also Type 94 Tankettes and, as late as 1942, in Burma, Type 89B Medium Tanks. The last two were obsolete and could only be effective against hostile forces devoid of tanks and anti-tank weapons.

With the end of the offensive phase and the passing on to the defensive the tank position deteriorated. As the initiative passed into Allied hands, Japanese armament development was largely dictated by their enemies and, as a result, production concentrated on aircraft and anti-aircraft weapons and on naval requirements. Tanks, like motor-vehicles and heavy artillery, were given a low priority, and after reaching the peak annual production figure of 1,290 tanks in 1942, their production began to decline.

In the meantime, one important step had been taken since the 1935–37 tank designs—the overdue introduction of a new medium tank gun. This was a tank version of the Type 1 47 mm. anti-tank gun and it was installed in the *Chi-ho*, or *Shinhoto* (" New Turret ") *Chi-ha*, a modified version of the Type 97 Medium Tank. A little later, in 1940, the up-gunned model was completely redesigned into the Type 1 *Chi-he*.

The *Chi-he* was basically the same as the *Shinhoto Chi-ha* but with thicker, welded armour instead of the riveted construction used largely on earlier Japanese tanks. As its maximum armour thickness increased to 50 mm., its weight increased also over that of the *Chi-ha*, to 17.2 tons, but the possible effect of this on performance was offset by increasing the output of the V-12 diesel from the 170 b.h.p. of the Type 97 engine to 240 b.h.p. of the improved Type 100. Production of the *Chi-he* was, however, late getting under way and the *Shinhoto Chi-ha* remained the principal Japanese medium tank throughout the rest of the war. Its first action appears to have been on Bataan at the beginning of 1942 but it was only in 1944 that the first fell into Allied hands, in Burma, during the Imphal campaign.

With the *Shinhoto Chi-ha* as the only new equipment, the use of tanks in the field made little progress. In spite of doctrinal emphasis on the advantages of concentrated employment and lip-service to mobility, Japanese tanks continued to be used in piecemeal engagements in support of the infantry.

In 1942 the 2 tank divisions in Manchuria were combined into a tank " army " and in the following year were joined by the 3rd Tank Division previously stationed in North China. The nominal organisation of each division included 2 tank brigades with a total of 4 tank regiments, but in practice, because of individual regiments being detached for service in other theatres, the divisions had 2 or 3 tank regiments only. In addition to the 3 tank divisions, in 1943 the Japanese also had an independent tank brigade, all stationed in Manchuria, 4 tank regiments in Japan, and a number of regiments deployed in China and the Pacific. In 1944, one of the tank divisions was used successfully during the Japanese offensive in Honan, in China, but a little later the 2nd Tank Division went into action against the American forces landed on Luzon in the Philippines and was frittered away in piecemeal attacks, showing that even in large armoured formations the Japanese were still behind in the effective employment of tanks.

The vehicles used in the Philippines indicated, however, that the Japanese were making further progress with equipment. Apart from the *Shinhoto Chi-ha* and earlier tanks, there were now self-propelled 75 mm. guns and 150 mm. howitzers on *Chi-ha* chassis and fully tracked armoured personnel carriers.

These were but a few of a whole series of new wartime Japanese developments, most of which did not get beyond experimental models or a small production batch. The most important in this category was the Type 3 Medium Tank, or *Chi-nu*, developed in 1943 to provide a better-armed tank than the Type 1 *Chi-he*. The type 3 differed from the Type 1— there was, incidentally, no Type 2—mainly in having a new turret with a medium-velocity 75 mm. gun. The gun was a tank version of the Type 90 field gun and with it the Type 3 was comparable to the contemporary American M4 Medium, which was proving an embarrassment to the Japanese. But its production did not begin until 1944 and only 60 were actually completed.

Springing from the same desire to up-gun the existing medium tank chassis was another version of the Type 1 re-armed with a 75 mm. howitzer and known as the " Gun Tank

Type 2," or *Hoi*. Its companion, the Gun Tank Type 1 *Ho-ni*, used the same Type 90 mm. gun as the Type 3 *Chi-nu* but mounted behind a fixed shield, instead of the turret. Gun Tank Type 3 was similar but armed with a more powerful 75 mm. Type 88, originally an anti-aircraft weapon, while the *Ho-ro*, a similar semi-improvised self-propelled gun, mounted a 150 mm. howitzer. Both the *Ho-ro* and the *Ho-ni* were first used in the Philippines in 1944.

In the meantime, while the Type 3 *Chi-nu* was beginning to be produced, a new medium tank was being developed, the Type 4 *Chi-to*. It followed the general arrangement of the Type 1 and 3 but was, in fact, a new design which employed thicker armour, up to 75 mm. thick, a more powerful Type 4 75 mm. gun with a muzzle velocity of 2,790 ft. /sec. and a more power-ful 400 b.h.p. engine.

Six experimental models of the *Chi-to* were built, but in 1944 an even heavier tank was demanded and this led to the Type 5, or *Chi-ri*. The main armament of the *Chi-ri* was the same as that of the *Chi-to*, but for no apparent reason it also had a 37 mm. gun beside the driver. Its armour was thicker, however, and it had a more powerful 550 b.h.p. engine.

There was also no lack of activity in the light tank field. No less than 5 different models were built, derived to a greater or lesser extent from the Type 95, whose production ceased in 1942. They showed chiefly progressive improvement in arma-ment, first to higher-velocity 37 mm. guns and finally to the 47 mm. gun, with some increase in armour and engine power. In other fields also the Japanese were not idle. Among others they built the *Ha-to* gun carrier with a 300 mm. mortar, the *Taha* anti-aircraft tank with two 37 mm. guns, turretless engineer tanks, including a bridging type, the fully tracked *Ho-ki* armoured personnel carrier and the half-track *Ho-ha*. In addition, the Navy as well as the Army experimented with several amphibious tanks, ranging in size up to the Navy's 26-ton Type 3 *Kachi-sha*.

Out of the whole collection only a few vehicles were used in the field. They included the Navy's Type 2 *Kami-sha* 11-ton light amphibious tank, the successful *Ho-ki* carrier and the *Ho-ni* and *Ho-ro* self-propelled guns. Some of the others were developed too late but the majority had little chance of getting into service in view of the deteriorating production situation.

In 1944, the year of decision in the Pacific, the total number of tanks built in Japan amounted to only 295, equivalent to less than 2 per cent. of the American production for that year. It is true that in the spring of 1945, when the decision was taken to concentrate on the defence of the home islands, tank production was for the first time given high priority. But in view of the deteriorating industrial situation it is doubtful whether any increase in the production of tanks could have been expected at this stage and in the event the total production for the first eight months of 1945, that is right up to the end of the war, amounted to 130 tanks.

In such circumstances, and indeed long before this in view of the limited industrial capacity, utmost economy of effort was imperative. To some extent the Japanese were aware of this, as shown by their attempts at standardisation, particularly in suspensions and engines. The air-cooled diesel engines were probably their most notable achievement. Not only did they introduce them in their tanks when diesel engines were only just entering the road transport field but with two exceptions—one American and one German—they were the only ones to use air-cooled diesel engines, in spite of the many attractions of this type from the tank point of view. After 1935 the Japanese used air-cooled diesels exclusively and toward the end of the Second World War they even evolved a family of engines of 6, 8 and 12 cylinders all based on the same cylinder size.

However, achievements in this field were not matched in others nor was standardisation of engines a sufficient answer to the need to concentrate. All the vehicles used in the field showed weaknesses in detail design, such as cramped interiors, absence of coaxial machine-guns and inadequate means of vision. Another weakness was the very limited provision of radio sets and this, among other things, made all the more questionable the far-fetched experiments with radio-controlled tanks, which started with the 1931 vehicle built by Major (later General) Nagayama. But by far the most serious weakness of the Japanese tanks was their main armament, for they were generally under-gunned and particularly so in the case of the medium tanks.

The failure to provide, or provide sufficiently quickly, more powerfully armed tanks was in the main due to three things: manufacturing difficulties, underestimates of battle-field requirements and lack of a sufficiently clear policy. The last resulted largely from a division of responsibility in tank matters between the General Staff, War Ministry and Ordnance and was also responsible for the failure to concentrate development and production on one or two of the most useful types.

An example of the avoidable dispersion of effort is provided by the manufacture of the Type 95 Light Tank and Type 97 Tankette which should have been merged into a single model. The effort devoted to the earlier Type 94 Tankette was also largely wasted, for the utility of this type of vehicle was strictly limited. That the Japanese could produce an effective tank was shown by the new turret *Chi-ha*, the up-gunned version of the Type 97 Medium Tank. When it first appeared in 1941 it compared quite favourably with such contemporary tanks as the British Crusader I and the German Pz.Kpfw.III Model F, and its main armament of the Type 1 47 mm. gun was probably superior to the gun of either of the two. But though a few were used in the Philippines in 1942 this tank did not appear in quantity until 1944. It was still the only tank used in quantity in the following year, when the Soviet T-34/85 rode through Manchuria, when its position could only be described as hopeless.

In view of the limited productive capacity and the steel and skilled labour shortages caused by prior claims of other armaments there was probably little that could be done to expand substantially the total volume of tank production. There can hardly be any criticism of the Japanese decision to give priority to the weapons of air war or, in the type of struggle they had to wage, of giving prior claim to naval requirements. But there was all the more reason to concentrate all energy on production of one really effective type of tank. This is what the Russians very largely did with their T-34 in 1941 and 1942 and this is what the Japanese should have done but did not do.

Whatever their shortcomings, the Type 97 *Chi-ha* and the Type 1 *Chi-he* medium tanks were satisfactory basic designs on which the Japanese might well have concentrated. They and their development, the Type 3 *Chi-nu* were certainly within the capacity of the Japanese industry and transport system, unlike the 40-ton Type 5 *Chi-ri*. Or, even less, the 120-ton *Oi* experimental heavy tank built in great secrecy in 1941 at the Sagami Arsenal, the tank development and production control centre of the Japanese Army. Concentration on the medium tank series would have been wiser and also a far better investment than the lightly armed light tanks, or the special purpose vehicles which the Japanese tried to develop and which were a luxury they could afford least of all.

The Japanese surrender of 1945 and the short-sighted policies of the United States and its allies brought about a complete, though only temporary, disarming of Japan. In consequence, further development of Japanese armoured vehicles ceased for several years and when Soviet policies in the Far East forced the rearmament of Japan her forces were initially equipped with American-built tanks. The first of these were M24 light tanks, supplied in 1952 and by then suitable for little more than training and police duties.

This somewhat inauspicious revival of Japanese tank forces was improved upon by a revival of Japanese tank development. Its first fruit were two experimental vehicles completed in December 1955 by the Komatsu and Mitsubishi companies. Designated the SS-I and SS-II respectively, they were both low silhouette turretless 3-man vehicles mounting twin 105 mm. recoilless guns. A year later, in December 1956, these light 6-ton vehicles were followed by a much more powerful model, the prototype of a new medium tank by Mitsubishi, whose specially built·Tokyo tank factory was the main medium tank manufacturing centre during the Second World War. The general layout and 90 mm. gun of this vehicle are similar to the American M47 medium tank but at 35 tons it is considerably lighter and it is also an improvement on the American tank in having a diesel engine.

The use of diesel engines in both the Mitsubishi medium tanks and the lighter SS vehicles provides an interesting link with the good features of earlier Japanese tanks. At the same time both categories show up-to-date ideas and indicate that the development of Japanese armoured vehicles has restarted on a sound footing.

20

Poland

DISCUSSIONS of the development of armoured forces generally centre on four or five of the major Powers. This is inevitable as between them these Powers hold most of the world's tanks and set the fashion in equipment, organisation and methods of employment. It should not be forgotten, however, that there are other armoured forces, of smaller size, which, at various times, have made their contribution to the general development.

One such armoured force, whose development is both interesting and instructive to consider, was that of Poland. Its first elements came into being in 1918, when Poland regained her independence, after more than a hundred years of occupation and partition between Russia, Germany and Austria, and began building a national army. A major component came from France, where a Polish corps was organised towards the end of the First World War, and consisted of a tank regiment with some 150 Renault F.T. light tanks. This regiment arrived on Polish soil in June 1919 and its first battalion was sent immediately to the front in north-eastern Poland, where its actions against Soviet forces were the first instance of the use of tanks in eastern Europe.

The other battalion of the regiment became a training and replacement unit which gradually supplied the specialist cadre to replace French officers and N.C.O.s originally with the units. By the middle of 1920 a total of 5 companies was operational. Acting independently, they participated successfully in a number of local defensive and offensive actions in various parts of the Polish-Soviet front, in spite of the fact that the Renault tanks, designed for the static conditions of the Western Front, had a maximum speed short of 5 m.p.h. and were not particularly suited to the fluid conditions which prevailed in Poland.

The same conditions were, on the other hand, very favourable to the employment of armoured cars. Small units of these,
equipped for the most part with cars captured from the Russians, were quickly formed and used in a variety of roles. On
two notable occasions the employment of armoured cars took
the novel form of spearheading strategic raids by Polish motorised forces. The first such raid was in April 1920, against
Zytomierz in the Ukraine, and the second in September 1920,
against the railway junction of Kowel, well in the rear of the
Soviet troops retreating from before Warsaw. On both occasions the main body consisted of 2 truck-borne infantry battalions with some truck-drawn field guns and on the second,
which involved an encircling sweep of about 100 miles, the
armoured cars were Fords, built in Poland on the famous Ford
Model T passenger car chassis using armour plate left behind
by the Germans at the Modlin fortress; they were the first
armoured vehicles built in Poland. Otherwise, in their use of
armoured cars and scope, the two Polish raids represented a
significant advance on an earlier German strategic thrust by a
battalion-size force of motorised infantry which seized Turnu
Severin on the Danube in advance of the main German forces,
during the Roumanian campaign of 1916, and a further step
forward towards the deep mechanised thrusts of the Second
World War.

After the signing of the peace treaty in 1921, in the post-
war reorganisation, armoured cars became part of the cavalry.
This practice, adopted by most armies after the First World
War, followed the example set by the French Army. Tank
units followed French ideas even more closely, being equipped
for many years with the French Renault F.T. light tanks.
They formed part of the infantry and, like the French *chars
d'accompagnement*, were regarded as auxiliaries which would
help the infantry by destroying hostile automatic weapons and
crushing barbed wire. The peacetime strength was fixed at a
tank regiment with three battalions, which represented a sizeable force at a time when the Royal Tank Corps consisted of

only four tank battalions and when in countries such as Italy and Japan tank forces were only of company size.

During the twenties little progress was made beyond the point reached at the end of the First World War. Apart from experiments aimed at improving the wartime Renault tanks, which most countries possessing a stock of them did, activity was confined to the provision of some new armoured cars. These were built in Poland on imported French Citroën-Kegresse half-track chassis model 1927, which attracted a good deal of attention at the time.

In 1930, however, a significant step was taken in Poland when the infantry tank regiment, the cavalry armoured car squadrons and the armoured trains, which had been under the control of the engineers and then of the artillery, were all combined into a single armoured arm, the *Broń pancerna*. The existing units were re-formed into 2 tank regiments, one armoured car group and 2 armoured train groups.

At the time the tank units were still equipped with the 12-year-old Renault F.T. but the reorganisation was accompanied by considerable activity in the equipment field, which bore fruit in several new types of armoured vehicles. One of the first steps in this direction was the purchase in Britain of a dozen or so Vickers Carden Loyd Mark VI. This was one of the most popular armoured vehicles of the period and was also purchased by Russia, Italy and several other countries. In Poland, after trials of the British-built vehicles, it was decided to adopt this type and to manufacture it, in a modified form, in Poland.

The Polish version, deliveries of which commenced in 1932, was designated the TK and weighed 2.5 tons ; it looked like a box on tracks and carried a crew of 2 and a Hotchkiss machine-gun. Like its British predecessor, this small turretless vehicle was powered by a Ford Model T car engine but a later, improved version, the TKS (or TKF), had a Polish-built Fiat engine. The TKS also had its frontal armour increased from 8 to 11 mm. and it had a Gundlach periscope which was subsequently adopted on British tanks, showing at least one instance of a flow of ideas in the other direction.

A new Ursus armoured car was also built in Poland but it was still of the road-bound type and in view of this and the appearance of fast light tanks it was decided to abandon further development of armoured cars after only a few were built. Much more important, in any case, was the purchase in 1932 of some more tanks from Vickers-Armstrongs. These were of the Six-Ton type, manned by a crew of 3 and armed either with 2 machine-guns in twin turrets or, much more sensibly, with a 47 mm. gun and machine-gun in a single turret. About 25 were purchased and it was decided to develop its design into a general-purpose light-medium tank. At the time the Vickers-Armstrongs Six Ton tank was very highly thought of, in spite of the fact that the British Army did not adopt it, and several countries beside Poland purchased it. Some were still in service, in Thailand for instance, in the late forties, while in Russia they served as a model for the T-26 series and in the United States they influenced considerably the development of the T1 light tank series.

Interestingly enough, Polish activity in the equipment field extended also to American tanks. In 1931, after demonstrations of new high-speed vehicles built by Walter Christie, the Polish Government contracted for 2 Christie tanks, as did the Soviet. But while the Soviet Government took delivery of its 2 tanks the Polish defaulted and the 2 tanks were taken over by the United States Army, which had already purchased from Christie 5 similar vehicles.

The progress which resulted from all the activity and interest of the early thirties was not, however, either uniform or consistent. Although in 1935 the strength of the tank forces was nominally increased to 9 battalions there was, in general, little understanding of the potentialities of mechanised forces, in spite of the fact that in Germany the first panzer divisions had already appeared and that the Russians were known to be producing tanks in large numbers. Even a year later the possibility of motorised German thrusts was dismissed—yet it was known that such thrusts had been considered several years earlier by the *Reichswehr*, when von Seeckt was at its head. At the same time, in Poland's weak economic position, funds for the provision of new equipment were very limited and tanks, let alone mechanised formations, were a particularly costly item. In consequence, the actual growth and re-equipment of the Polish armoured forces was limited and slow.

In 1936–37, however, the rearmament of the two neighbouring countries brought about a programme of modernisation and expansion of the Polish armed forces. One of its main points was to be a partial mechanisation of the cavalry, 4 brigades of which were to be motorised, and the formation of 8 independent tank battalions.

At the same time work on new types of tanks was begun. A new 4-ton light tank armed with a 20 mm. gun and coaxial machine-gun was to replace the earlier TK and TKS tankettes. Its design was again derived from a Vickers-Armstrongs light tank, a couple of which were purchased, and it was designed in an amphibious as well as standard form. The mechanised cavalry was to receive a Polish-designed 11-ton fast tank of the Christie type intended mainly to combat hostile tanks, work on which was still in progress when the war began. For the independent tank battalions, French Renault R-35 and Somua S-35 tanks were deemed most suitable.

In the meantime, until these plans could be implemented, production of the 7 TP, the improved Polish version of the Vickers-Armstrongs Six Ton tank, which began in 1935 was to continue. A total of 150 was ordered, although they were already considered inadequately armoured, and this in spite of the fact that the maximum thickness was already increased from 15 mm. of the Vickers model to 20 mm. on the 7 TP, bringing the fully laden weight up to 10 tons. The other characteristics of the 7 TP included a high-velocity 37 mm. Bofors gun coaxially mounted with a machine-gun, a 3-man crew and a Saurer 100 b.h.p. diesel engine imported from Switzerland ; it was, in fact, one of the very first diesel-powered tanks to go into service.

The first practical result of the rearmament programme of the mid-thirties was the conversion in 1937 of 2 of the 40 horse cavalry regiments into motorised units. Together with other units they formed the first Polish motorised brigade, the 10th Cavalry Brigade, which came into being in the same year. As planned, this brigade was to consist of a reconnaissance unit of light tanks and motorised riflemen, one battalion of the 11-ton Christie-type tanks, 2 motorised cavalry regiments, each the equivalent of a truck-borne rifle battalion, and a motorised battalion each of field artillery, 37 mm. anti-tank guns and engineers. In its cavalry origin and some other respects this brigade resembled the earlier French *Division Légère Mécanique*. It had, however, one feature which differentiated it from that and other contemporary motorised or mechanised cavalry formations, namely, the relatively high proportion of anti-tank guns and engineers. This revealed it as an " anti-mechanised " motorised formation which could be used for blocking hostile armoured thrusts, a role in which the brigade was, in effect, chiefly used in the 1939 Polish campaign.

In practice, the weakness of this brigade and of the second created later was their equipment and particularly the lack of suitable tanks. Polish industrial capacity was very limited and the production of heavy military equipment was only just beginning so that neither of the 2 new types of tanks had gone beyond the prototype stage when the war started. Even the production of the 7 TP was considerably delayed by the difficulties of making armour plate and its turrets had to be made in Sweden. At the same time foreign exchange for the purchase of equipment or the necessary materials was very limited—not that what there was of it was always best spent. For example, during the period in question 2 large destroyers, one minelayer and 2 ocean-going submarines were added to others purchased abroad earlier. Each one of these units was equivalent financially to a fully equipped medium tank battalion. To a country like Poland the latter was much more useful and in the event the naval units proved useless from the point of view of national defence.

The military loan granted by France in 1936 did little to improve the situation, for all transactions were hampered by prior claims of French forces, procrastination and troubles arising out of the contemporary nationalisation of some French industries and labour unrest. For example, delivery dates for some types of guns extended well into 1942. As for tanks, efforts to obtain Somua tanks met with refusal and, of the 2 ordered, only one battalion of 45 Renault R-35 tanks was delivered a few weeks before the outbreak of the Second World War.

On September 1, 1939, when the war began, the mobilised strength of the Polish armoured forces consisted of 2 battalions of 7 TP and one of R-35, 18 independent companies, each with 13 TK or TKS, attached to different infantry divisions, and 11 reconnaissance squadrons, one to each horse cavalry brigade, each with 13 TK and 8 armoured cars. Each of the 2 motorised brigades had one company of Vickers Six Ton Tanks and 2 companies of TKS. All this represented a total of about 190 tanks of the 7 TP, R-35 and Vickers type, 470 TK or TKS reconnaissance tankettes and 90 obsolescent armoured cars. There were also a few old Renault F.T. left, the majority having been sold to the Republican Government during the Spanish Civil War, and there were also 10 armoured trains, which soon came to grief under German air attack.

Although the number of modern gun-tanks was higher than that possessed at the time by Britain or the United States, Polish armoured forces were completely outnumbered and outclassed by the German. On September 1, the German Army had a total of 3,195 tanks, two-thirds of which were in the field against Poland, organised into 6 regular and one improvised panzer divisions and 4 light divisions which represented the whole of the German armoured forces at the time.

The existence of the powerful German armoured formations was well known to the Polish High Command and their concentration on the Polish-German border was anxiously watched, for their striking power was well appreciated. What, however, was not appreciated were their operational, as opposed to tactical, characteristics and, in particular, their capacity for deep and rapid penetration. In Poland, as elsewhere at the time, the difficulties of moving armoured formations cross-country and of their fuel supply were greatly exaggerated, as was the effectiveness of anti-tank weapons on which considerable emphasis was placed before the war. At the same time it was hoped that Allied action in the West would draw off some of the German armoured forces, as well as aircraft.

The hope proved false and the Polish campaign, which was the first of the *Blitzkrieg* campaigns, was very largely decided by powerful and rapid German armoured thrusts. The only thing to be said about the reaction of the Polish command is that if it was surprised by the German methods it had at least somewhat better reason than the French did 8 months later.

As for the part played by Polish armoured units, these, scattered among various formations, quickly crumbled away in a series of local actions. Of the 2 motorised brigades, the 10th fought a series of successful delaying actions and after 16 days of fighting was forced to cross the frontier into Hungary, where it was interned. The other, the Warsaw Cavalry Brigade, was still organising when the war began and it did not go into action until the closing stages of the campaign, unsuccessfully fighting off encirclement by superior German forces. By a strange twist of fortune the battalion of French-built R-35 tanks never saw action : held in reserve, it was ordered to cross the frontier into Roumania when the Soviet Army invaded Poland's eastern provinces on September 17.

While the fighting in Poland was drawing to a close, a new Polish Army was being born in France and first one and then another French-type infantry light tank battalions were created. In April 1940 the French command rather reluctantly agreed to the formation of a Polish mechanised division on the lines of the *Division Légère Mécanique* and the 2 light tank battalions and the reconstituted 10th Cavalry Brigade became its first units.

Hardly had the organisation of the division started when the German offensive in the West began. At first it made little difference and the tank units still only had a few old Renault F.T. of the First World War vintage for training. In the last days of May 1940 new equipment suddenly became available and orders were issued for the formation, as quickly as possible, of a mechanised brigade of 2 tank and 2 rifle battalions. Then, in the first days of June, under the pressure of events, the French command insisted on such units as were ready being thrown into battle. In spite of frantic activity the whole brigade could not be made ready in a few days and a scratch force was made up of the 1st Tank Battalion equipped with R-35 tanks, some motorised rifle companies and anti-tank guns. Optimistically designated the 10e *Brigade Motorisée Polonaise*, it went into action in Champagne and fought for 5 days, from the Marne to Montbard, amidst the confusion of the general retreat. By then France capitulated and the remnants of the force, cut off, out of petrol and ammunition, were ordered to disperse and make their way individually to unoccupied France.

The other mechanised units were saved from this fate and in the last days of June were evacuated to Britain from various ports in the Bay of Biscay. At first the tank battalions were formed into a British pattern Army Tank Brigade, starting with a few Infantry Tanks Mark I and then going on to Valentines and Churchills, and the 10th Cavalry Brigade was a motorised rifle brigade. On the creation of the 1st Polish Armoured Division in the spring of 1942 both brigades were turned into armoured brigades equipped with Covenanter cruiser tanks and then, in 1943, re-equipped with Crusader III's with 6-pounder guns. The Polish division was the last armoured formation in Britain to change from the earlier 2 armoured brigade organisation to the 1943 pattern with a single armoured brigade ; by then, like others, it began receiving American-built M4 Sherman tanks for its armoured brigade and British-built Cromwells for its armoured reconnaissance regiment. With these it landed in Normandy at the beginning of August

1944 and took part in the fighting around Caen and in the Falaise Gap, and then in the advance into northern France and Belgium and the fighting in Holland and Germany, all as part of the 21st Army Group.

In the meantime, an independent armoured brigade was formed in 1943 in Iraq from personnel saved from Soviet camps and evacuated in 1942 to Persia and Iraq. It experienced only one major change in equipment, from Valentines to Shermans, with which in April 1944 it landed in Italy as part of the 2nd Polish Corps of the 8th British Army. It was used as a " swinger " brigade right through the Italian campaign by the end of which it was expanded into the 2nd Polish Armoured Division. In 1946–47, on demobilisation of the Polish forces in the West, the 2 divisions were disbanded and with them closed another chapter in the history of armoured forces.

Armoured forces were re-established on Polish soil after the Second World War and in the early fifties armoured vehicles were again being produced in Poland. The equipment and the armoured forces are all, however, on the Soviet pattern and constitute little more than a branch of the Soviet armour.

17. United States M4A1 medium tank of 1942-43. (*US Army*).

18. German Panther medium tank with a long barrelled 75mm gun.

19. British Centurion 7 with an 83·4mm 20 pounder gun. (*Ministry of Defence, Crown Copyright Reserved*).

20. United States M48 medium tank of the fifties. (*US Army*).

21

Sweden

SWEDEN'S unique geopolitical position and her independent approach to questions of national defence would, in themselves, be sufficient reason for a look at her armoured forces. Moreover, the development of Swedish armoured forces exhibits a number of interesting features, some of which illustrate particular conditions and others which highlight the development of armour in general. There are, therefore, several reasons why Swedish armoured forces should be singled out here.

The case of the Swedish armoured forces is all the more interesting in view of the emphasis placed by the Swedish Army on mechanisation after the Second World War. The emphasis on mechanisation was something new to Sweden, even though armoured vehicles themselves were not. In fact, the first Swedish tank unit was formed soon after the First World War, in 1920, when 10 light tanks were assembled from components purchased in Germany. These vehicles, which were known as the Strv m/21, were very similar to the wartime German L.K. I and II light tank prototypes and their assembly was actually supervised by the designer of the latter, J. Vollmer.

Little further progress was made during the following decade and in 1930 the Swedish tank force still amounted to only 2 companies. However, by this time mechanisation and armoured vehicles began to attract attention throughout the world and in 1930 the Swedish Defence Committee approved the formation of an armoured force. Two tank battalions were proposed but these were not approved by the Swedish Parliament until 1937. To make matters worse, the 2 battalions were, in the manner of the times, assigned to the infantry and split between 2 so-called mixed infantry regiments. Moreover, they did not become effective until the autumn of 1939.

The equipment of the tank battalions was of Swedish manufacture, all of it produced by the Landsverk Company of Landskrona in southern Sweden. The origin and early development of this company, as well as its designs, benefited from the interest which the Germans took in the Swedish armament industry as a result of the restrictions placed after the First World War by the Allied control of Germany and the terms of the Versailles Treaty. The Landsverk Company came into being in the late twenties and in the early thirties it produced several advanced experimental tank designs, which foreshadowed a number of features later adopted on German and Soviet tanks, as well as a wheel and track vehicle and some conventional armoured cars.

The two designs which were standardised by the outbreak of the Second World War were the light, machine-gun-armed Strv m/37 and the 37 mm. gun m/38. Both were well up to the contemporary standard in tank design at the time of their introduction but the Swedish tank development did not live up to its early promise. In 1941, for instance, the m/38 was succeeded by nothing better than its modified version, the m/40, a 9.5-ton 3-man vehicle with a 37 mm. gun and 2 machine-guns. Nor were the tanks Swedish produced in sufficient quantity. To supplement them the Army purchased Czech designed 11-ton 37 mm. gun tanks which became the Strv m/41. This was one of the most successful tanks ever built: similar tanks were purchased on the eve of the Second World War by the Swiss and the Persians, and others saw extensive service as the Pz.Kpfw.38t in the German armoured forces, including Rommel's 7th Panzer Division in France in 1940, and subsequently as the basis of a large number of self-propelled and assault guns. By 1942, however, on account of their 37 mm. gun armament, the m/41 as well as the m/40 could be regarded as little more than light reconnaissance tanks.

Thus, during the early part of the Second World War, the equipment of Swedish tank units fell below the average standard in armoured fighting vehicles and with the intensive development which took place in all the belligerent countries it became increasingly difficult for Sweden to maintain its position in the tank field. One might have thought that the tank experience of Landsverk, coupled with the armament development resources of the world-famous Bofors works and the general automotive background of firms such as Scania-Vabis, would provide all that was necessary for continuous tank development. But the wartime rate of tank development and the progressive increase in the size and power of tanks made the task much more difficult than it had been hitherto. Production of tanks became a major industrial undertaking as the 40-odd ton tanks of the period came to require tens of thousands of parts, and engines, transmissions and other components out of the normal run of automotive engineering. Consequently, manufacturing facilities for them involved a heavy outlay of capital, difficult to justify by the relatively small quantities of this type of tank required by the Swedish Army. It is not surprising, therefore, that the Swedes did not make much progress in this field.

To be true, they did produce about the middle of the Second World War a 22-ton 4-man medium tank with a short 75 mm. gun, the Strv m/42. This model was very similar in many ways to the early versions of the Pz.Kpfw.IV medium tank which the German Army used in quantity until 1942, and within the limits implied by this comparison was a good tank. But, because of its armament, it became obsolete almost as soon as it was introduced and was not succeeded by a more powerful model until 1953, when the Swedish Army purchased its first 80 Centurion III tanks from Britain.

An attempt was made to up-gun the existing Strv m/42 chassis by turning it into a self-propelled carriage with a long 75 mm. gun but the resulting Pvkv m/43 could hardly be adjudged superior to some of the German wartime semi-improvised self-propelled anti-tank guns. More successful, within its particular field, has been the post-war Ikv 75 mm. infantry assault gun intended for the heavy companies of the infantry brigades, but this vehicle could not, of course, meet the needs of more mobile armoured units.

More surprising than the failure to produce a satisfactory medium-heavy type of tank has been the delay in developing lighter-weight armoured vehicles. Vehicles of this type were much more within Swedish industrial capabilities and their various possible applications would have ensured an economic production cost. Judicious concentration of development effort on a powerfully armed light-weight vehicle might well have led to the type exemplified by the German Jagdpanzer 38 and its associated 88 mm. gun *Waffentrager*, or by the French AMX 13 light tank series. Such a vehicle would have satisfied the most urgent need of the Swedish Army, as that of others, for a well-armed light-weight tank and it would also have provided a chassis suitable for a wide variety of purposes, such as self-propelled gun carriages, anti-aircraft tanks, command vehicles and armoured personnel and cargo carriers.

Manufacturing problems apart, the principal reason for the lack of progress in the development of new armoured vehicles was the changing attitude towards armoured forces. In the first 2 years of the Second World War the German Army proved armoured forces to be the decisive element in land warfare and its example in the effective employment of armour was followed by almost all other armies. This included the Swedish Army, which in 1942 finally abandoned the earlier ineffective method of tying tanks down to the infantry and constituted an independent armoured force embracing tank, anti-tank and armoured infantry units. A peacetime establishment of 4 tank regiments was planned and the employment of armour was intended to be in armoured brigades, each based on 2 tank and one armoured infantry battalions. These plans, were not, however, ever fully implemented.

The end of the Second World War and the contemporary confusion concerning the employment and value of armoured forces put a stop to almost all development of armour in Sweden. The Swedish Army fell full prey to the misguided opinion, which was particularly rampant in the United States after the Second World War, that there was no future for armoured forces. So much so that no money was made available for the procurement of new armoured equipment until 1953.

By this time North Korean-manned Soviet tanks had demonstrated once again the power of armour and in the wake of the resultant world-wide revival of interest in armoured forces the Swedish Army set about mending the error of its ways. Badly needed modern tanks were purchased in Britain and the reconstituted armoured brigades were allotted the important role of a mobile striking force.

At about the same time armoured brigades became one of the two types of basic formations—infantry brigades being the other—which the Swedish Army adopted in place of the earlier divisional organisation. Originally the armoured brigades were reconstituted on the basis of one tank battalion with some 60 tanks and 2 infantry battalions backed by a 105 mm. howitzer battalion. Apart from these units, there were also in each armoured brigade 2 anti-aircraft companies with 40 and 20 mm. guns, and one each of heavy tank, self-propelled 75 mm. gun, mortar and engineer companies, as well as a brigade maintenance group which very sensibly embraced all the service and supply units.

From some points of view the Swedish armoured brigade of the early fifties looked like a smaller edition of the 1944–45 German panzer division. It certainly had the same ratio of infantry to tanks and the same incomplete mechanisation.

The 2 infantry battalions, for instance, were only partly equipped with wheeled armoured personnel carriers of the 4 x 4 Skpf m /42 type. These were essentially armour-plated trucks and as such lacked cross-country performance but they were an advance on the unprotected trucks in which most of the infantry of the armoured divisions has been transported throughout the world.

Part of the infantry was also equipped with bicycles, which were claimed to provide a degree of mobility comparable to that of motorised troops under many conditions. Interestingly enough, this tallied with German experience in the closing stages of the Second World War, when the Germans found bicycle troops particularly useful for co-operation with tanks in night operations and in close country, which, of course, many parts of Sweden are. Another point about the infantry of the Swedish armoured brigades has been a high proportion of light automatic weapons which are more useful in close country and in the short, violent engagements of mobile warfare than conventional rifles with their unnecessarily powerful long-range ammunition. The infantry also has been well provided with recoilless guns and rocket launchers on which the Swedish Army, like the American, has placed considerable emphasis since the Second World War.

However, in spite of the emphasis which has been placed on these light-weight anti-tank weapons, it has been officially recognised that armoured fighting vehicles themselves are the best anti-tank weapon. This is one of the principal reasons why much more attention has been given to tanks, especially as the employment of armour by a potential attacker was not expected to be confined to a few of the most favourable areas but to extend to practically the whole of the country. Much of it might have been classified as " impassable " to tanks but note has obviously been taken of the 1940 lesson of the Ardennes and the 1950 lesson of Korea.

Likewise, Sweden's own armoured brigades came to be regarded as versatile fighting formations capable of operating under a variety of conditions and suitable for mobile defence as well as offensive operations. The capabilities of armoured units in face of nuclear weapons are a further reason why more attention has been paid to tanks and this aspect of the problem has held a particularly important place in Swedish operational research as it concerns armour.

In other respects the smaller size of the Swedish armoured formations made them better fitted to meet probable operational conditions. So did the attention realistically given to operating under conditions of enemy air superiority. As for the Achilles' heel of the logistical requirements of armoured formations, the Swedish brigades have been less vulnerable to threats to their supplies because of their more frugal scale of equipment. In this respect the Swedish Army has again resembled the German in the closing stages of the Second World War, rather than the armies of the West with their swarms of trucks and an over-abundance of various special units and services.

There remained, however, room for considerable further improvement, particularly in the equipment of the Swedish armoured brigades. The greatest room for improvement has been in the basic type of tank, a problem by no means confined to the Swedish Army. The principal need has been for tanks combining powerful armament with a high degree of operational mobility. This requirement is not met by the existing relatively heavy medium tanks, especially in the varied terrain of a country like Sweden, and to obtain the necessary mobility and reduced logistical dependence new and lighter equipment is essential.

Part 4

Equipment and its Problems

22

The Mechanics of Design

THE creation of mechanised equipment involves, in general, 3 major and successive stages. The first is the evolution of the broad conception of the particular type of equipment. The second is the realisation of the original conception in the form of a practical design. The third is the reproduction of the approved design for delivery, in quantity, to the users.

The broad conception, which is the starting point of the whole process, stems from considerations of what the user does or may need and what is technically feasible. It combines the facts of the existing strategic and tactical situation, or deductions about possible or probable future conditions, with others drawn from the fund of scientific knowledge gained by research and the existing technological capabilities, into a tentative technical solution to a military problem.

Once the broad conception of the equipment has been evolved, the next step is to define its military and technical characteristics. This is done in the form of a specification or, directly, in the form of a preliminary design which establishes the basic configuration of the equipment and its general performance. In addition to the functional characteristics, a preliminary design must also give some consideration to the manufacture of the equipment with existing or obtainable facilities and to the cost aspect, for the best design is one which achieves its object at minimum cost.

Preliminary design is followed by detailed design, which determines the shape, dimensions, material and other particulars of individual parts, and then the construction of one or more, frequently 3 to 6, prototypes. Prototypes or test models are an indispensable part of design, to prove it functionally and to develop reliability and durability, none of which can be done on paper. Development testing of prototypes invariably reveals the need for some modifications of the original design and serves to refine it. Usually prototypes are also used for evaluation and acceptance tests by the user.

Successful trials of prototypes are normally followed by a re-examination of the design from the point of view of manufacturing economy, re-design of parts to make them more suitable for production and the preparation of a complete set of detailed production drawings which provide the information necessary for the manufacture of the equipment.

Frequently, before any quantity production is embarked upon, a pre-production batch of equipment is manufactured for troop trials or service tests. This serves the double purpose of trying out the equipment under field conditions in the hands of the troops and of providing preliminary experience for the manufacturing organisation. It also serves to indicate further improvements to the design which can be introduced before full-scale production begins, just as service experience with early full-production units serves to improve those produced at a later stage.

To a large extent the whole process from the conception of the equipment to its production has been systematised and responsibility for the different phases divided between a number of groups or units. The usual procedure is, first, for the General Staff to establish an operational requirement from analysis of strategic and tactical conditions, enemy or foreign intelligence reports and technological developments. The broad requirement is then translated into a specification, formulated by a committee containing representatives of the user arm and technical services, which defines the military characteristics of the equipment in the light of what is considered technically feasible. Commonly the specification contains such things as the required armament, crew, armour protection, speed and endurance.

Next, the general specification is issued to an engineering establishment, such as the Fighting Vehicles Research and

Development Establishment in Britain or the Tank Automotive Engineering Centre in the United States, which carries out preliminary design studies on its basis. The outcome is a general arrangement, or layout, drawing and a detailed engineering specification which are submitted for approval by service representatives. Either as a supplement to the preliminary design, or shortly after its approval, a mock-up—full-size wooden replica of the proposed vehicle—is also built to check the location of the components and as a visual aid to the assessment of the design.

If the preliminary design is accepted the engineering establishment proceeds to the detailed design of the vehicle and, as the detailed design drawings become available, to the construction in its experimental department of one or more prototypes. In the first instance, the experimental prototypes are used for engineering tests which prove the functional design and reveal shortcomings which need to be rectified ; subsequently they pass into the hands of using services which may carry out their own development tests, as well as evaluation of the equipment.

When the prototypes have successfully passed the various tests and the design, after modification, is accepted by the services it is then arranged that its production be undertaken by an industrial organisation possessing the necessary manufacturing facilities. Its engineering department reviews the design from the production point of view, recommends modifications to facilitate manufacture and issues the complete finalised engineering information required for production. In addition, of course, the industrial organisation assumes responsibility for all the other functions related to production which are described in the next chapter.

The above procedure has evolved over a number of years and is followed in principle in Britain and the United States. It has proved workable but it is not in every respect an ideal arrangement.

For one thing, it is doubtful whether the General Staff is, in fact, the body best placed to synthesise the different military and technological factors into an idea of a new equipment, which is expected of it if the accepted procedure is strictly adhered to. It possesses, of course, the necessary knowledge of strategy, tactics and military intelligence. But it is neither in close nor continuous contact with technological problems, and yet it is responsible for generating what is essentially a technical idea—a role for which it is obviously ill fitted, either as a corporate body or in its various committees. In consequence, its requirements are more likely to envisage improvements to existing equipment than really new types and progress closely directed by it, like that dictated by its civilian management counterparts, is apt to be slow and mediocre. Indeed, had it been left to General Staff requirements, the tank itself would probably still have to be conceived.

Those who are concerned with design studies should be in a far better position to take the initiative and evolve ideas of really new equipment which is, in fact, usually the consequence of inventive thinking at the design level. They live in a technical environment and they are closer to the research which provides information and data necessary to devise new equipment. Their common difficulty is insufficient knowledge of operational conditions, partly from lack of opportunity and partly of their own making, which prevents them from visualising what the user needs or, better still, anticipating his needs.

A way out of the dilemma is for the General Staff to provide a maximum of information with a minimum of direction and leave it to technical groups, which it should foster and encourage, to integrate the various factors into broad conceptions of new equipment. Ideally, these groups should work in competition with each other and the General Staff can then confine itself to the proper executive function of objective review and selection of the proposals put to it. This implies a state of affairs akin to that existing in the aircraft and guided missile fields where a number of firms compete with each other in the design and development of similar equipment. To a limited extent such conditions have also existed in the tank field, particularly in Germany and France during the thirties when tanks were designed in competition and the final decision was taken on the basis of competitive trials of prototypes. For instance, Renault, Hotchkiss and F.C.M. submitted designs to a 1933 French light tank specification and 2 to 5 firms submitted prototypes to each German tank specification from the Pz.Kpfw.I of 1933 to the Tiger and Panther of 1942, with beneficial results to the final product.

In the absence of a sufficient number of competent firms, or of a sufficient incentive for such firms to undertake work on tanks, research, design and development must be centralised in a single government establishment. Centralisation unfortunately removes the stimulus of competition but at least it ensures one body of competent personnel and eliminates some of the duplication of effort which is inseparable from a competitive system. It also provides easier co-ordination and control of research sponsored in connection with mechanised equipment and makes easier the provision of adequate facilities to support the development of design.

The development facilities which have come to be considered necessary are quite extensive. They include laboratories with test beds and rigs for testing components, test rooms for stimulating tropical and arctic conditions and a proving ground covering at least 1 or 2 square miles, where the performance of the vehicle can be tested over different surfaces, on steep slopes, wading through water, and so on, and where it can be subjected to accelerated endurance testing, to determine as quickly as possible its durability.

The time factor in development is important for it is essential that it be carried out quickly. Indeed, if the development cannot be carried out quickly enough it might as well not be done at all because the results will arrive too late to be of use.

Bearing in mind the time factor, it is debatable whether or how much prototype development should be done by the services in place of, or in addition to, that carried out by an engineering establishment to develop the design. Service development tests are bound to indicate further design modifications but they are not close enough for effective support of design and are too artificial, on the other hand, to provide real service experience. The demand for them is understandable and contrasts well with the unrealistic attitude of the early days of the tank when equipment was expected to be perfect straight off the drawing board. There are, also, strong historical arguments in favour of separate service prototype development, for it was essential when the designers of tanks had little or no experience of them and little or no development facilities, as was the case when automotive and railway firms were brought into the tank field in the Second World War. In general, however, design and development activities are best maintained together and performed in the closest possible contact.

Service evaluation tests or troop trials are a different matter, for while they too provide valuable technical evidence their main object is operational suitability. Naturally, the users want to satisfy themselves that the equipment will perform under the expected field conditions, that it can be operated by personnel of average qualifications and that it is tactically effective. Whether the evaluation tests are performed with prototypes or pre-production models, or both, is largely a matter of time. Tests with a few prototypes enable a decision to be reached quickly but the equipment may not be fully representative of that later issued in quantity ; tests with a pre-production batch are more representative but mean that decisions are delayed until a later stage in the process and involve extensive manufacturing commitments. The safest course, on the " belt and braces " principle, is to do both, as well as service prototype development, and delay decisions on full-scale production until the completion of tests with pre-production models. This is commonly done in peacetime and accounts for the fact that it usually takes so long from the conception of the equipment to its issue to the troops.

In wartime evaluation tests with pre-production batches of equipment are often dispensed with entirely and development testing cut down to a minimum. This was the case with all the

21. British Conqueror, a 65 ton tank with a 120mm gun. (*Ministry of Defence, Crown Copyright Reserved*).

22. United States M60 medium tank with a 105mm gun. (*US Army*).

23. United States M50 Ontos anti-tank vehicle with six 106mm recoilless guns. (*US Marine Corps*).

24. SS-11 anti-tank guided missile at launch from a French AMX-13 light tank. (*Nord Aviation*).

tanks of the First World War and such Second World War German tanks as the Panther and Tiger, where operational experience was obtained in action with vehicles from full-scale production. It meant that vehicles reached service without all the desirable modifications and improvements but they did reach the troops quickly : in less than a year in the case of most First World War tanks and 13 months in the case of the Tiger I. They were not as reliable as they might have been but frequently a less perfect vehicle available early is much more effective than a superior vehicle which appears late. It is, in fact, possible to carry development, testing, trials, evaluation and all the rest to such perfection that by the time the vehicle is finally put into production its design is obsolescent or obsolete. This particular danger prevails in peacetime, when the direct stimulus of enemy developments is removed and no other form of competition exists.

A further weakness of the prevailing procedures for the evolution of the equipment is the emphasis which they place on committees. A particularly important aspect of this are the committees, boards or commissions which formulate the original requirements. To be fair, they are very valuable for bringing together the many different viewpoints and as a forum for discussion but unfortunately committees and similar bodies do not have the gift of vision and intitiative which are found in individuals. In consequence, committee decisions do not, as a rule, represent the integration of the best thought but mere compromises.

This is yet another reason why a small technical study group or team led by a man or men who have some knowledge of every technological and operational aspect of the equipment are more likely to originate new equipment. One man, or even a small group of men, cannot design a whole tank in detail but, given the necessary basic knowledge, opportunities to acquire a maximum of information and encouragement or stimulus, they are more likely to produce really new ideas.

The design of a tank in detail is a considerable undertaking which involves the creation of a drawing for every one of its many parts. Even a tank as simple—by latter day standards —as the American Renault F.T.-type M1917 light tank was made of 1,200 different parts, or about as many as the current agricultural tractor. By the outbreak of the Second World War the design of a tank involved 7,000 to 10,000 parts and a typical wartime tank, such as the American Medium M4, 31,150. Tanks produced since the Second World War, such as the M46 and the Centurion, are also made of over 30,000 different parts.

Because of the large number of parts which goes into the making of a tank it is desirable, and indeed essential, to use as many existing parts or complete assemblies as possible in the design of any new vehicle. In consequence, and to reduce development effort and manufacturing problems, it is common

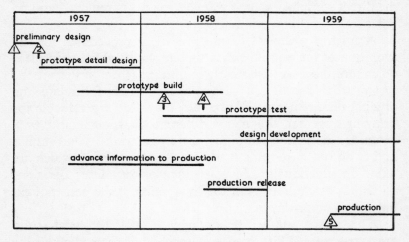

1—Issue of specification 2—Mock-up approval 3—Completion of first prototype
4—Approval of design 5—Commencement of production

FIG. 1. Design and development programme.

practice to use previously designed and fully developed engines, transmissions and electrical components. But even so the design of a fighting vehicle involves 4,500 to 5,000 drawings. This number of drawings means about 65,000 to 75,000 design man-hours or, at the average rate of 2,000 man-hours per man per year, a design team of 30 to 40 men working for 12 months. In terms of cost, it also means £65,000 to £75,000 since the pay and cost of supporting facilities per engineering man-hour amount to about £1.

The effort and money necessary to bring the design to the prototype stage are only a fraction of the total involved in bringing up a new tank to the production stage. The making of prototype parts by tool-room methods and their assembly into one or half a dozen vehicles require more man-hours and money. So does development testing and subsequent design modifications : the preparation of a complete set of production drawings often consumes as many man-hours as the original design, and development testing costs at least as much as all the design work combined.

As far as time is concerned, some of the work can overlap, as indicated in fig. 1, which shows an idealised programme timing chart. The timing depends, to some extent, upon the available engineering manpower but under normal conditions two and a half years is about the minimum time required from the issue of a specification to the commencement of production. If adequate manpower is available and, even more, if several fully developed components, such as engines or transmissions, can be incorporated in the design, then the time can be reduced without adverse effect on the performance of the first production vehicles. On the other hand, with limited personnel and under more leisurely peacetime conditions 5 to 6 years are by no means exceptional.

23

Production and Costs

THE manufacture of tanks, like that of other automotive vehicles, is a considerable and complex undertaking. It calls for large-scale industrial resources and involves a wide range of activities, from the moment it is first contemplated to the actual delivery of the vehicles to the user.

In the general sequence of events the manufacturing phase follows the policy decision, which establishes the broad specification of the vehicle and its design and development into a reliable product. However, both the policy decision and the design are interwoven with questions of manufacturing facilities and must, of necessity, be commensurate with them. Manufacturing considerations consequently appear as early as the proposal stage of most products and the preparatory stages of the manufacturing phase run concurrently with design— or should do, if an undue amount of time is not to be lost between the completion of a design and the commencement of production.

In view of this overlapping, it is often better to think in terms of the main production functions than, say, a strict sequence of events. Moreover, each main function corresponds, in general, to a separate department or division of an organisation concerned with the manufacture of armoured vehicles.

The first is that of design or product engineering, or just plain engineering where there is no chance of confusing it with other activities to which this name may also be applied or misapplied. Whatever the name the function is basically the same, however, namely to design and develop the vehicle into a reliable product and to supply blueprints and other engineering information in order that other departments may perform their functions.

Often the engineering department which designs the vehicle does not form an integral part of the organisation manufacturing it. This is the case, for instance, with the British ordnance factories producing tanks to the design of a centralised design establishment represented by the Fighting Vehicles Research and Development Establishment. Nevertheless, the existence of a design department is an essential prerequisite to the operation of a manufacturing organisation and the closest contact between it and the other departments is most important.

Given a satisfactory design and a decision to proceed with it, the next question is that of the sources of supply for components of the new vehicle. It is one of the characteristics of automotive vehicle production that no one factory or firm attempts to make more than a certain proportion of the total number of parts which make up the vehicle and the rest is bought-out from sub-contractors or specialist suppliers.

In fact, the manufacturing organisation responsible for the production of the complete vehicle is often mainly an assembly plant. Engines are supplied from one plant, transmissions from another, armament from yet a third and so on, until the list literally includes hundreds of suppliers. For instance, production of the 1944 British Comet tank by the Leyland Company involved more than 900 suppliers; that of the 1951 American M41 light tank at the Cadillac-operated Cleveland plant over 2,000; and of the M48A2 medium tank by Alco, 1,500. Even a relatively simple vehicle, such as the Ontos produced by Allis-Chalmers, involves 370.

A preliminary survey of the necessary plant, manufacturing equipment, manpower and sources of supply is usually made while the vehicle is being designed, and the choice of whether to make or buy is dictated by the available facilities, established practices which confine many components to specialist manufacturers and the relative cost of the two alternatives. In the main, the decision is arrived at between the manufacturing departments and the purchase department, which handles the actual procurement of the components and parts which are bought-out as well as the material for those which are made-in. The magnitude of the raw material problem alone may be gauged from the fact that its weight per vehicle is almost twice the finished weight of the latter. The additional material is required by the unavoidable scrap, and the ratio of final weight to the material required, or material utilisation, in tank production is generally of the order of 50 to 60 per cent.

The methods by which parts are made-in and assembled are the responsibility of the production engineering department which decides on the machinery, its arrangement within the factory and the sequence of operations which has to be planned for each part produced. Thus, information derived from the design drawings is eventually translated into plant layout and the facilities for manufacture and assembly. Even where a considerable number of parts is bought-out, over 1,000 machine tools are required and several acres of factory floor area.

For quantity production actual operations are arranged on a flow-line principle where one operation follows another in a finely synchronised sequence. Where small quantities do not justify specialised equipment more flexible methods have to be used and the work is done in batches on multi-purpose machinery which is changed over at intervals from making one part to another.

The operation of all the machinery and the building of the actual vehicles are the responsibility of the production departments which provide and control the necessary labour. A vehicle may require, say, 8,000 man-hours to produce and if produced at the rate of one per day will require a labour force of about 1,000 men working the normal 8-hour day. Taking it one step further, this would mean a factory employing a total of about 2,000 people, as the ratio of productive to non-productive personnel is usually about one to one.

As this example indicates, the work of a factory is geared to the rate of flow of work rather than the total quantity of an order. It is the delivery schedule of so many vehicles per week, or per month, which determines the production programme and this, in turn, governs the scheduling of material supplies and the production of parts. The continous flow of work, which is essential to efficient flow production, is ensured by material and production control and demands that the production programme be established several months in advance of the completion of the vehicles, for the purchase department may have to place orders on outside suppliers 6, 9 or more months in advance of delivery.

The amount of work involved in scheduling and controlling the production of parts is best indicated by the fact that even a simple vehicle, such as the American M1917 light tank was made of 1,200 different parts or 33,000 individual pieces, when every nut and bolt was counted. A tank such as the British Matilda of 1940 had about 8,000 parts and 40,000 pieces and the American Medium M4 of 1943, 31,150 parts and 85,000 pieces; on the M46 the number of pieces has increased still further to about 100,000, all of which have to be made, delivered and assembled on time.

Quality of the complex end-product is ensured by the quality control, or inspection, department which tests the performance of the completed vehicle, as well as inspecting incoming material and checking, on a percentage basis, parts at various stages of the manufacture. Final inspection now includes a wading test to check waterproofing and a test run of several miles, as well as static inspection; when through, the tank is finally ready for shipment to the user.

The cost of the finished tank is established by the financial department, which maintains cost data and pays wages and suppliers, and its cost figures provide a good measure of all the work involved in producing tanks. To give a few typical figures, the cost of the British Mark IV heavy tank of the First World War was estimated at about £5,000, while the cost of the French Renault F.T. light tank was £2,250 at the contemporary rate of exchange ; Carden Loyd tankettes of the late twenties cost about £500 each and the light tanks of the midthirties, such as the British Mark I and the French Renault

R-35, £1,500 to £2,200. During the Second World War such typical vehicles as the British Churchill infantry tank cost £15,000 and the American Medium M4 £10,300 to £16,600 depending on the date of the contract; tanks built in quantity since the Second World War, such as the Centurion and the M48, cost £40,000 and £47,000 respectively, in 1957.

This gives some indication of the effort and money involved in producing tanks. It also shows that costs of tanks vary considerably, even when allowances are made for monetary depreciation which has taken place over the years. Several factors are involved, one of which is weight. With tanks, as with other vehicles, the cost per pound of net vehicle weight is substantially constant over a wide range of models produced under similar conditions. In consequence, the cost of a tank is, in the first instance, a matter of how many pounds it weighs. From the cost point of view low weight is, therefore, highly desirable, but weight is usually determined by other than cost considerations. Therefore, however desirable it may be to reduce the total weight of a vehicle, the achievement of economy must concern itself with other things.

Beside weight the principal factors which affect economy are the complexity of the design and the way in which tanks are produced. Both are reflected in the cost per pound figures which vary considerably as the conditions change. The lowest of the present costs of about 7s., or one dollar, per pound of vehicle weight are comparable to those of the more expensive quantity-produced civilian vehicles and are about twice the cost per pound of the cheapest mass-produced models. This is commensurate with the quantities involved and to reduce production cost of tanks would require greater quantities, which would justify more high-output special-purpose machinery to reduce the man-hours per tank and which would spread the cost of development, tooling, etc., over a greater number of tanks and thus automatically reduce the cost per tank.

Conversely, there is no more certain way of increasing costs per vehicle than to produce tanks in small quantities and at a low rate of production. For instance, produced in a small

batch of about 300 vehicles the cost per tank may be almost
three times the unit cost of the same tank which is part of a
production run of about 2,000. Thus, the Mark VIII heavy
tanks, 100 of which were completed in the United States
immediately after the First World War, cost $85,000 each,
whereas in quantity production originally envisaged they would
have cost $35,000, or £7,350 at the contemporary rate of ex-
change; 30 years later the unit cost of the first batch of M41
light tanks was as much as $330,000 but in 1953, in quantity
production, it came down to $77,000, or £27,200.

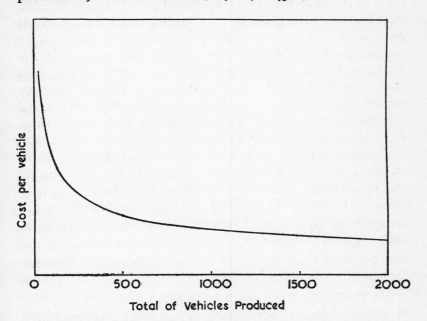

FIG. 2. Variation of vehicle cost with the total quantity of vehicles produced.

As the number of a particular tank increases, the unit cost
or cost per tank gradually tends towards a constant value, as
indicated in fig. 2, but, nevertheless, the greater the quantity
the lower the unit cost. The same applies to components and
it is commonly far easier to achieve long economical production runs with components, such as engines and transmissions,

than complete vehicles by using as many common units as possible in a number of different designs. The ultimate in this approach towards reduced costs is to use components from large quantity civilian production, as has been done in several instances, particularly with engines.

The opposite of such rationalised production, where the number of special components and complete vehicles is held down to a minimum, is to produce simultaneously two or more different tanks with similar military characteristics. In contrast to the competitive design and development of different tanks to the same broad specification the continuation of more than one into production is quite inadmissible. Yet, in several cases, instead of the best design being singled out, two or more similar tanks were produced in parallel. For instance, in the late thirties the French manufactured 3 very similar light tanks, the R-35, H-35 and F.C.M., and in 1940–41 the very similar Covenanter and Crusader cruiser tanks were being manufactured in Britain. To make matters worse in the latter case, contemporary British production was spread over a total of 5 different tanks, each with a different engine and transmission, but with identical main armament. The Russians, on the other hand, managed to confine themselves for several years to the two T-34 and KV tanks and a single engine and transmission type common to both and several other armoured vehicles, with obvious advantages from the manufacturing and cost points of view, as well as that of operation and maintenance.

In peacetime, when the total quantity of a particular type of tank is often very small not only is its cost inherently high but the situation is further aggravated by the fact that its production is at a low rate, which makes it almost impossible to maintain an efficient manufacturing organisation properly staffed with the necessary personnel. For instance, a study performed in connection with the American Cleveland plant manufacturing the M41 light tank showed that it required a minimum output of 20 tanks per month, or one tank for each working day, to justify its existence and even then its operation would be far from economical.

Because of the small peacetime orders for armoured vehicles, in most cases their production could not be undertaken by manufacturers with experience of low-cost industrial methods and has had to be placed with others, capable of handling small quantity orders but frequently wanting in low-cost methods and general cost-consciousness. Among them have been the manufacturers of some of the best and certainly the most expensive cars in the world who were unlikely to bring the question of low costs to the fore and who have been aided and abetted by the services who were apt to ask for nothing but the best, instead of the best at the lowest cost.

In a few cases only has competition between manufacturers been used to lower costs: a notable example occurred in the mid-thirties when competition between the Renault and Hotchkiss companies for a French light tank order brought the already low cost of the Renault-designed tank from 250,000 francs down to 190,000. Usually, however, competitive conditions do not exist to stimulate economical production and about the best that can be done is to place the manufacture of tanks under the wing of an efficient industrial organisation, to allow the general low-cost approach and production techniques of the latter to influence to the fullest extent the work on tanks.

Cost-consciousness can do much not only to reduce production costs but also to keep in check the inevitable tendency towards complexity, which is a further cause of high costs of armoured vehicles. A good deal of the complexity stems directly from the original specification and one school of thought insists that all user requirements which can be technically met should be incorporated. Another believes that beyond the principal requirements a design should be governed by manufacturing considerations. The more extreme forms of designing for production might reduce the effectiveness of the equipment in the hands of the users, but the Russians, who have favoured this approach, have shown that it need not do so seriously and it certainly allows more tanks to be built for any given amount of money. The usual solution is some form of compromise between user requirements and manufacturing considerations and it is largely left to the skill of the designers to make the tank as suitable as possible for production. If in the process they avoid elaboration and make the tank simple and robust they also make it a much better piece of military equipment.

A further contribution towards reduced costs can also be made by designing tank components for a shorter working life than is generally the case. Analysis has shown that the field life of a tank is about 5,000 to 6,000 miles and yet most components are designed to last much longer. Were a shorter component life accepted, the cost of a tank could be reduced and for the same expenditure of resources more tanks could be built or, what is perhaps even more desirable, they could be replaced more quickly by improved designs.

However, of all the possible ways of reducing costs none is as likely to succeed and ensure effective economical equipment as a general cost-consciousness on the part of all concerned with armoured vehicles: the users, the designers and the producers.

24

Tank Armament

A FIGHTING vehicle and its weapons are interdependent. The vehicle is essentially a weapon carrier and serves to increase by its mobility the overall effectiveness of the weapons which are mounted in it. Inversely, the effectiveness of its weapons largely determines the battle-worthiness of the vehicle.

This reciprocal relationship between vehicles and weapons makes the problem of tank armament complex, for it generally involves vehicle characteristics and weapon installation, as well as the weapons themselves. Ultimately, however, the effectiveness of tank armament may be simply related to its ability to disable or destroy enemy personnel, weapon emplacements and fighting vehicles.

When tanks were conceived, the need to attack fighting vehicles did not exist and the other two main functional requirements were met by a combination of two different weapons : the machine-gun, which answered the need for an anti-personnel weapon, and the gun, which fired high-explosive shells necessary against dug-in machine-guns and pill-boxes.

The combination of machine-guns with guns has since remained the common basis of tank armament. Tank machine-guns have remained, as they were originally, adaptations of existing rifle calibre, 6.5 to 8 mm., infantry weapons firing 140 to 230 grain bullets with a muzzle velocity of 2,000 to 2,900 ft. / sec. Tank guns, on the other hand, have changed considerably over the years.

The gun which was contemplated for the first British tank, the Little Willie of 1915, was a small naval 2-pounder, but the second tank carried 2 Hotchkiss 57 mm. naval 6-pounders and these were adopted for the British tanks of 1916. The choice of

301

the 6-pounder, and its mounting in sponsons projecting out of the side of the tank, were influenced by the naval experience of the tank's designers, and the gun was approved by army representatives as sufficiently powerful against dug-in machine-guns. The final decision, however, was based on its availability from naval stocks rather than functional requirements.

The naval 6-pounder used on the Mark I tanks, which was 40 calibres long, was later superseded by a shorter-barrelled version manufactured especially for tanks. This second version, only 23 calibres long, was used on the principal First World War British heavy tanks, such as the Mark IV and V, as well as the Anglo-American Mark VIII and the post-war American experimental medium tanks down to the T1 of 1925.

The short 6-pounder gave satisfactory service and, in spite of its low 1,350 ft./sec. muzzle velocity, even proved capable of dealing with hostile tanks on the rare occasion when the need for this arose. However, soon after the war its place as the standard British tank gun was taken by a smaller calibre weapon, the 47 mm. 3-pounder. This was introduced in 1921 as a light tank gun, but as the second Vickers design, in which it was installed, was not only up-graded into the medium tank category but also became the only tank in service, the 3-pounder became the only British tank gun in use during the twenties. It retained this position well into the thirties and, in addition to the Vickers Medium Mark I and II, was also used in the later and heavier A.6. and A.7 medium tanks and even on the 31-ton A.1 Independent heavy tank.

By comparison with the 6-pounder, the 3-pounder possessed the advantage of higher muzzle velocity and consequently flatter trajectory and greater accuracy. But, as indicated by the archaic designations, the weight of the shell fired by it was only about one-half that of the 6-pounder and it was thus considerably less effective against weapon emplacements and troops behind any form of protection. This, however, was in keeping with the post-war British operational ideas which visualised a return to more open warfare and no longer saw the need for an effective shell-gun in tanks. In fact, the gun was regarded as no more than an adjunct to the machine-gun which was elevated to the position of the primary tank weapon. According to some contemporary views the only real need for a tank gun was to be able to fight other tanks.

A tendency to concentrate on machine-guns had already manifested itself during the First World War, when one-half of the Mark I and similar Female versions of the later heavy tanks were only armed with 5 to 6 machine-guns ; the Medium A tanks were also only armed with 5 machine-guns. The use of a multiplicity of machine-guns continued after the First World War : the Medium Mark I, in addition to its 3-pounder, had 2 Vickers and up to 4 Hotchkiss machine-guns ; the Independent had 4 Vickers in separate machine-gun turrets grouped round the main 3-pounder gun turret and the A.6, or Sixteen Tonner, had 5 Vickers machine-guns, 4 of them in 2 auxiliary turrets placed on either side of the driver's position. The practice of mounting several machine-guns, although principally a British phenomenon, also showed itself in other countries, particularly in the United States, where the M2E1 medium tank carried the record number of 9 machine-guns, including 2 mounted externally.

All such emphasis on machine-guns was usually at the expense of other weapons and had an adverse effect on the capabilities of tanks because of the limitations of the machine-gun armament. Machine-guns could be highly effective against troops caught in the open, as was shown on a few occasions by the Medium As, or in what used to be called " colonial warfare," but in other, more usual circumstances, other weapons were necessary.

The limitations imposed by the machine-gun armament applied especially to the light 2-man tanks which came into fashion in the late twenties and early thirties. In most cases these tanks were armed with nothing more than a single rifle-calibre machine-gun and their offensive power was correspondingly limited. Because of this they were only effective in auxiliary or secondary roles and powerless in the face of hostile tanks.

The inability to fight hostile tanks was more difficult to ignore than lack of shell-power and by the mid-thirties even the light tanks were provided with some type of armour-piercing weapon in addition to one or more rifle-calibre machine-guns. The weapons varied in size and performance but they were of relatively small, 12.7 to 47 mm., calibre and although the larger ones could also fire high-explosive shells they were, in the main, specialised armour-piercing weapons.

The first specialised armour-piercing weapons were developed by the Germans towards the end of the First World War in response to the Anglo-French employment of tanks. One of them, and the first to be used, was an oversize single shot rifle of conventional design which used rifle-type ammunition scaled up from 7.92 to 13 mm. The ammunition was fairly effective against the armour of contemporary tanks but the anti-tank rifle did not prove a success, mainly because of its heavy recoil. The same 13 mm. ammunition was also used in a dual-purpose, anti-tank and anti-aircraft, *Tank und Flieger*, or *T.u.F.*, heavy machine-gun whose large-scale production was beginning when the war ended. A third anti-tank weapon was the 20 mm. Becker automatic cannon, which was originally developed for aircraft but some of which were later converted to ground use. All three were the forerunners of many later weapons of their type.

Of the three categories foreshadowed by German weapons of 1918, the anti-tank rifles took the longest to come into use. It was only just before or in the early part of the Second World War that they were introduced by several armies and their service life proved to be short. They ran the gamut from 7.92 mm., such as the Polish Model 35 and the German Pz.B. 38 and 39, to the 20 mm. Japanese Type 97, the German-Swiss Rheinmetall-Solothurn S18-1000 and similar heavy anti-tank rifles used by the Italian and Swedish Armies. About the last to appear, in 1942, shortly before anti-tank rifles began to go out of use elsewhere, were Soviet 14.5 mm. anti-tank rifles, some of which were still used by North Korean troops in 1950. All had high muzzle velocities, of up to

3,600 ft. /sec., or more, and with their tungsten core shot could penetrate about 30 mm. of armour at 100 yards. But by the time they were developed their performance was only considered adequate for close defence. The only weapon of this type used in armoured vehicles was the British .55 in. (14 mm) Boys which was carried by scout carriers and several light armoured cars of the 1939–41 period.

In contrast to the anti-tank rifles, the heavy machine-guns foreshadowed by the 13 mm. *T.u.F.* were employed fairly extensively and from an early date in tanks. The *T.u.F.* itself was contemplated by the Germans for use in light tanks of the LK series. Nothing came of this but in 1930, in Britain, the somewhat similar .5 in. (12.7 mm.) Vickers machine-gun was introduced on the Lanchester armoured car and experimental models of the A.4 light tank series and was also mounted on the small Carden Loyd Mark VI carrier as a mobile anti-tank weapon. In France a 13.2 mm. Hotchkiss machine-gun was mounted in the A.M.R. model 1935 and in the United States the .5 in. Browning machine-gun, which used a cartridge copied from the *T.u.F.*, was installed in 1931 in the Christie-designed T1 Combat Car and in 1934 in the T2 Light Tank.

The half-inch Browning was the heaviest American tank weapon during the middle thirties, even on the T4 medium tank, and it continued on light tanks until 1940. The Vickers continued to be used on British tanks up to 1942, being a standard weapon of the light tanks Mark IV to Mark VIB. The Russians, too, came out with a 12.7 mm. heavy machine-gun but its use was confined to the T-40 amphibious light tank of 1941.

The different 12.7 to 13.2 mm. heavy machine-guns had roughly similar characteristics : muzzle velocities of the order of 2,800 ft. /sec. and 700 /800 grain bullets. Thus, their bullets had five or six times the punch, or kinetic energy, of rifle-calibre bullets and could penetrate about 20 mm. of armour at 100 yards. At that they were reasonably effective against the armour used in the twenties but by the late thirties they were definitely inadequate against armoured vehicles. As for other ground targets their effectiveness has always been questionable as they were more powerful than necessary against personnel and not powerful enough against anything else. Their use has continued, however, on American and to a lesser extent on Soviet tanks, although mainly as anti-aircraft weapons.

The descendants of the 20 mm. Becker automatic cannon have been fewer in the tank field although they better deserved to be employed than the half-inch machine-guns. Not only did their projectiles have more than twice the weight and twice the punch but in addition to the superior penetration of up to 40 mm. at 100 yards at normal impact they also fired shells effective against soft vehicles and other equipment.

The development of the Becker itself was transferred after 1918 from Germany to Switzerland where it led first to the Semag and then to the 20 mm. Oerlikon widely used later as an aircraft and anti-aircraft gun. In the early thirties the Oerlikon was tried in Britain as the .8 in. anti-tank gun, but nowhere does it appear to have been used in tanks, except as an anti-aircraft tank gun during the latter part of the Second World War. However, another German-sponsored Swiss gun, developed by the Rheinmetall-controlled Solothurn company, was adopted in the early thirties by the German Army as the 2 cm.KwK 30. This and its later KwK 38 version became the main armament of the Pz.Kpfw.II light tank series down to the Model L of 1942. Earlier a 20 mm. Madsen automatic cannon was used in some Swedish Landsverk light tanks, a Breda in the Italian L /6 light tank and a similar Soviet gun in the T-60 light tank of 1941.

Useful as the 20 mm. guns might have been, in the late thirties the minimum calibre considered necessary even for light tank guns was 37 mm. Guns of this calibre, originally devised by Benjamin Hotchkiss within the limit imposed by the St. Petersburg Convention of 1868 on the minimum weight of explosive projectiles, had been used for several years in French light tanks, starting with the Renault F.T. But the

37 mm. *S.A. Modèle 1918,* which was used on that tank and carried into the Renault, Hotchkiss and F.C.M. light tanks of the thirties, was short-barrelled and had a muzzle velocity of 1,270 ft./sec. What was generally specified were guns of similar calibre but twice the muzzle velocity. The French attempted to answer the need by bringing out a Model 1938 with barrel length increased from 21 to 33 calibres, but by then gun barrel lengths had crept up from the 30-odd calibres of the early thirties to well over 40 calibres and with them came even higher muzzle velocities and greater penetration. Somewhat larger-calibre tank guns were also being developed, as shown by the British 40 mm. 2-pounder, the Soviet 45 mm. tank gun, the French, Czech and Italian 47 mm. guns and the 50 mm. gun which the Germans were about to introduce.

Thus, on the eve of the Second World War, typical guns of the most common light-medium tanks of 10 to 20 tons were of 37 to 47 mm. calibre with barrels 32 to 52 calibres long and muzzle velocities of 2,000 to 2,800 ft./sec. The least powerful had five and the most powerful fifteen times the punch of the 20 mm. guns, which made it possible for them to penetrate 40 to 60 mm. of armour plate at 500 yards at normal impact. This fulfilled adequately the contemporary requirement for an armour-piercing tank weapon, just as similar characteristics fulfilled the requirements of the contemporary towed anti-tank weapons which were developed concurrently with tank guns, the one being frequently a modified version of the other. What the 37-47 mm. tank guns did not have was shell-power which would have enabled them to deal effectively with such targets as anti-tank guns. In this one respect, in fact, the average tank of 1939 was inferior to the original British and French tanks of 1916–17.

In Britain an attempt was made to remedy this situation by the development, from about 1930 onwards, of special " close support " tanks. These were standard tanks rearmed with 3.7 in. or, later, 3 in. howitzers, and they were distributed on the scale of 2 to 4 per tank company to support the 47 or 40 mm. gun tanks with smoke or high-explosive shells. They did not however, provide a satisfactory solution : they were too few and their low-powered howitzers could not provide the shell-power necessary against anti-tank guns, as was demonstrated during the Libyan campaigns of 1941 and 1942, where the lack of shell-power proved a severe handicap to British tank units.

In contrast to the British ideas which favoured machine-guns and small-calibre guns, the artillery-minded French went in for good size guns from the start. The first French tank, the Schneider, carried a shortened version of the 75 mm. field gun and the second, the St. Chamond, a normal *soixante-quinze*, 36 calibres long and with a muzzle velocity of 1,790 ft. /sec. Pursuing this line further, the French were the first to mount a gun of this size in a turret, on the 2C heavy tank, and they even fitted a short 75 mm. gun on a small number of the Renault F.T. light tanks. After the First World War the French devoted considerable attention to the light infantry-accompanying tanks but they did not lose sight of the need for a fully-fledged 75 mm. gun battle tank. Unfortunately for them, they took so long over its development that by the time the resulting B1 tank was finally produced in the mid-thirties it was obsolescent.

Others, who took up 75 mm. gun tanks after the French but proceeded more rapidly, did much better. The Germans started in 1926–28 with a secretly built medium tank which carried a turret-mounted 75 mm. gun 24 calibres long. In 1933 this was followed by the design of the multi-turret Nb.Fz. tanks, whose main turret had a similar 75 mm. gun coaxially mounted with a 37 mm. gun, and the development was brought to fruition with the Pz.Kpfw.IV medium tank designed in 1935, whose main armament consisted of the 7.5 cm. KwK (L /24). The Russians started in the early thirties with the multi-turret T-28 and T-35, which carried 76.2 mm. guns in their main turrets. By the late thirties they drew abreast of the Germans by mounting more powerful guns on the T-28, 26 calibres long instead of the original 16.5, and in 1940 jumped ahead of everybody else by going to even longer, 30.5 and then 41.5 calibres long, guns on the heavy KV and medium T-34 tanks. The United States, which made a late start in 1940 with the M3 medium tank, caught up with the Russians in 1942 with the M4, when the Germans regained a slight lead by going to longer-barrelled guns on the Pz.Kpfw. IV.

Combined with machine-guns, the 75 or 76.2 mm. guns of the Pz.Kpfw.IV, T-34 and M4 fulfilled all the main functional requirements. Hitherto, to accomplish this, it had been thought necessary to employ three types of weapons and the French B1, Soviet T-35, American M3 and the British Churchill I did, in fact, carry a shell-gun of 75 to 76.2 mm. and a smaller calibre, 37 to 47 mm., anti-tank gun as well as machine-guns. But in 1941 the 75–76.2 mm. guns, whose muzzle velocities had reached 2,000 to 2,400 ft./sec., were recognised as effective for both anti-tank and high-explosive fire.

An exception to the general trend was provided by the contemporary British policy which clung to the use of smaller-calibre guns as the primary tank weapon. Thus, in 1942 and 1943 tanks such as the Churchill, Crusader, Cavalier, Centaur and Cromwell were all armed with a 57 mm. 6-pounder which took the place of the earlier 40 mm. 2-pounder. It was only reluctantly that a " general purpose " 75 mm. gun, very similar to that already used on American medium tanks, was adopted in 1943.

In 1943, however, the 75–76.2 mm. gun formula of 1941 had already outlived its usefulness and more powerful guns were necessary to match the new tank guns which were being developed elsewhere and to defeat the thicker armour of opposing tanks. The German answer to this problem was to go to a much higher-velocity 75 mm. gun on the Panther medium tank and to an 88 mm. gun on the Tiger I heavy tank. The Russians followed quickly with an 85 mm. gun on the KV 85 heavy tank and later on the T-34/85 medium which, like the German guns, had about twice the punch of the earlier 75–76.2 mm. tank guns. On the other hand, in Britain and the United States little was done for a time to achieve comparable results, due mainly to the fallacious doctrine that tanks should not be expected to fight other tanks and that it was unnecessary, therefore, to arm them with a better armour-piercing weapon than the existing 75. The result was an inverse of the pre-war situation when tanks were being provided with adequate, for their day, armour-piercing weapons but lacked shell-power ; now they had reasonable shell-guns but thes: guns no longer had sufficient penetration.

Fortunately, more realistic views prevailed and in 1944 the standard Allied M4, or Sherman, medium tank was rearmed with the more powerful American 76 mm. gun or the British 17-pounder of the same calibre but better performance, comparable, in fact, with that of the Panther's gun. Just before the war ended the United States Army also introduced the M26 tank with a 90 mm. gun of comparable performance with the 88 mm. gun of the German Tiger I and the Soviet 85 mm. and, like the other two, based on an earlier anti-aircraft gun. However, the Russians and the Germans had already moved a stage further with the introduction, in 1944, of the 122 mm. gun on the Stalin heavy tank and of the Tiger II with a much more powerful 88. The Germans also had the Jagdtiger with a 128 mm. gun which could penetrate 200 mm. of armour at 1,000 yards at 30° of impact and which was actually the most powerful tank weapon used up to the end of the Second World War.

As far as the majority of the medium tanks was concerned, when the Second World War ended, they were armed with 75 to 85 mm. guns with muzzle velocities of between 2,600 and 3,000 ft./sec. After the war, in the late forties, the average calibre of medium tank guns increased further with the adoption of 90, 83.9 and 100 mm. guns on the American M46 Patton, British Centurion III and Soviet T-54 respectively and the lower limit of muzzle velocity rose to 2,800 ft./sec. Post-war light tanks, which had generally lagged one stage behind the mediums, also acquired more powerful guns and the American M41 and French AMX have been armed with 76 and 75 mm. guns with 3,000 ft./sec. muzzle velocities. On the other hand, the armament of the heavy tanks has stabilised itself at about 120 mm., although guns of 150, as well as 128, mm. were being considered towards the end of the Second World War for the German E.100 heavy tank, and the American T30 experimental heavy tank of the same period actually mounted a long 155 mm. gun. However, both the American M103 (T43) heavy tank produced in 1954 and the contemporary British Conqueror and the experimental French AMX have been armed with 120 mm. guns.

In fact, at about 120 mm. and muzzle velocities of the order of 3,000 ft./sec. the development of conventional tank guns and ammunition had just about reached its practical limit. Throughout its course the main object of the development had been to achieve progressively greater armour penetration. In essence, this meant achieving sufficient kinetic energy at the target to be able to penetrate the armour plate by a combination of projectile weight and velocity, kinetic energy being, of course, half the product of projectile mass and the square of its velocity.

Progressive increases in calibre from 37 to 120 mm. increased projectile weight from about 1.5 lb. to 60 lb., but the larger calibre also meant a larger diameter hole and more work to be done in penetrating a given thickness of armour, so that the performance increased in proportion to the calibre of the projectile rather than its weight, which increased as the cube of the calibre. At the same time, as the calibre increased so did the weight of the tank gun, which is roughly one hundred times the weight of the projectile. Thus, the German 128 mm. gun of 1945 weighed 7,380 lb., which is about as much as some of the earlier tanks did complete. Only heavy vehicles could carry such guns and withstand their recoil loads, even when muzzle brakes came into use, as they did from 1942 onwards.

Increasing muzzle velocity, which rose from less than 2,000 ft./sec. to 3,000, brought somewhat better returns initially but rapidly approached its limit at the latter figure. Higher muzzle velocities necessitate disproportionate increases in gun

[*continued on page 314*

Table of Tank Guns
Arranged in chronological order by countries

Gun	Calibre (mm.)	Length (calibres)	Muzzle Velocity (ft./sec.)	Mounted in
British				
6-pounder (naval)	57	40	—	Mark I of 1916
6-pounder	57	23	1,350	Mark IV and V of 1917–18
3-pounder	47	—	1,750	Vickers Mediums
2-pounder	40	52	2,650	Light, cruiser and infantry tanks of 1938–42
6-pounder	57	45	2,675–2,800	Crusader III
6-pounder	57	52	2,950	Churchill III
75 mm.	75	40	2,050	Churchill VII, Cromwell IV
17-pounder	76.2	—	2,950–3,950 APDS	Sherman Firefly, Centurion I
77 mm.	76.2	—	2,575	Comet
32-pounder	94	—	3,050	Tortoise
20-pounder	83.9	—	—	Centurion III
French				
75 mm. *raccourci*	75	—	656	Schneider of 1916
75 mm. M1897	75	36	1,788	St. Chamond
37 mm. M1918	37	21	1,273	Renault F.T., R-35, F.C.M., H-35
75 mm.	75	17.1	—	B-1
47 mm. M1935	47	34	2,200	S-35, B-1
37 mm. M1938	37	33	2,300	H-39, R-40
75 mm.	75	—	1,970	E.B.R.
75 mm.	75	—	3,280 app.	AMX 13
100 mm.	100	—	3,280 app.	AMX 50 early model
120 mm.	120	—	3,280 app.	AMX 50 late model

United States

37 mm. M1916	37	—	1,204	M1917 light tank
37 mm. M6	37	53	2,900	M3–M5 light tanks
75 mm. M2	75	31	1,850	M3 medium
75 mm. M3	75	40	2,050	M4 medium
3 in. T12	76.2	50	2,600	M6 heavy
75 mm. M6	75	40	2,030	M24 light
76 mm. M1A2	76	53	2,600	M4A3E8 medium
90 mm. M3A2	90	53	2,800–3,350 APCR	M26 and M46 medium
76 mm. T91E3	76	—	3,000	M41 light
90 mm. M41	90	—	—	M48 medium
120 mm. T123	120	—	—	M103 heavy

German

3.7 cm. L/45	37	45	2,445	early Pz.Kpfw.III
7.5 cm. L/24	75	24	1,263	early Pz.Kpfw.IV
5 cm. L/42	50	42	2,247–3,444 APCR	Pz.Kpfw.III E to H
5 cm. L/60	50	60	2,700–3,930 APCR	late Pz.Kpfw.III
7.5 cm. L/48	75	48	2,461	late Pz.Kpfw.IV
8.8 cm. L/56	88	56	2,657	Tiger I
7.5 cm. L/70	75	70	3,068	Panther
8.8 cm. L/71	88	71	3,340–3,708 APCR	Tiger II
12.8 cm. L/55	128	55	3,020	Jagdtiger

Russian

37 mm.	37	—	2,500	early B.T.
45 mm.	45	46	2,490–2,740	B.T. and T-26
76.2 mm.	76.2	16.5	—	T-35, early T-28
76.2 mm.	76.2	26	—	late T-28
76.2 mm. M1938/39	76.2	30.5	—	early T-34
76.2 mm. M1940	76.2	41.5	2,172	T-34 and K.V.
85 mm. M1944	85	53	2,600	T-34/85
122 mm.	122	45	—	Stalin
100 mm.	100	—	—	T-54

barrel length, chamber pressure and weight of the propellant charge, while barrel life decreases rapidly as muzzle velocity increases. Once this limit was reached with any given tank gun the only way to obtain increased armour penetration was either to increase the gun calibre or else to depart from orthodox designs, particularly in ammunition.

The way was actually opened before the conventional guns approached the limits of calibre and muzzle velocity or even before the conventional ammunition reached the degree of refinement common to naval guns. That is, before the projectiles of tank guns acquired armour-piercing caps to

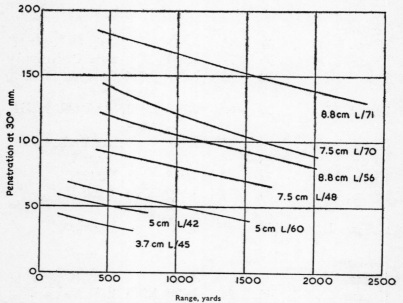

FIG. 3. Armour penetration achieved by a number of German tank guns of the Second World War using standard armour-piercing ammunition against armour plate inclined at 30° to the vertical.

assist penetration and ballistic caps to reduce air resistance. The latter, or APCBC, type of ammunition began to come into use in 1942, but a year earlier the Germans had already introduced, in their standard 37 and 50 mm. guns, a new type of armour-piercing shot. This was of composite construction and consisted of a hard tungsten carbide core in a soft light-metal jacket. As it was lighter than the conventional projectile fired from the same gun, the composite shot could attain a higher muzzle velocity and it made penetration easier, as the latter was confined to the smaller diameter of the sub-calibre hard core. The disadvantage of this type of shot was its cost and its rapid loss of velocity and performance with range, due to the fact that it was lighter than the normal AP projectile and yet retained the same frontal area. Nevertheless, this type of composite rigid or high-velocity armour-piercing shot (APCR or HVAP) was used with some success by the Germans in 1941 and their example was followed by the Russians, who started using similar ammunition in 1942. In 1944 high-velocity tungsten core ammunition was also introduced on American 76 and 90 mm. guns and has been used in them since.

To achieve still higher muzzle velocities, several countries had begun work before the Second World War on weapons with tapered or cone bores, originated in Germany by Gerlich. In 1941 the Germans introduced the first anti-tank weapon of this type, with 28 mm. at the commencement of rifling and 20 mm. at the muzzle, which fired a tungsten core shot with a muzzle velocity of about 4,600 ft. /sec. Two larger, 42 /30 and 75 /55 mm., cone bore anti-tank guns were also introduced at about the same time, but because of a shortage of tungsten the use of all three was limited and none was applied to tanks. In fact, the only tank application of the cone bore was on the British airborne Tetrarch light tank of 1944, which had a " Littlejohn conversion " muzzle squeeze attachment fitted to the 40 mm. 2-pounder. In general, this type of equipment produced the desired high velocity but, apart from high production costs and short barrel life, it also had the serious drawback of less effective high-explosive ammunition.

A more practical type of very high-velocity armour-piercing ammunition which could, moreover, be fired from conventional parallel bore tank guns was the APDS, or discarding sabot, type. This was, in a way, a logical development of the light tungsten-core ammunition which discarded its envelope or jacket after leaving the muzzle and thus reduced the air resistance of the armour-piercing sub-calibre core in proportion to its cross-sectional area. In consequence, the velocity and penetration of the APDS type fall off less rapidly with range than those of the APCR or HVAP.

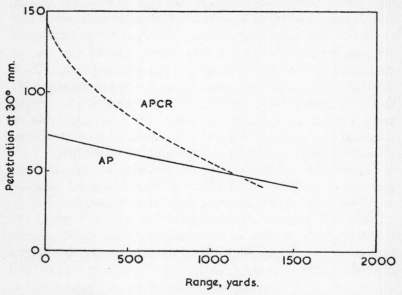

FIG. 4. Comparison of the armour-piercing performance of the German 5 cm. KwK 39 L/60 gun using standard armour-piercing ammunition (AP) and high-velocity composite rigid shot (APCR).

The discarding sabot type of ammunition was introduced in 1944 in the British 57 mm. 6-pounder gun of the Churchill infantry tanks and improved penetration at up to 2,000 yards by 30 to 50 per cent. over that of the APCBC projectile from the same gun. Up to the end of the Second World War its use was still limited but it has increased since.

Yet another type of high-velocity sub-calibre ammunition was being worked on in Germany when the Second World War ended. It was fin-stabilised and fired from smooth bore guns but so far this type has not appeared in service. Instead, smooth bore guns have been applied to an entirely different type of armour-piercing ammunition. This is the shaped, or hollow, charge ammunition which does not rely on the kinetic energy of the projectile but on the focused blast energy of its explosive content. To be more precise, the shaped charge, or HEAT, ammunition functions by virtue of the fact that on

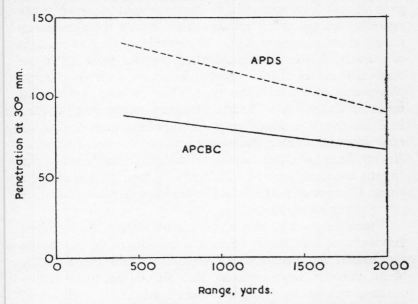

FIG. 5. Comparison of the armour-piercing performance of the 57 mm. 6-pounder using standard armour-piercing ammunition and high-velocity discarding sabot shot (APDS).

detonation the thin metal liner of the conical cavity in the nose of the projectile forms a long thin jet travelling at very high velocities, of up to 30,000 ft./sec. and that the impact of this high velocity jet produces extremely high pressures which perforate the armour plate.

The first tank use of shaped charge shells appears to have been with the German Pz.Kpfw.IV and *Sturmgeschütz* in 1942, but since then similar ammunition has been developed for many other guns. The shaped charge principle was also applied at an early date to anti-tank rifle grenades, such as the British No. 68 grenade, the British PIAT anti-tank spigot

mortar of 1943 and the German *Panzerfaust* recoilless anti-
tank grenade discharger of 1944. The latter, with a 7 lb.
6-in. diameter projectile was able to penetrate as much as
200 mm. of armour at normal impact.

Of the different applications, the use with conventional
guns was the least successful because the spin imparted to the
projectile by the rifling reduces considerably the penetrating
ability of the shaped charge. Nevertheless, other advantages
of spin-stabilisation and established practice have led to the
continued use of shaped charge projectiles with rifled guns,
particularly of the recoilless type. The Germans introduced
the latter in 1941 as a 75 mm. airborne infantry gun but they
later developed a whole range of recoilless guns and at an
early stage considered their application to armoured vehicles.
Among the possibilities considered were the installation of two
75 mm. recoilless guns on a Pz.Kpfw.IV type of tank and of a
single 105 mm. gun on a light armoured carrier, both of which
got to the mock-up stage.

From the point of view of vehicle installation the recoilless
gun is almost ideal, for it is light and imposes no firing loads on
the chassis. In consequence, it has made possible the mounting
of an effective high-explosive and shaped charge armour-
piercing weapon on the lightest armoured vehicle. However,
the development of light armoured vehicles with recoilless guns
was slow and it was only in the mid-fifties that a few such
vehicles appeared : the French *Even*, the Japanese SS-I and II
with twin 105 mm. guns and the American Ontos with six
106 mm. guns adopted in 1956 by the United States Marine
Corps as its anti-tank vehicle.

The slowness was surprising in view of the need for light-
weight armoured vehicles, particularly in airborne operations,
and of the equal need to make recoilless guns more mobile
because of their conspicuous back-blast which gives away their
position and makes it essential for them to change their position
quickly and frequently. Apart from the back-blast, the main
disadvantage of recoilless guns is the fact that they require
three to five times as much propellant as conventional guns of

similar ballistic performance. The additional propellant is necessary to produce the rearward thrust which balances the forward thrust on the projectile, but it also makes recoilless gun ammunition bulky and heavy.

Because of the drawbacks of recoilless guns the Germans had by 1945 already developed another type of weapon for use with shaped charge ammunition. Logically they went to fin-stabilised projectiles fired from smooth bore guns and evolved the 8 cm. PAW 600, which answered to these characteristics. In addition, its design employed a perforated throttling plate interposed between the propellant case and the projectile which reduced the peak loads on the projectile and the gun. The shaped charge projectiles of this original anti-tank gun were stable and accurate at up to 700 yards and could penetrate 140 mm. of armour at normal impact. The gun had undergone successful troop trials towards the end of the Second World War and a larger-calibre version was contemplated for use on the light Panzerjäger 38t. However, it was only in 1955 that a weapon of this type actually appeared on an armoured vehicle—the Swiss 4-wheeled Mowag tank destroyer.

The next logical step would have been to extend the range and accuracy of the fin-stabilised projectiles by rocket assistance or to go to rockets fired from closed-breech launchers. But, so far, neither type has appeared in service, in spite of the extensive use of shaped charge rockets with such short-range infantry anti-tank weapons as the original 2.36 in. American "bazooka" of 1942, the 8.8 cm. German *Raketen-panzerbüchse*, the American 3.5 in. rocket launcher and others.

Instead, the next and latest armour-piercing weapon to come into the picture is the short-range surface-to-surface guided missile. This, in its anti-tank form, is essentially a rocket with a shaped charge warhead which can be controlled in flight to achieve a high degree of accuracy.

Its development began towards the end of the Second World War in Germany, which seized the initiative in the field of guided missiles. Among its many missile projects was the X-7, a wire-controlled slow-speed anti-tank missile, work on which began in 1944 and which was about to go into production when Germany surrendered in 1945. This put an end to further development in Germany but in 1946 the X-7 type was taken up in France and evolved into the S.S.10 which in the early fifties became the first operational anti-tank guided missile. Apart from the French Army, the S.S.10 has also been supplied to the United States, Sweden and the Federal German Republic and to the Israeli Army, which successfully used a few against Soviet-built Egyptian tanks during the 1956 Sinai campaign.

By then several other countries were also developing similar missiles of their own, ranging from the small British Vickers-Armstrongs Type 891, with a body diameter of 4.5 in. and a firing weight of about 35 lb. to the large American SSM-A-23 Dart, with a body diameter of 8 in. and a firing weight of 98 lb.

Missile launchers, like recoilless guns, impose no firing loads and can be installed in the lightest armoured vehicles. The main disadvantage of the anti-tank guided missiles, apart from complexity and cost, is their bulk, for even the small Vickers 891 has a span of 11 in. over its aerodynamic lift and control surfaces and the Dart as much as 40 in. The installation of several guided missiles in a vehicle is consequently difficult. But, otherwise, they open the possibility of light highly mobile tanks able to attack the most heavily armoured hostile vehicles and to that extent promise to solve the problem of an adequate armour-piercing weapon which does not impose unduly upon the vehicle which serves as its carrier. The S.S.10 can penetrate 400 mm. of armour at normal impact and the larger missiles can do even better.

Other probable targets remain to be dealt with by other means, however. For the moment, at any rate, it is unlikely that the guided missile will be used as a general purpose high-explosive carrier, while the machine-gun seems likely to remain as the main anti-personnel weapon. Thus, the future of effective tank armament appears to lie more than ever in a combination of weapons which will provide the necessary ability to attack the main types of battlefield targets.

25

Vehicle Components

Since the tank is essentially a weapon carrier, logically it should be designed around its armament. In general, however, tank design has not been governed by armament alone but also by the armour protection specified concurrently with armament. Indeed, in many cases, particularly when tanks were regarded as " mobile pill-boxes " or " perambulating fortresses," armour took precedence over armament.

To some extent, armour protection and armament are interrelated for, under some conditions, the one can compensate for the other. For instance, greater protection may enable the tank to approach some targets more closely and make do with somewhat less powerful armament. Conversely, the more effective the fire power of the tank the less it needs rely on its protection. In general, however, the amount of protective armour carried by tanks stems from requirements which are not directly related to their armament.

Basically, the amount of armour which any given model carries is a function of the weapons likely to be used against it and of the degree of protection against them which is desired, or deemed practicable. The weapons range from small arms to large calibre high-velocity guns and shaped-charge missiles ; the degree of protection has varied no less, from attempts at almost complete immunity to much more modest and realistic aims.

The majority of the early tanks were satisfied with protection against bullets and shell fragments and this is still the criterion for the armouring of many self-propelled guns, personnel carriers and reconnaissance vehicles which content themselves with plates 6 to 15 mm. thick. Tanks, on the other hand, have steadily thickened their armour in attempts to

secure immunity from the increasing number and power of
tank and anti-tank weapons. A common aim has been to have
sufficient armour to make the front of the tank immune to the
armament of a similar hostile tank, and to the concurrent types
of anti-tank guns, at 1,000 to 500 yards. As a result, by the
outbreak of the Second World War the frontal armour had
risen to 20–30 mm. on the average light-medium tank and
60–75 mm. on the French and British infantry tanks. By the
end of the war the maximum frontal thickness on several
medium tanks exceeded 100 mm. and on the German Jagdtiger
it reached 250 mm., but even this was improved upon by the
American T28 experimental heavy tank which carried the
record thickness of 12 inches or 304 mm.

Armour of such great thickness afforded a high degree of
protection but its weight imposed severe handicaps. Since
armour weighs .283 lb. /c.in., a square foot even of half an inch
(12.7 mm.) plate weighs 20 lb. while the 250 mm. frontal plate
of the Jagdtiger weighed about 400 lb. per square foot. Such
weight limits the armour which can be carried even by heavy
vehicles and offers every inducement to the most effective use
of the least amount rather than increasing it, and with it the
weight of the whole vehicle.

One method of making the most of the armour used, which
has been practised almost from the start, is to distribute it
unevenly according to the probable directions of attack. Thus,
the front of most tanks, where they are most likely to be attacked,
has been given the most effective protection, while the top of
the hull is usually made of the thinnest armour. Another
method is to slope the armour away from the vertical. This
increases its effectiveness against high-velocity projectiles, at
first in direct proportion to the increased horizontal thickness
of metal which the projectile has to penetrate and then more
rapidly because of the uneven stresses set up in a projectile
when it strikes a plate at an angle : with a slope of about 50° to
the vertical the plate is approximately twice as effective against
horizontal attack as a vertical plate which offers the same thickness in the horizontal direction.

The use of sloped armour only came into prominence during the Second World War, particularly with the appearance of the Soviet T-34 medium tank with a one-piece sloping glacis plate, but its advantages were known and to a limited extent employed earlier. It was introduced on a few vehicles, such as Christie's experimental models and a Krupp armoured car, in the late twenties at about the same time as welded construction, which gave greater freedom in the arrangement of plates than the earlier method it began to replace. Hitherto, the accepted method had been to bolt or rivet armour plates on to a frame, and this heavier, less efficient, construction survived on American tanks down to the M3 medium of 1941 and on British tanks to the Cromwell of 1943. The Germans and the Russians, however, had already adopted welded construction in the early thirties. The French, on the other hand, had by then successfully evolved the technique of making large castings, and with the D-1 of 1931 introduced into service the first tank with a cast turret.

Cast armour, though slightly inferior ballistically to rolled armour plate, gave particular scope for improving resistance to penetration by suitable shapes. Castings were applied with particular success on the Stalin tanks of 1944 and the experimental British Valiant of the same period in the form of hull fronts with double curvature, which meant that frontal attack against them was at large composite angles. The construction was improved upon further on the later Stalins and on the American ellipsoidal one-piece cast hull introduced on the experimental T42 medium tank and adopted, after thickening up, on the M48 medium and the M103 heavy tanks. However, the production of such large hull castings is apt to tax industrial resources and the general trend has been to limit large castings to turrets where, in addition, welded construction out of rolled plate is more difficult to apply than to hulls.

Another mode of application of the armour is in the form of spaced plates, which were originally a by-product of attempts to give some protection to the suspension components.

Against high-velocity shot spaced armour has proved less effective than a single plate of the same thickness, and the space in between creates high-explosive pockets. But the use of a second, relatively thin, external armour plate has become much more attractive since the introduction of shaped-charge ammunition, as a means of setting off shaped charges as far away as possible from the main armour plates and thus decreasing their powers of penetration. To this end the Germans first fitted thin mild steel plates, or wire mesh, round the turret and to the sides of the later Pz.Kpfw.IV tanks. Skirting plates have been used also on the British Centurion tank, the particular attention given to side protection being based on the theory that infantry rocket launchers, against which the skirting has been principally intended, are likely to be most dangerous when in ambush to the sides of the tank.

If the widespread employment of shaped-charge ammunition makes more attractive the use of spaced armour, which is relatively inefficient against other forms of attack, it is unlikely on the other hand to have much effect on the quality of the armour plate. In fact, mild steel is almost as effective against it as highly alloyed armour plate. But effective protection against high-velocity projectiles still demands high quality steels which are both tough and ductile. The two qualities are to some extent, opposed to each other and armour which has been hardened right through to achieve the desired toughness is apt to lose its ductility and crack under impact. In consequence, softer machineable quality armour with a Brinell hardness number of about 400 to 500 is commonly used as the best all-round solution, although occasionally it is hardened on its outside surface to about 700 Brinell. Such face-hardened armour is intended to cause shot break-up, but piercing caps fitted to armour-piercing shot spall away the hard layer and enable the uncapped shot to attack the softer armour underneath. In general, therefore, protection is sought mainly in the thickness and arrangement of homogeneous machineable quality armour.

Apart from its thickness and arrangement, or disposition,

the total amount of armour which a vehicle carries depends, of course, on the space which it has to envelop. In fact, the internal space of a tank determines directly the least amount of armour which it might carry and which is equal to the envelope of the thinnest useable armour, required for protection against bullets and shell fragments. The upper limit is indefinite and as the total weight of the vehicle increases so does the size and weight of its various components. In practice, however, the range of possibilities is such that for a given type of armament and performance the heavily armoured vehicle will weigh about three times as much as the lightest.

In general, armour accounts for about half of the total weight of a tank and not only provides a protective envelope but also a framework or structure within which to mount the armament and such other components as the power plant, transmission and running gear. Were one to ignore the protective function of the armour shell and confine it to structural duties its weight would still amount to something like 20 per cent. of the total weight of the lighter vehicle. The contribution of the other components to the total weight of typical tanks is indicated in the table of weight distribution and except for the external running gear, the space requirements of these various components and crew add up to the total space which the armour has to envelop.

As far as crew space is concerned, the functional division of duties results in the crew being accommodated in separate fighting and driver's compartments, as in the case of most vehicles where the fighting compartment is surmounted by a revolving turret. In the case of turretless vehicles, however, the whole crew may be accommodated in a single compartment whose height need be no more than 40 inches, the minimum necessary to accommodate the average man sitting on the lowest possible seat with his legs almost horizontal. This low height means a low vehicle silhouette, which is difficult to aim at and hit since the necessary accuracy in elevation of hostile guns is the most difficult to attain, and gives turretless vehicles a significant advantage over turreted types. In the latter the turret requires its occupants to sit in a more upright position and this increases the minimum height of the vehicle by at least 15 inches.

Table of Tank Weight Distribution

Component	Typical component weights per cent. of total weight	Range of component weights per cent. of total weight
Armament and mountings	5	2 – 6
Ammunition and racks	5	2 – 6
Crew and Stowage	5	3 – 10
Electrical and radio equipment	1	$\frac{1}{2}$ – $1\frac{1}{2}$
Power plant	4	2 – 10
Fuel and tanks	3	2 – 4
Transmission	7	6 – 12
Suspension	15	10 – 16
Tracks	8	7 – 12
Hull and turret armour	47	30 – 60
Total	100	–

Against the advantages of lower silhouette, simpler construction and the possibility of somewhat better utilisation of the armour, turretless vehicles suffer from the serious disadvantages that their armament has limited traverse. This means that beyond narrow limits the whole vehicle must be turned to train its weapons on target and on the move turretless vehicles can only engage targets to their immediate front, so that, in general, they take longer to aim.

Because of the serious disadvantages of turretless vehicles, the majority of tanks, from the Renault F.T. onwards, have had rotating turrets which permit 360° traverse of the armament with respect to the rest of the vehicle. The size of the turrets has grown steadily in parallel with the size of the armament mounted in them and the number of personnel necessary to operate the weapons. Thus, a rifle-calibre machine-gun operated by a single man can be accommodated in a turret with an inside ring diameter of about 30 in. but a 37 or 47 mm. gun with coaxial machine-gun and a 2-man crew requires a minimum diameter of about 45 in. ; a 75 mm. gun and a 3-man crew about 60 in. and the contemporary 83.9 to 90 mm. guns about 70 in. Even this does not represent the limit, for the turret which was being developed for the German Maus and E.100 super-heavy tanks had an inside ring diameter of over 100 in.

The turret ring diameter in turn determines the minimum width of the vehicle and, on account of steering requirements, also the length. Conversely, limits imposed on overall width of the vehicle limit the size of the turret and the armament which a conventional turreted type can carry. Such overall width limits have been commonly imposed, in fact, mainly from the point of the established dimensions of railway equipment which they were expected to use, and they have, to some extent, hampered the development of tanks, although not as much, perhaps, as has sometimes been claimed. For instance, on the eve of the Second World War the Germans allowed themselves 9 ft. 7 in. but British tanks were being designed to a width of limit of 8 ft. 9 in. During the war the limits were relaxed and the British Centurion and American M46 introduced since the Second World War have overall widths of 11 ft. 1 in. and 11 ft. 6 in., respectively, while the Conqueror and M103 120 mm. heavy gun tanks have 13 ft. and 12 ft. 2 in. On the other hand, the Soviet Stalin was still limited by the Russian railway gauge to 10 ft. 3 in., although this did not prevent the mounting in it of a 122 mm. gun.

In the majority of cases turret armament of a gun and a machine-gun has been combined in a single mounting. The first combination mount appears to have been used on the American Medium A experimental tank of 1921 but it was generally adopted only in the early thirties. Until then turret machine-guns were usually mounted independently of the gun and even after the adoption of coaxial mountings additional, separately mounted, machine-guns continued to be fitted. A common location was in the rear turret plate, as on the French White armoured car of 1918, several Japanese tanks of the thirties, and the Soviet T-26B, KV and the early Stalin tanks. Another method, confined almost entirely to American tanks, has been to mount the additional machine-gun in a cupola or small turret on top of the main turret. It was introduced on the original 1919 Christie experimental tank and used on such later models as the M3 medium of 1941–42 and the recent M48A2, but it suffers from the disadvantage that the tank commander, who mans the cupola, is apt to become preoccupied with the machine-gun to the detriment of his more important command functions.

Additional machine-guns have also been mounted in the sides of the high superstructures of such tanks as the British Vickers Medium of the twenties and the American T5 medium of the thirties, and in small machine-gun turrets placed below the level of the main turret, as on the British Independent which had as many as four of them, the German Nb.Fz., the Soviet T-35 and T-28, as well as several later British tanks down to the Crusader I and the Canadian Ram I of 1941, both of which still had an auxiliary, machine-gun turret alongside the driver's position. The latter has been by far the most common location for additional machine-guns, and occasionally other weapons, but in almost all other cases the weapon was mounted directly in the superstructure or hull front plate. From the mid-thirties until recently there were, in fact, more tanks with this feature than without it. However, since the Second World War the view has rightly prevailed that the additional machine-gun did not justify the space required by the forward machine-gunner—although the machine-gun itself might have been retained under driver's control for close-in defence.

The elimination of the forward or hull machine-gunner reduced the average tank crew from 5, common in the latter part of the Second World War, to 4 and with it the total space required by the crew. This was all the more important in view of the increasing size of ammunition, which has had to be reduced steadily in number. Up to the early stages of the Second World War, in the days of 37 to 47 mm. tank guns, most tanks carried over 100 rounds of gun ammunition, but by the end of the war, with the adoption of larger-calibre high-velocity guns, 60 to 80 rounds became common and on such heavy gun vehicles as the Jagdtiger and the Stalin the number came down to 38 and 25 respectively. Over the years the amount of machine-gun ammunition has also shown a tendency to decrease and no tank has improved on the British Mark I Female of 1916 which carried no less than 31,232 rounds ; on the majority of tanks the number of machine-gun rounds has fluctuated between 2,000 and 5,000.

To some extent, the reduced number of rounds has been compensated by improved means of observation and fire control. These have advanced from the primitive methods of sighting through open slits, still used in the early thirties on light tanks, to periscopes, commanders' cupolas with several episcopes and optical range-finders. The latter were being developed for the German Panther at the end of the Second World War and were put into service for the first time on the American M47 medium tank using the turret and fire control system developed originally for the T42 medium. Similarly, internal and external means of communication have greatly improved. In the First World War, for instance, the use of radio was confined to a few British and French command tanks. The value of a more extensive use of radios was demonstrated in the British experiments of the early thirties but in 1939 the great majority of tanks was still without them. In the latter part of the Second World War radios were finally recognised as an essential part of tank equipment, but Soviet and Japanese tanks usually still lacked them.

All the development in armament and other equipment progressively changed the size and contents of the fighting compartment of tanks. But, on the whole, it had little effect on the latter's position in relation to the rest of the vehicle. That is, from the Renault F.T. onwards the layout of most tanks has placed the driver's compartment forward, the fighting compartment in the middle and the engine at the rear. A few of the early tanks, such as the British Medium A, German LK and the American T1 light tank, had the engine at the front, ahead of the driver, but this interfered with the latter's field of view unless he was placed high up, as has been done on the American T97, T98, T99 and T108 self-propelled guns where this practice has been revived recently. A somewhat similar but much more attractive solution, where engine size allows it, is to place the driver's and engine compartments alongside each other. This leaves the rear half of the body clear for the fighting compartment and can produce a compact vehicle, as shown by the French AMX light tank, although this particular disposition of units can be traced back through the British Mark VI light tanks to the Vickers Medium Mark I. The location of the driver and the engine at the front also provides an attractive proposition for self-propelled guns and armoured personnel carriers, as it allows a maximum of unobstructed body space and good access from the rear. Yet another layout was used on the German Maus and the proposed Löwe heavy tanks which had the driver at the front, the engine in the middle and the fighting compartment at the rear. With turreted vehicles this layout offers no advantage over the conventional rear engine location but it is suitable for limited traverse vehicles and has been used with several self-propelled guns.

If for most vehicles the location of the engine is thus predetermined its size is not, for it depends on the weight of the vehicle and the desired power to weight ratio, as well as its output per unit of engine capacity. In turn, the engine affects to some extent the total weight of the vehicle both by its own weight and, even more, by the weight of the armour needed around it. In theory, therefore, engine size can only be determined by a process of successive approximations but in practice it is more often decided by the availability of particular types, as described in the next chapter which deals specifically with the development of tank engines.

As far as the general relationship between the vehicle and

the engine is concerned, power to weight ratios have increased steadily from a mere 3.7 b.h.p. per ton of the early British tanks. At present more than 10 b.h.p. per ton is considered essential and 12 to 16 is commonly met, while a few tanks have attained or exceeded 20. Increasing power to weight ratios imply the possibility of higher maximum speeds since the forces resisting motion, or rolling resistance, are roughly proportional to weight : the ratio of rolling resistance to weight of tanks is of the order of .05 on hard ground and .1 on soft ground. However, high engine horsepowers are now sought less to give high maximum speeds than to provide an excess of power for acceleration and greater overall agility.

The possibility of a substantial increase in maximum speed above the 4 to 8 m.p.h. of the tanks of the First World War was demonstrated quite early, by the Light Infantry Tank, designed in Britain by Colonel Johnson, which attained 30 m.p.h. during its 1921 trials. Ten years later maximum speeds of 20 to 30 m.p.h. were becoming common and to this day most tanks fall within this bracket. Some of Christie's later vehicles and their Soviet and British derivatives could do 40 m.p.h. or more on hard level ground, but during the Second World War French and British infantry tanks still could do no better than 10 to 15 m.p.h. Better results were desirable even then but moderate road speeds do not, necessarily, mean a correspondingly low overall performance and, in particular, a low cross-country speed. Even with a high power to weight ratio, which is a better criterion of overall performance than maximum road speed, cross-country speed may be relatively low—limited by the suspension and ride characteristics of the vehicle.

The full utilisation of the available engine power depends to a large extent on the transmission, which must provide a sufficient range of torque multiplication to meet the requirements of rapid acceleration and climbing ability. The maximum slope which tanks are generally expected to ascend is one of 30° to 35°, or a 60 per cent. grade. Some of the earlier tanks were designed to climb slopes of as much as 45°

but the actual ascent of such steep slopes has always been limited to favourable surface conditions.

The majority of tank transmissions has been of the conventional mechanical type with 4 to 8 forward speeds and one or more reverse gears. In this category gearboxes with 5 forward speeds provide a reasonable compromise between a sufficient number of gear ratios and complexity. As an alternative to mechanical transmissions electrical transmissions have been used on a number of vehicles, starting with the French St. Chamond of 1917. They have also been used in the American T23 medium tank of 1943 and heavy tanks, such as the French 2C of 1918, the British TOG and German Maus and Ferdinand of the Second World War, for which they could be developed more rapidly from standard-type generators and motors than suitable mechanical transmissions. By comparison with the latter, however, they have been heavier and less efficient, although easier to control and readily applicable to the steering of tracked vehicles.

Another type, which appeared as attractive but proved even less efficient than the electrical transmission, was the hydrostatic transmission, with a positive displacement pump coupled to the engine and a similar hydraulic motor in the final drive to each track. A Williams Janney transmission of this type was first tried in 1917 in an experimental version of the British Mark IV heavy tank and was subsequently applied to the Mark VII of which 3 were built in 1918. The application was suggested by previous successful use of hydrostatic transmissions in warships but what was not realised was the difference between the application of the relatively inefficient apparatus to the intermittent low-power auxiliary naval drives and to driving tanks. Once the transmission was installed in a tank the inefficiency made itself obvious by the heat it generated but the discouraging results, or, much more likely, ignorance of what was going on elsewhere, did not deter the designers of the first Vickers tank of 1921 from trying again. However, hydraulic component efficiencies being what they were, the transmission overheated badly on trials and the tank itself was abandoned.

Another type of transmission unit which had also been used in the marine field well before the appearance of tanks was the hydro-kinetic torque converter. Its first armoured vehicle application was in the form of the Voith *Turbo-Getriebe* installed in the Austro-Daimler ADGZ 8-wheeled armoured car built in 1934. Seven years later, in 1941, a hydro-kinetic torque converter was applied to the American M6 heavy tank and by the end of the Second World War it was also incorporated in the transmissions of the M18 tank destroyer and the M26 heavy tank. Since then, hydro-kinetic torque converters have been applied in the transmissions of the post-war American tanks and several other tracked vehicles, their lower efficiency being accepted for the sake of ease of control and smoother drive.

Closely connected with the various devices for multiplying engine torque and frequently combined with them in one unit are mechanisms for steering the tank. The principle of steering tanks, whose tracks are virtually rigid in the lateral direction, is to slew or skid the tracks round over the surface of the ground by the application of unequal forces to each. The necessary difference in the forces applied to each track has been accomplished in a number of ways, the most elementary being to provide a separate engine to drive each track. Such a twin-engine system was actually used in the British Medium A, German A7V and the American Ford 3-ton tank of the First World War but the method is basically unsound, as well as troublesome, for it makes no attempt to obtain the difference in track forces required for steering by transfer from one track to the other and can put no more than one-half of the total available horsepower into one track.

The clutch-and-brake system which tanks inherited from the Holt tractor was simpler and better in that it directed the whole of the available propulsive effort to the outer track when a turn was desired by disengaging or declutching the inner track and then slowing it down further by the application of a brake. This system, introduced with the French Schneider and Renault F.T., was used extensively during the twenties and thirties on light tanks and also on several heavier vehicles where it was far less successful because of the high power absorption in the steering brakes. The Russians applied it to vehicles as heavy as the KV, as well as the T-34 series and the earlier T-28 and T-35, but it proved troublesome and was probably the least satisfactory feature of those tanks.

A logical development of the clutch-and-brake system was the replacement of the on-or-off clutch in the drive to each track by a multi-speed gearbox. With this arrangement steering was effected by engaging a lower gear on one side and thus producing a difference between the speeds of the 2 tracks less extreme than with the clutch-and-brake system. Moreover, with geared steering, power generated at the inner track, instead of being dissipated in a brake, is transferred to the outer track and helps to bring it round. Geared steering is, therefore, regenerative and can be very efficient but, like the clutch-and-brake system, it is discontinuous for there is an undesirable interruption of the drive whenever a gear is changed. Supplementary track brakes are also necessary with it to provide tight skid turns.

What amounted to a provision for geared steering was incorporated in the British Mark I to IV tanks of 1916–17, which had a two-speed sliding-mesh secondary gearbox in the drive to each track. However, the normal method of steering these tanks was to lock out the differential, put the gearbox on one side into neutral and apply the track brake. This amounted to clutch-and-brake steering, and each set of gears and brake was operated by a man stationed on either side of the tank on signal from the driver.

For the Mark V its principal designer, Major W. G. Wilson, devised a much simpler, driver-operated, epicyclic clutch-and-brake system in which an epicyclic gear train performed the function of an on-or-off steering clutch. Similar more refined epicyclic clutch-and-brake systems were later used on many other vehicles, including the German Pz.Kpfw.

III and IV, and Italian and Japanese medium tanks of the Second World War. But a more advanced system had been introduced already in 1918 on the large Anglo-American Mark VIII : this tank incorporated a 2-speed epicyclic gearbox in the drive to each track and consequently possessed the first practical system of geared steering.

After a lapse of several years an improved Wilson epicyclic stepdown gear was applied to one of the Sixteen Tonners, the A.6 E.3 of 1931, and the A.14 experimental heavy cruiser of 1939, but it did not come into regular use in British tanks until the production of the Covenanter and Crusader cruiser tanks of 1940–41. Wilson-designed epicyclic steering, very similar to that of the Crusader, was also used in the Czech L.T.H., or Pz.Kpfw.38t, tank which the Germans employed extensively during the Second World War. But in Britain Wilson's epicyclic stepdown geared system was abandoned, after the 1942 Cavalier experimental cruiser tank, in favour of a controlled differential transmission.

The simplest and oldest type of differential steering system consists of a conventional differential with brakes added to the half-shafts. When one of the brakes is applied it slows down the track on its side and speeds up the other. Unlike the clutch-and-brake or geared system it is continuous, but like the former it is non-regenerative and the energy dissipation in the brake is very high. The disadvantages of the braked differential outweigh, in fact, its simplicity, and because of its inefficiency its application was confined to a number of very light vehicles of the late twenties and the thirties, such as the Carden Loyd tankettes and the Bren Gun carriers. Earlier, braked differential steering had been used on the Hornsby tractor of 1905 and it was also available on the British Mark I to IV tanks of the First World War, but the latter were normally steered by clutch-and-brake methods, as already described.

The simple braked differential steering can be converted to a much more efficient regenerative system by the addition of gears, so that the application of the brake on one side does not bring the corresponding half-shaft to rest but merely reduces its speed—and increases that of the other—according to the ratio of gears. This type of geared differential steering was evolved in the late twenties and was first applied to French tanks, as well as the American Cletrac commercial tractor of 1927, after which it has commonly been called. It was first used in quantity in such light tanks as the AMR, R-35 and H-35 of the mid-thirties and, even earlier, in the Renault *chenillette* designed in 1930–31. At about the same time, in 1932, the Cletrac geared differential was also applied to the American T1E1 light tank and was subsequently used on all light tanks up to the M24 of 1944, and on medium tanks from the T4 to the M26 of 1945, as well as the M6 and other experimental heavy tanks.

A much more advanced type of differential transmission was adopted on the French type B heavy tank whose development started in 1926. It employed a double differential system with a hydrostatic unit in the steering drive which gave it an infinite number of turning radii, in contrast to the single fixed radius of turn of the Cletrac geared differential which was that system's main drawback. A slightly different all-mechanical double differential steering system was also used on the S-35 medium tank designed in 1934 by S.O.M.U.A.

In the meantime, a controlled epicyclic system equivalent to the double differential was designed in Britain by Major Wilson for the A.7 E.1 experimental medium tank. It was not adopted, but it led to further development of the regenerative differential steering systems. Thus, in 1938 another transmission, known as the Merritt-Maybach, was evolved from the principles of the 1928 Wilson design. Like the double differential type, the new transmission split the drive from the engine into a main transmission drive and a steering drive and then recombined the two in an epicyclic gear train at each output shaft, the steering drive when engaged being used to slow down the drive to the inner track and simultaneously increase the speed of the outer track. The system was continuous and fully regenerative so that there was a minimum loss of power and speed when making a turn ; it also gave turning radii which varied with the transmission gears—the lower the gear the tighter the turn—and a neutral or pivot turn : when one track drove forward and the other reversed and the vehicle turned about its centre.

The Merritt-Maybach was installed in the A.16 E.1 experimental heavy cruiser but was quickly superseded by an improved and simplified version known as the Merritt-Brown. First fitted to the Churchill infantry tanks of 1941, the Merritt-Brown was also applied to the Centaur and Cromwell cruisers of 1943 and ousted all other British tank transmissions ; with few modifications it is still used on the current models of Centurion and Conqueror tanks.

A Henschel transmission similar to the Merritt-Maybach was also adopted in 1941 for the German Tiger heavy tanks but the contemporary German Panther medium tank was fitted with another regenerative steering system which was similar to the previous three in some respects but was actually discontinuous and behaved like a geared steering system. Since the Second World War a steering system similar to the Merritt-Maybach has been employed also in the American Allison Cross-Drive transmission, which incorporates a hydrokinetic torque converter in the input drive from the engine. The Cross-Drive was first applied to the M46 medium tank of 1948 and then to the T41, T42 and T43 light, medium and heavy tank designs and several other tracked vehicles.

Transmissions such as the Cross-Drive represent a high degree of mechanical refinement but the basic mechanism of tank steering remains rather brutal, for it relies on skidding or slewing the tracks over the surface of the ground. An alternative is to use laterally flexible tracks and a track setting mechanism to lay the tracks down on the ground in a curve. This was first attempted on the Light Infantry Tank designed around 1921 by Colonel Johnson but the laterally flexible " snake " tracks, which used spherical joints, proved troublesome as well as expensive. A limited degree of track setting by lateral displacement of one bogie was also employed on the Bren Gun carrier designed in the mid-thirties by Vickers-Armstrongs. In this case the track was of conventional type and laterally flexible only to the extent permitted by the clearances between the track pins and their holes in the track links. This was also the case with the more successful application of curved track steering on the Vickers-Armstrongs Tetrarch light tank designed in 1936, and its later derivatives, the Harry Hopkins airborne tank and the Alecto self-propelled gun. But on these 3 vehicles all 4 road wheels on each side were pivoted and turned to curve the track for large radius turns. This absorbed less power than the other methods of steering but for tight turns the track still had to be slewed round and the pivoting of the road wheels complicated the suspension.

Whatever the transmission and steering mechanism, the drive from the power unit must eventually be transferred to the tracks. In essence, the latter are endless chains which the vehicle lays down on the ground and then propels itself along by positive engagement between the driving sprockets and the tracks. But, since every action must have an equal and opposite reaction, the tractive effort at the sprocket must be balanced by a horizontal thrust at the ground and, because the capacity of the soil to withstand horizontal, or shear, forces is limited, the reaction between the track and the ground limits the tractive effort of the vehicle to about 70 per cent. of the total vehicle weight.

In general, because of the slip which occurs when a horizontal force is applied at the ground, long tracks are advantageous from the point of view of traction. But the longer the track the more difficult it is to slew it round and, therefore, from the point of view of steering, long tracks are undesirable. In consequence, the length of track in contact with the ground has been generally limited to less than twice the distance between the track centre lines. To be more precise, on most tanks the ratio of ground contact length to track centre to centre distance has been between 1.1 and 1.8 but on some, such as the Mark VIII and IX of 1918, it has been over 3. The 1940 British TOG, derived from the same 1918 ideas, even had a ratio of 3.5, but then it was most unsteerable.

The construction of the track itself originally was similar to that still used on agricultural tractors. In other words, each track consisted of steel links connected by pins and track plates, attached to the links, which formed the outer surface of the track ; the links provided a running surface for the suspension rollers and one edge of each track plate was usually formed into a grouser. Such early tracks were heavy and since their pitch, or the distance from pin centre to pin centre, was as much as $7\frac{1}{2}$ to 11 inches, as on the British tanks for instance, they were noisy and wore out rapidly. To lighten the track the separate link and plate construction was abandoned in favour of an integral one-piece track link and to increase the flexibility of the track the pitch was gradually reduced. The first successful application of very short pitch tracks was with the Carden Loyd tankettes of the late twenties, where the pitch was as low as 1.75 in., and at about the same time track design was improved further by the adoption of work-hardening manganese steels for the track links. By the out-break of the Second World War both features were widely adopted and short-pitch manganese-steel track links of skeleton or recessed form, with single or twin guide horns, superseded most earlier forms of construction.

Immediately after the First World War attempts were made to improve the working and life of track pins by lubrication. This was attempted on the Vickers Medium and the American Medium A but the approach was not successful and the lubri-cated track had to wait for the German half-track vehicles of the thirties for its first really successful application. In the latter case a sealed pin joint with needle rollers was used, giving very long track life, but the track was expensive to manu-facture and was never applied to tanks.

A less elaborate approach was adopted in the early thirties in the United States where the limited amount of movement between the pin and the track link was taken up by a flexible rubber bush. In this way, metal to metal rubbing contact was eliminated and again track life was increased above that of the conventional dry pin type. The rubber bushed track was first used on the T2 light tank of 1934 and has been employed since on the majority of American tracked armoured vehicles.

Complete elimination of the track pin problem was attempted with the Kegresse continuous rubber track which was taken up in France around 1921 and which was applied experimentally to some Renault F.T. tanks. This type of track proved too vulnerable for tanks and after the appearance of the light short-pitch steel track its use was confined to half-track vehicles. Its development continued however, first in France and then in the United States, and it was strengthened by the addition of steel cable reinforcement, with the result that since the Second World War it has been reapplied to some American full-track vehicles, such as the Ontos.

As a result of all this development track life increased considerably over that of the original British tanks, where it was pessimistically estimated at a mere 20 miles, or over that of the lighter Renault F.T. tanks, where it was of the order of 50 to 60 miles. By the time short-pitch manganese-steel tracks were introduced some tanks, such as the Vickers-Armstrongs Six Ton, could cover 3,000 miles before new tracks were necessary and a track life of 2,500 to 5,000 miles was recorded on some of the better designed 10-ton tanks of the late thirties. However, the life of medium tank tracks during the Second World War was not much more than about 1,000 miles, and has remained at that since, while many tanks, particularly of the heavy type, wore their tracks in less than 500 miles. Both before and since the Second World War the rubber bushed tracks of American light tanks have had a life of up to 4,000 miles, but the average life of the same type of track on medium tanks during the 1944–45 operations in Western Europe was only 1,300, while the life of the German tracks with sealed needle roller joints varied even more, from 3,000 to 15,000 miles, or better.

In general, track life is still a major problem but this disadvantage has to be accepted for the sake of the other advantages of the track, which include the ability to provide a large bearing area to support heavy loads in soft terrain.

The importance of distributing the weight of the tank over a large area of soft ground, or, in other words, of a low load per unit of track contact area, was recognised at an early date and low ground pressures were already a design objective during the First World War. Seven to nine pounds per square inch of projected track area was considered desirable to enable tanks to pass over the same ground that infantry could cross but on the British heavy tanks of the period the ground pressure varied from 10 to 25 lb./sq. in., depending on the amount of track sinkage. After the war, during the twenties and thirties, the design of light tanks followed the 7 lb./sq. in. example of the Renault F.T. and employed ground pressures of 6 to 8 lb./sq. in. while about 10 lb./sq. in. was accepted on heavier vehicles. During the Second World War, as the weight of tanks increased, ground pressures went up to about 12 to 14 lb./sq. in. and in the case of the British Matilda infantry tank to as much as 15.8. Soviet tanks, which had a reputation for good cross-country performance, were something of an exception with a ground pressure of 10 lb./sq. in. on the T-34 medium tank and only 11.5 lb./sq. in. even on the Stalin heavy tank. Towards the end of the Second World War, with the introduction of wider tracks, the ground pressures of American medium tanks were also reduced to about 10 but the British stayed at about 13; since the war the tendency has been to use 12 to 13 lb./sq. in. on the heavier vehicles and 8 to 10 lb./sq. in. on the lighter ones.

The above ground pressures arrived at by dividing the weight of a tank by the nominal ground contact area of its two tracks are, however, only a very rough guide to performance over soft ground. In the case of frictional sandy soils, for instance, the shape of the ground contact area is important and, in general, the calculated mean ground pressure bears little relation to the actual soil stresses under the track.

The actual distribution of stresses under the track depends on, among other things, the suspension which transfers the weight of the tank on to the tracks through a number of rollers or bogie wheels. In general, the more wheels there are the more even is the load distribution and the lower the peak stresses under the track. On the other hand, a large number of wheels is apt to interfere with the provision of adequate springing which is necessary if the suspension is to perform its other function of absorbing the reactions of surface irregularities.

The latter requirement was ignored by the British tanks of the First World War which had as many as 33 rigidly mounted rollers per side. The contemporary French tanks, like the Holt tractor, had rollers mounted in sprung bogies but the degree of springing on them and many later tanks was very limited. During the twenties development concentrated on articulated systems in which rollers or bogie wheels were mounted in pairs and the vertical wheel movement, required to absorb the irregularities of the ground surface, was mainly taken up by articulation, or walking beam action, and only to a limited extent by a rise against the springs. Indeed, a few of the early suspension schemes relied entirely on the equalising effect of interconnected rollers, as in the case of the British Medium D and the American Medium M1922, which had rollers connected by cable, and the American T1E1 light tank where the same result was achieved with links.

The cable and link methods were quickly abandoned but the articulated systems with springs proved reasonably satisfactory at low speeds and paired bogie wheels were used up to the end of the Second World War on such vehicles as the German Pz.Kpfw.IV medium tank and even later on the American M4 medium tanks and their derivatives. Some of the earlier tanks, such as the Renault F.T. and the Vickers-Armstrongs Six Ton, went even further and coupled bogie pairs so that two pairs rocked about a common point. Similar multiple bogie suspension assemblies survived up to the middle of the Second World War, on the British Valentine and the Italian M/13, but as tank speeds increased articulated systems became less and less satisfactory and during the thirties there was already a move towards independently sprung wheels.

The lead in the development of independently sprung wheels with large vertical movement was taken in 1928 in the United States by J. Walter Christie and, in combination with the use of power to weight ratios of more than 30 b.h.p. per ton, enabled him to set up new standards in performance. Christie's 1928 suspension consisted of four large wheels per side, the wheels revolving on pivoted axle-arms controlled by long coil springs and having a vertical movement of about 14 inches. This type of suspension was successfully applied to the T3 medium tank built in 1931 for the United States Army and the later, Ordnance-designed, T4 and has been employed on a large scale on Soviet medium tanks, from the B.T. series derived directly from two of Christie's 1931 tanks, through the T-34 to the T-54. It was also used on British cruiser tanks from the A.13 of 1938 to the Comet of 1944.

In the thirties other forms of independent suspension also appeared, such as the leaf spring type used on the majority of the German Pz.Kpfw.II light tanks and the torsion bar type introduced with the Pz.Kpfw.III Model E of 1939. Shortly afterwards the Russians also introduced several tanks with torsion bar independent suspensions: the T-40 and T-60 light tanks and the KV heavy tank from which this type of springing has been carried into the JS series. In 1942 the Germans extended the use of the torsion bar independent suspension by adopting it on the Tiger and Panther tanks and in 1944–45 it also began to appear on American vehicles, such as the M18 (T70) tank destroyer, the M24 light tank and the M26 heavy tank from which it has been carried on as the standard type of springing on post-Second World War American tanks.

One of the advantages of torsion bar springing is that it lends itself to a neat lateral installation in the vehicle where it is protected by armour. But this also means that it requires space within the armour envelope and to that extent makes the latter heavier. The same criticism applies to the usual mounting of the coil springs of the Christie suspension within the hull, while a further point against torsion bar springing is that it increases the height of the tank. For this and similar reasons, in the latter part of the Second World War the Germans decided to abandon torsion bar springing, as well as front sprocket drive, in favour of externally mounted springing on the " E " tank series ; in the majority of cases, tanks of this series were to use nests of conical, or Belleville washer, springs. At about the same time the Germans were developing the " E " series British tank design also abandoned Christie-type suspensions in favour of externally mounted suspension units, each consisting of a pair of wheels connected by coil springs, which were adopted on the Centurion.

Apart from the independent suspension, Christie also pioneered two other tank suspension features which were generally applicable : large-diameter wheels and rubber tyres. Christie's introduction of both was rather fortuitous for it was essentially a by-product of his aim to design tanks so that they could operate without tracks as well as with them. The twenties saw several attempts to develop tanks which could travel along roads on wheels and save their tracks for off-the-road operation by providing them with two sets of running gear. Christie's scheme, which used the same set of wheels for both modes of operation, was far simpler and more promising than the others but his convertible tank was also gradually abandoned. On the other hand, rubber tyres, which he introduced on his 1919 experimental tank, and large-diameter wheels have been widely adopted. The former came into wider use with the British Independent of 1926 and the Carden Loyd tankettes and were generally adopted during the thirties. However, the British Churchill infantry tank designed in 1940 still used small plain steel rollers and during the Second World War steel tyred wheels staged something of a comeback with the Soviet introduction of the steel tyred resilient type on the KV heavy tank. The Germans copied it for the Tiger II and intended to standardise it for the " E " series ; since the Second World War it has been used on the British Conqueror as well as the Soviet JS (Stalin) heavy tanks. The attraction and the principal advantage of the resilient steel tyred wheel over the rubber tyred type is that it allows a higher loading per unit of tyre width and its advantage over the plain steel type used earlier is that it has some resilience ; it also saves a good deal of rubber over the former since the rubber is confined to a ring between the hub and the rim. But this is at the expense of track life and, in general, any return to steel tyred wheels can only be regarded as a retrograde step.

So far there has been no sign of a similar retrograde move to small-diameter rollers which are liable to get clogged up with mud. The one advantage of a more uniform load distribution over the track length possible with small rollers can largely be obtained with overlapping large-diameter wheels, as was shown on the Tiger II. Earlier German vehicles, such as the Tiger I and the Panther, had interleaved as well as overlapped wheels but, although this arrangement was theoretically attractive, in practice it was liable to suffer from mud and snow packing between the wheels.

The most recent development is the use of pneumatic tyred wheels on some of the lighter vehicles, such as the American Ontos, which improves the resilience of the suspension. The particular method may be questioned but in general any improvement in the suspension characteristics is to be commended, for improved cross-country performance depends largely on the development of better suspension. At present the pitching and bouncing of tanks are still such that their crews cannot operate effectively off the road at high speeds and this limits the average cross-country speed of tanks to less than 10 m.p.h. even if they are capable of 30 or 40 m.p.h. on the road.

If higher cross-country speeds are to be attained improved low periodicity suspensions with large wheel movement are essential and so, probably, is stabilisation of the crew stations. Stabilisation has already been applied to the main armament, first in elevation on the American M3A1 light tank and M4A1 medium tank of 1942 and then in elevation and traverse on the

British Centurion. The next logical step is to extend stabilisation to the crew, along the lines indicated by the oscillating turret of the French AMX light tank.

Apart from the suspension, the quality of the ride is also affected by the vehicle configuration. For instance, tanks with short tracks and relatively high centres of gravity, such as the British Mark VI light tank of the late thirties, have been notorious from the point of view of pitching. Conversely, relatively long vehicles can travel faster off the road. Vehicle length is also desirable for other reasons, from the point of view of the crossing of trenches, ditches and similar obstacles, just as a clearance of 12 to 18 inches from the ground to the belly is essential if the tank is to be able to straddle minor obstacles and a concomitant of suspensions with large wheel movement.

In general, suspension characteristics and the interrelationship between the vehicle and the ground, as well as that between the vehicle and its occupants, which falls within the province of human engineering, provide important and potentially fruitful fields for further development.

26

Power Units

For more than 40 years the petrol or spark ignition reciprocating engine has been the source of power of the great majority
of tanks and other armoured vehicles. However, a number of
other power units have also emerged as actual or potential
challengers to the petrol engine and it is necessary to consider
these alternative units as well as the development of the petrol
engine.

The petrol engine was already well established when the
first tanks came into being during the First World War. It
had behind it some twenty-five years of development in the
automotive field and by 1914 Henry Ford was already producing it by the thousand for cars. As a result, a number of
proved automotive engines was available and it was from
among the existing models that the first tank engines were
chosen.

For instance, the engine which powered the first British
tanks of 1916 was originally built by the Daimler Company
for a large wheeled tractor. It was a 6-cylinder, in-line,
water-cooled engine which developed 105 b.h.p. at 1,000
r.p.m. The first French tank engines, used on the Schneider,
St. Chamond and Renault tanks, were also of the automotive,
in-line, water-cooled type.

Engines of this type fulfilled the requirements of the early
tanks reasonably well, particularly as far as the lighter vehicles,
such as the Renault F.T., were concerned. But the heavier
tanks presented a more difficult problem because of their
greater power requirements. For instance, the Daimler engine
of the British Mark I tank gave a power to weight ratio of less
than 4 b.h.p. per ton, and when better performance was
demanded engines of suitably large size could not be found
in the automotive field.

In consequence, by the time British tank development reached the Mark V a special engine was produced for it giving 165 b.h.p. at 1,200 r.p.m. This engine was the first ever to be designed and produced specifically as a tank engine and its designer, H. R. Ricardo, laid it out on very robust lines, employing a crosshead in the manner of the steam engine, from which, of course, the gasoline engine was mechanically derived; otherwise the engine was of the water-cooled, 6-cylinder, in-line type.

An alternative way of satisfying the increasing power demands of tanks was to draw on engines from the aircraft field. There great progress was made during the 4 years of the First World War, resulting, towards the end of that conflict, in relatively light and compact engines of over 300 b.h.p. It was inevitable that some of these should be tried in tanks: the 360 b.h.p. Rolls-Royce Eagle and the 240 b.h.p. Siddeley Puma were fitted experimentally in British tanks and the 338 b.h.p. Liberty engine was applied to the Anglo-American Mark VIII heavy tank which was planned to be produced on a large scale in 1919. The Liberty engine itself was hurriedly designed by the pooled talent of the American automotive industry along the lines established in Europe and was intended to meet a contemporary Allied demand for a high-powered aero engine.

The aero engines adopted for tank use were of the water-cooled V-12 type and their use set a pattern which was to be repeated several times since. In the post-war decade, however, Britain, which then held a lead in the field, continued to develop special tank engines. The actual development was entrusted to the Armstrong Siddeley company which at the time was the dominant British air-cooled engine manufacturer. Naturally enough, the tank engines which it produced were air-cooled, the first production model being a V-8 of 90 b.h.p. used to power the Vickers Medium Mark I. A smaller 4-cylinder model was produced for the very successful Vickers-Armstrongs Six Ton tank and 2 larger air-cooled engines were built for experimental medium and heavy tanks: a 398 b.h.p. V-12 for the A.1, or Independent, multi-turret heavy tank and a 180 b.h.p. V-8 for the A.6, or Sixteen-tonner, medium tank of the late twenties.

The Armstrong Siddeley engines were somewhat expensive and bulky but their basic simplicity and the ability to dispense with the coolant, radiator and the vulnerable plumbing were sufficient to offset any drawbacks associated with the use of air-cooling. By the early thirties the British Army was not alone in holding this view : the application of air-cooled engines was taken up in earnest in the United States ; the Russians, who purchased 15 of the Six Ton tanks from Vickers-Armstrongs and copied them on a large scale as the T-26, copied also their air-cooled engines. The Germans also used an air-cooled engine, a Krupp flat-4, in their first quantity produced tank, the Pz.Kpfw.I Model A. The Czechs, too, designed a flat-6 air-cooled engine of 60 b.h.p. for one of the early Skoda tanks and the Japanese went into air-cooled engine development on some scale.

Of all the countries which tried them, the United States was the only one to standardise eventually on air-cooled petrol engines. The American development of air-cooled tank engines actually began with the application of a Franklin 6-cylinder 67 b.h.p. engine to a 6-ton M1917 light tank in 1929. This was followed by the use of air-cooled Continental 7-cylinder radial engines in the Light Tank T2 and the Christie-type Medium T4, the earlier Christie vehicles having been powered by water-cooled V-12s, such as the Liberty, Hispano-Suiza and the American La France.

The Continental engine was an adaptation of an aircraft model and was chosen as the only near-suitable power unit which the United States Army could procure at the time out of its very limited tank funds. It was standardised and the Continental company became closely associated with American tank development: through most of the thirties it was, in fact, the only supplier of tank engines. The position changed only shortly before the Second World War, when the need for a more powerful tank engine led to the experiments with and subsequent adoption of the Wright 9-cylinder 400 b.h.p. air-cooled radial aircraft engine for the Medium M3.

In the meantime, Britain, having pioneered the air-cooled tank engine, abandoned it completely. The reasons were almost entirely economic. In the wave of financial stringency which followed the Depression tank development funds were cut down drastically and the special air-cooled tank engines, such as the V-8 of the A.6 medium tank, had to be abandoned together with the rest of the project. Cost became a most important consideration and as a result the new British tanks of the mid-thirties came to be powered by commercial automotive engines. Thus, the Cruiser Tanks Mark I and II were powered by 6-cylinder in-line water-cooled A.E.C. engines, converted from the Associated Equipment Company's standard range of bus and truck engines, and the Infantry Tank Mark I was powered by a standard British-built Ford V-8.

Something of this sort was foreshadowed in the late twenties in the development of the British machine-gun carriers, which were designed down to a price from the start. In consequence, they made use of the cheapest engine available at the time—that of the Ford Model T. Subsequent developments of the Carden Loyd machine-gun carriers, the Bren Gun carrier series, continued to be Ford-powered, although by this time the engine size went up to a V-8. The other offshoot of the Carden Loyd machine-gun carriers, the Vickers Carden Loyd light tanks, were powered by Meadows industrial water-cooled engines or, in a few cases, by Rolls-Royce car engines.

Once more, the use of all these commercial engines was satisfactory as long as only moderate horse powers were required. When the demand for performance and power went up aero engines had to be resorted to again, as in the case of the first British Christie-type tank, the A.13 or Cruiser Tank Mark III. By the time this tank was being designed the pressure of events was such that there was no question of designing a special tank engine for it. At the same time, the only up-to-date aero engine which was available—apart from air-cooled radials which in Britain were not considered suitable for tanks—was the water-cooled V-12 Rolls-Royce. But the Rolls-Royce engines were all required for aircraft which had a much higher priority in British defence planning than tanks. In consequence, the choice fell back on the First World War Liberty : cleaned up a little, the 350 b.h.p. Liberty was put into production by the Nuffield organisation and was used on cruiser tanks right up to the Centaur of 1943.

An exception among the cruiser tanks was the Covenanter, which had a special water-cooled flat-12. However, this engine suffered from inadequate development and, in any case, it did not have a sufficient reserve of development potential for extended application. A water-cooled flat-12 was also designed by Vauxhall Motors, the British subsidiary of the General Motors Corporation, for the Churchill heavy tank but though robust it was far too heavy for its 325 b.h.p. and again it did not have sufficient development potential for use beyond this tank.

French tank engines of the period were generally of the same type as those of the British light tanks, that is fairly robust, water-cooled in-line automotive engines. Others too relied on this type of engine, for the light tanks at any rate.

This applied also to the lighter German tanks, such as the Pz.Kpfw.I Model B and Pz.Kpfw.II, even though their engines belonged to a special series evolved for tanks by the Maybach company. The more powerful German tanks, the Pz.Kpfw.III and IV, used a water-cooled V-12, the Maybach HL 108 TR of 230 b.h.p. later replaced by the more powerful HL 120 TR of 320 b.h.p. The Russians also used a water-cooled V-12 for all their medium and heavy tanks of the thirties. This large 2,860 c.in. engine was based on a German B.M.W. aircraft design and developed about 500 b.h.p.

In general, by 1939, tank engines could be grouped into 2 fairly distinct categories : the in-line 6-cylinder water-cooled engines of automotive origin and the large V-12s adapted from the aircraft field ; a third and separate group was formed by the American air-cooled radial engines which, like the V-12s, were also of aircraft origin.

The Second World War changed little in the general situation with regard to the two main categories of engines. Power requirements went up, however, and where commercial engines were used twin installations became quite common, not only with petrol engines but also with diesels. The earliest example was the British Medium A of 1918 and the practice was revived in the mid-thirties on the British A.7 experimental medium tank. It was then used on the British Infantry Tank Mark II, or Matilda, and several other tanks such as the American Medium M3A3 and M4A2, which had twin General Motors diesels, the M5 and M24 light tanks, which had twin Cadillac V-8s, and the Soviet T-70, which had 2 GAZ 202 engines. The ultimate in this line of development was to be found in the American M3A4 and M4A4 medium tanks whose power plant consisted of five 6-cylinder Chrysler automobile engines geared together to give a total output of 370 b.h.p.

For the more powerful vehicles using V-12 engines there was no other way out but to go to bigger units, although a twin V-12 installation was used on the German Ferdinand (later Elefant) heavy self-propelled gun of 1943. For their heavier tanks, such as the Tigers and the Panther, the Germans developed larger Maybach V-12s developing 650 to 700 b.h.p. at 3,000 r.p.m. In Britain, beginning with the Cromwell cruiser tank, the not-too-successful Nuffield-Liberty was replaced by the Rolls-Royce Meteor, a de-rated ground version of the V-12 Merlin engine which powered the Hurricane and Spitfire fighters of the Battle of Britain; it had a swept volume of 1,649 c.in. and developed 570 to 600 b.h.p. at 2,550 r.p.m. The Russians, like the Germans, developed a new V-12 of 500 to 550 b.h.p. for their medium and heavy tanks but this was a diesel and not a petrol engine like the others. The United States, in addition to air-cooled radials and adaptations of commercial engines, introduced a large 450–500 b.h.p. V-8, a sawn-off version of a V-12 engine originally designed for

25. German 105mm assault howitzer of 1943.

26. United States M40 155mm self-propelled gun developed in 1944. (*US Army*).

27. German Sd.Kfz.251 half-track armoured personnel carrier of 1942.

28. United States M113 aluminium-armoured personnel carrier which has become the most numerous armoured vehicle outside the Soviet bloc. (*FMC Corp.*).

aircraft, which was used on the later models of the Medium M4 series and the M26 Pershing.

After the Second World War the United States Army made a clean sweep and replaced the various types of tank engines by a standardised series of air-cooled engines, horizontally opposed in the smaller sizes and V-12 for the high powered units. This series was designed especially for military use by the Continental company in co-operation with the Ordnance Corps and was introduced in 1948 with the M46 medium tank, which was powered by the AV-1790-5A engine, a V-12 of 1790 c.in. swept volume developing 810 b.h.p. at 2,800 r.p.m. and the largest engine of the series.

After the Second World War the British Army too introduced a standardised series of military engines, the Rolls-Royce B series, but these were water-cooled and covered only the requirements of the smaller armoured vehicles. The largest is a straight-eight of 160 b.h.p. used on the Saracen wheeled armoured personnel carrier and the Saladin armoured car. In British tanks the standard engine is still the V-12 Meteor but its parentage has passed from the Rolls-Royce organisation to the Rover company.

The French also developed several special engines, including a large 1,000 b.h.p. V-12 for the AMX 50-ton tank which was not, however, put into production. Then, disregarding the advantages of rationalisation, they produced 2 horizontally opposed engines of similar output : a 270 b.h.p. Mathis water-cooled flat-8 used on the AMX 13-ton tank and its derivatives and a 200 b.h.p. Panhard air-cooled flat-12 used in the EBR 8-wheeled armoured car.

More recently the United States also departed somewhat from the advantages of rationalisation and air-cooling offered by the Ordnance-Continental series of engines and adopted the less expensive General Motors commercial-type, water-cooled, in-line, 6-cylinder engines in the M59 armoured personnel carrier and the Ontos.

The differences between commercial automotive engines and aircraft engines adapted to ground use, or special military engines, have diminished, however, in recent years, partly because of the slowing down of development of reciprocating engines in the aircraft field, where their place is being taken over by turbo-prop and turbo-jet engines, and partly because the design of automotive engines has followed increasingly aircraft practice. There are still a few examples of the older, purely automotive practice, represented, for instance, by the Rolls-Royce B series with their F heads. But, in general, the technical characteristics of armoured vehicle engines follow a fairly common pattern, except for the method of cooling, on which there is still no unanimity. Otherwise there seems less reason than ever for not using commercial engines for the lighter vehicles. For the heavier vehicles, however, special engines appear inevitable, especially as the reciprocating aero engines slowly disappear from the scene.

The accepted practice in petrol engine design is the use of short strokes and large bores, overhead valves and high compression ratios which together with improved engine breathing and knowledge of combustion processes have resulted in increased engine speeds and higher cylinder mean effective pressures. These in turn have resulted in greater power outputs for a given size of engine and, at the same time, greater efficiency. Compared with the position 40 years earlier the average piston speed, compression ratio and mean effective pressure have just about doubled. At the same time specific fuel consumption at full load has been nearly halved.

In spite of all the progress, it is generally considered that further development is still possible. The 3 main lines envisaged are :

    (1)   still further increases in compression ratio ;
    (2)   supercharging ;
    (3)   fuel injection.

The first depends very largely on the development and availability of high octane fuels. If or when such fuels become available specific output and thermal efficiency will improve still further, or, in other words, if other things remain the same, the specific size of engines will decrease and the miles per gallon increase. However, as in other fields, this line of development will bring in the law of diminishing returns in terms of increased fuel and engine costs and a compression ratio of 12 to 1 is regarded as the practical limit, the average compression ratio of tank engines at present being about 7 to 1.

The second line of development has been followed for many years in the aircraft field and, in fact, because of their aircraft origin, several of the larger tank engines were originally developed in the supercharged form. The chief benefit of supercharging is greater specific output ; its drawbacks include increased complexity and cost of the power unit. In spite of this a number of supercharged engines has been used, a recent example being found in the American M41 light tank and its derivatives which are powered by the supercharged, horizontally opposed, 6-cylinder AOS-895 engine of 895 c.in. swept volume and 500 b.h.p. at 2,800 r.p.m.

The third line of development was started in the aircraft field in the late twenties and was widely applied to aero engines during the Second World War. Towards the end of that conflict the Germans began to extend its application to tanks and an experimental HL 234 version of their Tiger II heavy tank engine with petrol injection produced a maximum of 900 b.h.p. instead of the 700 b.h.p. of the standard HL 230 carburetted version.

Since the Second World War, the French used fuel injection on the 1,000 b.h.p. engine of the AMX 50-ton experimental tank and in Britain fuel injection was applied to the standard Meteor tank engine. Introduced on the Conqueror heavy tank, the modified Meteor IVB gave 810 b.h.p. compared with 650 b.h.p. of the standard carburetted version retained in the Centurion medium tanks. The same British S.U. fuel injection system, manufactured under licence in the United States by the Simmonds Aerocessories Inc., has also been adopted on the M48A2 medium tank and other American armoured vehicles.

The use of fuel injection is likely to expand. Apart from its immediate benefit of increased specific output resulting from better fuel distribution, fuel injection also offers the possibility of some improvement in overall fuel economy, acceleration and reduced fuel sensitivity, as well as reduction in overall dimensions of the engine.

With further development along those lines there are good prospects that the reciprocating spark ignition engine will maintain its position in the tank field for some time. It is all the more likely because of the demands of civilian peacetime economy, which makes petrol the most readily available fuel and one which can be most readily rationed in an emergency. This factor, of course, has been responsible as much as any other for the emphasis which military planners have placed on petrol and petrol engines.

However, in spite of factors such as the above, which have favoured the development of the petrol engine and the many satisfactory aspects of its performance, its position has not passed unchallenged in the tank field. The most serious challenger so far has been the compression ignition or diesel engine.

The development of the tank diesel began in the mid-twenties, in Britain, some 10 years after the appearance of the first tanks. It was prompted by the development of diesel engines for aircraft, which was initiated towards the end of the First World War by the German Junkers company and which was pursued after the war in Britain by the Royal Aircraft Establishment, and the early tank diesels actually preceded the application of diesel engines to commercial vehicles.

The first tank diesel engine, designed by the Ricardo research organisation at the request of the War Office, was completed in 1927 and was a 4-cylinder water-cooled unit which developed 90 b.h.p. at 1,300 r.p.m. It was installed in a Vickers Medium Mark I and orders for 3 more experimental designs followed, including one for a 6-cylinder engine of 180 b.h.p. which was installed in one of the experimental Sixteen-Ton medium tanks, the A.6 E.2.

Other experimental installations followed. In 1932 the French tried diesel engines in two prototypes of the type D infantry tank and a little later the Germans tried a diesel version of the air-cooled Krupp engine of the Pz.Kpfw.I Model A. In 1935 the Japanese introduced their first tank diesel, an air-cooled straight-six of 115 b.h.p., on the Type 89B medium tank and in 1937 the first 3 American light tanks were fitted with Guiberson diesels, 9-cylinder air-cooled radial engines originally designed for aircraft use. At about the same time the Guiberson was also tried in the United States Cavalry's T5 and then M1 combat cars and in 1938 it was installed in a few production models—the M2A3E1 light tank and the M1A1E1 combat car.

In the meantime, in the mid-thirties, the French and Polish Armies each procured 2 battalions of diesel engined tanks, the former of the F.C.M. Model 1936 powered by a Berliet engine built under licence from Ricardo and the latter of the 7 TP type powered by a Saurer engine imported into Poland from Switzerland. By the outbreak of the Second World War Italy adopted an SPA V-8 diesel for its M/11 and M/13 medium tanks and Russia was well advanced with the development of the powerful 500–550 b.h.p. V-12 diesel which was to power all the new Soviet medium and heavy tanks and assault guns during the war. By 1939 also, the British Army adopted A.E.C. and Leyland 6-cylinder engines of 95 b.h.p. each, in a twin engine installation, for the Matilda infantry tank. Similarly, the United States Army adopted commercial General Motors 2-stroke diesels, which were put on the market in 1938, for the M3A3 and M4A2 medium tanks of 1941 and 1942, having earlier standardised on the Guiberson diesel for the M2A4 and M3 light tanks.

This upsurge of interest in diesels in the late thirties and early forties did not, however, last even to the end of the Second World War. By that time, apart from the Russian and Japanese tank engines, the only tank diesel used in quantity was the General Motors, used in the M4A2 medium tank and the M10 tank destroyer. The Germans were about to extend considerably the employment of the Czech-built 220 b.h.p. V-12 Tatra air-cooled diesel in their lighter armoured vehicles but in 1945 they, like the Japanese, dropped for a time out of the picture. As the Western Allies had already decided to standardise on petrol engines, the post-war application of diesels was limited to Soviet tanks, including the JS heavy and T-54 medium.

The reason for this was twofold. There was the general question of the availability of fuels which has been mentioned already. Because petrol was adjudged to be more readily available, already in the early thirties the Germans decided to concentrate on petrol engines. The United States did likewise in 1942, and so did Britain and France. The other reason was the somewhat lower specific output of diesel engines compared with petrol engines.

The latter was partly due to the inherent combustion characteristics of the diesel engine. But, partly, it was also due to the fact that far less development effort had been devoted to high-speed diesels than petrol engines, which had vast sums spent on them in connection with military aircraft and passenger cars. More recent developments have shown that the differences in power output need not be as great as had sometimes been imagined. They have also shown that diesel engines can consume a variety of fuels. For instance, the General Motors 2-stroke diesel of the Second World War had already demonstrated its ability to operate on petrol and more efficiently than some contemporary petrol engines. More recently other diesel engines have demonstrated that direct injection 4-stroke diesels can run satisfactorily on 70 octane petrol and some diesel manufacturers have come to include instructions on running their engines on petrol as an alternative.

Examples such as these do not establish the diesel as a multi-fuel engine in the full sense of the word. But they show a possibility of running it on a wide range of fuels and remove, partly at any rate, the old objection that fuel for diesels is not as readily available as that for petrol engines.

Another factor which has made the diesel even more important is the belated realisation of the importance of fuel economy in armoured operations. Under conditions where the enemy possesses strong air forces, or, even more, of nuclear warfare, an uninterrupted flow of the large quantities of fuel required by armoured units is very doubtful. Any saving in their fuel requirements is, therefore, of the utmost importance and this is where a diesel engine really comes into its own. Because it is more efficient, the diesel can extend considerably the operating range of individual vehicles and reduce the overall fuel requirements of armoured units, thus achieving the double object of reducing their logistical support requirements and increasing their freedom of action.

In consequence, more attention has again been given to diesel engines at both the Detroit Arsenal and the Fighting Vehicles Research and Development Establishment in Britain ; the results can be seen in the turbo-blown diesel version of the American AV-1790 V-12 air-cooled tank engine adopted in the M60 medium tank and the British Rover V-8 tank engine designed with an eye for easy conversion from spark ignition to compression ignition. The Japanese, too, have installed a V-12 diesel of 550–600 b.h.p. in their 1956 Mitsubishi medium tank, as well as a smaller air-cooled diesel in the SS-I and II recoilless gun vehicles.

It could be asked whether further development of the high compression petrol engine will not nullify much of the present economy advantage of the diesel engine. At full load it is quite likely that the gap will be considerably narrowed but to arrive at this the petrol engine will require expensive, high-octane fuels and even then its overall economy is doubtful. This and considerations of engine design suggest that the trend to high compression engines might, in fact, be best met by a more extensive use of diesels rather than further development of the spark ignition petrol engine.

Apart from the diesel engine, the spark ignition petrol engine has a more recent potential challenger. This is the automotive gas turbine.

Study of the application of gas turbines to tanks began as early as 1944, in Germany where the first turbo-jet aircraft flew in August 1939. However, this first tank gas turbine project was brought to an end by the surrender of Germany in 1945. It was only in about 1951, soon after the appearance of the first Rover gas turbine powered car and of the Boeing-Kenworth truck, that the first turbine powered armoured vehicle was tried in France. The gas turbine in the French vehicle was a 540 b.h.p. twin Turbomeca unit and in 1954 a 1,000 b.h.p. Parsons gas turbine was demonstrated in Britain installed in an experimental Conqueror heavy tank chassis.

The advantages of the gas turbine type of power plant are its inherent balance, torque characteristics, ability to operate on a wide range of fuels and light weight. Its most serious disadvantages are high fuel consumption and the necessity to employ expensive strategic materials.

Work on improving the efficiency of gas turbines has made progress, almost entirely through the use of heat exchangers, which save much of the energy contained in the high temperature exhaust gases by transferring it to the air leaving the compressor. In this way a heat exchanger saves considerably the amount of fuel which has to be burnt to heat the air to the required working temperature and thereby increases the overall efficiency of the unit. Unfortunately, the use of a heat exchanger brings in its own penalties of increased power unit bulk and weight and of increased thermal inertia which slows down the response of the engine—a feature particularly undesirable in automotive applications.

An alternative to the use of heat exchangers and the second of the two divergent lines of gas turbine development is the use of high pressure ratios. With rotary compressors this implies the use of two, or more, compressors in series and such " two-spool " axial flow compressor units have already been applied to aircraft, giving pressure ratios of up to 10 to 1, instead of the 3 or 4 to 1 used in automotive gas turbines. But even such high pressure ratios are still low in relation to the compression ratios of reciprocating engines.

Under some conditions the gas turbine may well prove as efficient as the existing petrol engines but this does not mean that it is near to being able to compete under the variety of conditions and the low average load factor encountered in tank operation. Moreover, the aim should be to improve considerably on the existing engines and not to accept them as the best that can be done. An operating efficiency of less than 15 ton-miles per gallon of some of the existing tanks certainly leaves a good deal to be desired.

Further development of the gas turbine may eliminate some of its present shortcomings but in the meantime these preclude any thought of its immediate, large-scale application to armoured vehicles. On the other hand, there is a more immediate and promising field for the application of gas turbine components in combination with reciprocating engines.

The simplest example is provided by the turbo-blower. This is essentially a small gas turbine unit added to a reciprocating engine to increase the air intake and hence the power of the latter. The energy required to operate it is provided by the exhaust gases of the engine and the power developed at the turbine is used wholly to drive a centrifugal blower in the engine intake system.

From the turbo-blown engine it is, in principle, a relatively short step to a compound engine. Instead of being used only to drive the compressor, the exhaust gas driven turbine may be made larger and made to develop all the shaft power which the unit is capable of supplying externally. In such a case, the power unit acquires the excellent torque characteristics of the gas turbine, while at the same time it retains the high efficiency of the high compression reciprocating engine. The role of the latter becomes that of a high pressure gas generator, or, in other words, it performs the same function as the compressor, combustion chambers and the compressor turbine in a simple gas turbine unit.

The advantage of this scheme is that the reciprocating gas generator can operate at a much higher pressure ratio than one made of rotary components and that the gas supplied to the power turbine—which is the same in the two cases—is at a lower temperature. The first means that the compound engine can approach the efficiency of a diesel and the latter that the power turbine does not require such costly materials.

The reciprocating gas generators of compound engines have taken the form either of a 2-stroke diesel or of a free piston engine, which is essentially a highly supercharged, opposed-piston 2-stroke without a crankshaft.

One of the first examples of the former type was the British Napier Nomad compound aircraft engine developed soon after the Second World War. A later example was provided by the General Electric Orion whose development started in June 1950 to a United States Army Ordnance Corps specification for a 600 (originally 900) b.h.p. engine suitable for use with the M47 medium tank. The development was partly prompted by a belated realisation of the advantages enjoyed by Soviet diesel-powered tanks. However, this interesting air-cooled gas generator turbo-compound engine was abandoned in 1955 before a unit could be tried in a tank.

The first automotive example of the free piston type of compound engine was provided by the General Motors GMR 4-4 Hyprex experimental car engine demonstrated in 1956. The free piston gas generator or gasifier of this unit was actually designed by the Société d'Études Mécaniques et Énergétiques in France, where much of the pioneer work has been done and where a number of industrial units has been produced.

Whichever of the two types of compound engine is ultimately applied, its combination of high efficiency and torque characteristics makes it eminently suitable for tank use. In addition, the compound engine can consume a wide range of fuels, from kerosene or bunker oil to high-octane petrol. The compound engine is, of course, in an early stage of its development but given the right amount of effort it could become a serious competitor to the petrol tank engine and its successor, if the latter is not by then partly displaced by the diesel.

Although reciprocating spark ignition engines, compression ignition or diesel engines, gas turbines and compound engines cover quite a range of power units, they do not, by any means, exhaust the number of possibilities. They do not even cover all the engines which have already been used in the automotive field.

For instance, in the late thirties considerable attention was devoted in Western Europe to producer gas power units and they were seriously considered for armoured cars intended for long distance reconnaissance. Essentially these units consisted of conventional spark ignition reciprocating engines which were operated on gas produced by the combustion of coke, anthracite, charcoal or even wood in a separate gas producer. A number of civilian vehicles was operated on producer gas in Europe during the Second World War, but the gas producer units proved cumbersome and the whole idea was abandoned as soon as the fuel supply situation eased.

Since then civilian interest in engines operating on gaseous fuels has switched to highly compressed gases, such as liquefied petroleum gas. The latter, commonly referred to as L.P.G., has been mentioned as a possible fuel for armoured vehicles but in that application it has little to recommend it, except for some reduction in engine maintenance and good starting, which are more than outweighed by the inconvenience and the potential danger of having to handle high pressure containers of gas.

Since the Second World War also, a certain amount of attention has been attracted by reciprocating engines using the Texaco Combustion Process, or T.C.P. The T.C.P. engines combine spark ignition with fuel injection into the cylinder and an organised air movement which together produce a controlled rate of combustion and consequently make it possible to operate at high compression ratios on a wide range of fuels.

As a multi-fuel engine the T.C.P. engine has obvious military attractions. However, it suffers from the complication of having to use the ignition system of a petrol engine and the high pressure injection system of a diesel. Moreover, it has not shown the operating flexibility necessary for an automotive engine, and in view of the development of other engines capable of burning a wide range of fuels the application of the T.C.P. engine to armoured vehicles seems rather doubtful.

One or two of the earliest armed or armoured cars of 1900 were steam powered. In the First World War steam engines were still regarded as a distinct possibility for the larger types of tanks and a steam-powered tank was actually built in 1918 by the United States Corps of Engineers. However, as in other applications, the reciprocating steam engine proved too cumbersome. On a number of occasions steam turbine powered vehicles have also been mentioned and an aircraft powered by a steam turbine, the Travelair, was actually tried in the United States in 1933. But with the appearance of the gas turbine any justification for an automotive steam turbine using conventional fuels has disappeared because the gas turbine can produce similar results to the steam turbine without the complication of an additional working medium, *i.e.*, steam, interposed between the heat source and the power producing turbine.

Steam could, perhaps, still enter the automotive field were nuclear energy to become a practical proposition in small mobile power units. In principle such a nuclear power plant is not difficult to visualise : heat generated by fission in the nuclear reactor is extracted by a cooling medium and converted into mechanical work at a turbine wheel. In other words, the nuclear power plant using steam would be similar to a conventional coal or oil-fired steam plant but would have a different type of boiler. Or, if a gas such as helium were used as the cooling and working medium, it would be similar to a closed cycle gas turbine. In principle then, nuclear fuel would be merely a substitute source of heat energy to that which is released by the chemical processes associated with the combustion of the familiar fossil fuels.

In practice, however, the utilisation of nuclear energy in mobile systems presents immense difficulties. The greatest of these, so far as ground vehicles are concerned, is the development of sufficiently light shielding to protect the crew of the vehicle. Shielding is essential, of course, to reduce the radiation from the reactor well below the maximum allowable exposure level beyond which permanent damage to the human body may result.

Effective shielding of the reactor has so far involved a considerable weight of material such as lead or concrete. Even relatively small units require massive shielding and it is one of the unfortunate features of nuclear reactors that the amount of shielding does not decrease in proportion to reductions in reactor power. This, of course, imposes a much greater penalty on small nuclear power plants than the larger ones, such as that used, for instance, in the Nautilus nuclear powered submarine launched in 1954. The design problem of ground vehicles is also more difficult than that of aircraft, not only because power requirements are lower but also because the crew must be located nearer to the power unit and generally live longer with it and because partial shielding cannot be employed.

With regard to the actual weight, a 1,000 b.h.p. nuclear power plant for a heavy tank would weigh at least 40 tons, or some 80 lb./h.p. Even in the idealised case of a nuclear power source reduced to a point the weight of a 600 b.h.p. automotive nuclear engine would be about 12,000 lb., or 20 lb./h.p., as compared with 2 to 5 lb./h.p. of the existing engines using chemical fuels.

The above figures show something of the magnitude of the problem from the point of view of shielding, which is by no means the only one to be solved. Thus, in spite of the obvious attractions of a power unit which could be operated for long periods without refuelling, nuclear powered armoured vehicles are not yet a practical proposition. To become one they will require major technological advances beyond the present state of knowledge.

The general opinion, therefore, is that in spite of advances of nuclear energy in other fields petroleum fuels will continue as the source of energy for ground vehicles. This brings one back to the reciprocating engine and the gas turbine and, even more, to the combination of the two in the compound engine.

27

Self-Propelled Guns

SELF-PROPELLED guns are closely related to tanks and at times the two have been barely distinguishable from each other. In essence, both are automotive weapon carriers and their common function is to provide mobile fire power. Consequently, differences between self-propelled guns and tanks have been a matter of degree rather than principle and it is not easy to draw a clear dividing line between them. Neither the question of direct and indirect fire, range and calibre of weapon, nor the amount of armour protection provide an infallible basis on which to differentiate tanks from self-propelled guns although, in general, self-propelled guns have tended to larger calibre weapons with limited traverse and less protection than tanks and to be used for indirect, rather than direct, fire at longer ranges.

In their simplest form self-propelled guns are also simpler than tanks and consist of nothing more than guns mounted on ordinary trucks, or similar wheeled vehicles. Because of their simplicity wheeled self-propelled guns preceded tanks in time and their development can be traced to the earliest attempts at using automotive vehicles for military purposes.

The earliest attempts were exemplified by the armed motor cars developed from 1899 onwards by Major R. P. Davidson in the United States and conceived as highly mobile carriages for the newly introduced machine-guns. Motor vehicles mounting heavier weapons followed later, particularly for use against dirigible balloons and aircraft. The first was an automatic truck-mounted 37 mm. gun, intended for use against ground targets, built in the United States by S. M. McClean and unsuccessfully tried in 1904. In 1906, an Ehrhardt anti-balloon vehicle appeared in Germany mounting a 50 mm. gun on an armoured 4-wheeled chassis and in the same year a

366

truck-mounted Krupp 75 mm. gun was also tried for use against balloons. The French followed suit and in 1910 started experiments with a 75 mm. field gun mounted on a de Dion-Bouton chassis. This was the forerunner of several such self-propelled anti-aircraft guns and itself remained in service until 1936. It was the Italians, however, who were the first to use wheeled self-propelled guns in quantity following an order placed in 1915 for sixteen 4-gun batteries of 102/35 guns on Spa 9000 trucks.

Since then several other wheeled self-propelled guns have been built, particularly for anti-aircraft use and, more recently, to carry light anti-tank weapons, but since 1916, when the first tanks appeared, the great majority have been based on tracked chassis. The association between the artillery and tracked vehicles began even earlier, however, during the gun-towing trials of the British Hornsby tractor at Aldershot and in 1908 it was proposed by Major Donohue of the Mechanical Traction Committee to mount a gun on the tractor and give it some armour protection. Nothing came of this proposal and the War Office showed little further interest in the Hornsby tractors but by about 1911 at least a few far-sighted British artillery officers were convinced of the value of tracked tractors for towing heavy guns. Soon after the outbreak of the First World War they got the opportunity to put their ideas into effect, though only with Holt tractors imported from the United States because of the pre-war failure of the War Office to support the development of the Hornsby tractors. And this pioneer use of the Holt tractors for gun towing also helped Colonel Swinton to formulate the ideas which contributed to the conception of the first British tank.

Soon after the first tanks were designed the idea was also conceived, or revived, of using tracked vehicles to carry guns. As a result, the design of what was called a Gun Carrying Tank was commenced in July 1916 and in January 1917 the first vehicle was completed. It was based on the mechanical components of the Mark I tank and its role was to carry a 6 in. howitzer or a 60-pounder gun, after removing their wheels which were hung on the outside of the vehicle. The guns could be fired from the carrier although normally they were expected to be fired dismounted and in practice the 48 carriers built were used chiefly for bringing up ammunition.

The French started designing self-propelled guns a little later although, in fact, a French artillery officer, Captain Levasseur, submitted proposals for a tracked self-propelled 75 mm. gun as early as 1903 and the first French tanks of 1916–17 were employed and designated as *artillerie d'assaut*, beside being conceived by another artillery officer, Colonel J. E. Estienne. The first two were a 220 mm. self-propelled howitzer and a gun of the same calibre designed respectively by St. Chamond and Schneider, who built the first French tanks, but the former was actually preceded by an experimental mounting of a long 120 mm. gun on the St. Chamond tank chassis. Other designs followed and by the end of the war in 1918 there were 6 prototypes, including a 105 mm. and 3 different 75 mm. on the Renault F.T. light tank chassis and the 220 mm. on St. Chamond and Schneider chassis.

Immediately after the war General Sainte-Claire-Deville, inspector general of artillery equipment, envisaged that the whole of the French artillery, except for heavy long-range guns, would be self-propelled but his views met strong opposition from other artillerymen and the High Command. The superior cross-country mobility, speed in changing position and economy in personnel were grudgingly conceded. But arguments were advanced against self-propelled guns on the grounds that petrol was an imported product, that their reliability and road performance were poor and, above all, thinking in terms of traditional methods, that the gun could not be placed in position without its motor carriage. The opposition was officially backed by the Commander-in-Chief and as a result development of self-propelled guns ceased in 1918. Only a few 280 mm. and 194 mm. G.P.F. guns on St. Chamond chassis were completed and these, with modifications, were still the only self-propelled guns in service when the Second World War broke out.

29. Carden-Loyd Mark VIII with two 0·5in Vickers machine-guns, the first anti-aircraft tank.

30. United States LVT-1, the first production version of the Landing Vehicle, Tracked. (*FMC Corp.*).

31. Panhard EBR with the four centre wheels raised for road operation. (*French Army*).

32. Prototype of the Alvis Saladin armoured car. (*Ministry of Defence, Crown Copyright Reserved*).

In the last few months of the First World War, following the French example, the United States also took up the development of self-propelled guns and experiments continued until about 1922. At least 12 different models were built or sponsored by the United States Ordnance, ranging from a light 5-ton 75 mm. gun to a 240 mm. self-propelled howitzer and including the first tracked vehicles designed by J. Walter Christie, who later became famous for his tank designs. The Caliber, or Westervelt, Board established after the war to study the whole problem of artillery equipment advocated the adoption of self-propelled carriages for medium and heavy artillery but again further development was abandoned in 1922. Much the same arguments were used against self-propelled guns as in France, chiefly that if the engine of the carriage failed the entire unit was immobilised. Therefore, the arguments ran, tractor-drawn artillery was the more logical system.

Thus, what were in many ways very promising beginnings came to nothing in all three countries and in the following two decades little further progress took place. A few isolated attempts to revive the development of self-propelled guns were uniformly unsuccessful since the artillery saw no tactical need for them and the armoured forces concentrated on tanks.

Good examples of this were the self-propelled 83.8 mm. 18-pounders designed in Britain by Vickers in 1924 and first tried during the summer manoeuvres of 1925. Their chassis were very similar to that of the contemporary Vickers medium tanks and they represented a major advance on the original self-propelled guns of the First World War. Three slightly different versions were built: the original had all-round traverse and sufficient elevation for anti-aircraft fire but not even a gun shield, which was added on the second version, while the third version was fully armoured. Unfortunately, although their development was sponsored by the Director of Artillery they found little support and understanding elsewhere. To the majority of the gunners they looked too much like tanks while the tankmen would have nothing less than a tank. In consequence, after 1930 the self-propelled 18-pounders were abandoned and the place which they might have occupied in the development of British armoured forces was taken by the close support tanks. The latter were medium tanks rearmed with 3.7 in. 15-pounder mortars, intended mainly for firing smoke, and they were considerably less effective than the self-propelled 18-pounders.

A similar fate befell the few experimental self-propelled guns built in other countries, which were abandoned as a result of opposition by some and lack of support from others. Such was the fate of the self-propelled 37 mm. anti-tank and 75 mm. field guns built in Germany in the late twenties and of the 75 mm. Howitzer Motor Carriage T1 and T3 built in the thirties by the United States Ordnance Department. The French Army was the only one to resume seriously the development of self-propelled guns before the outbreak of the Second World War, and the 1936 defence programme authorised the creation of 5 self-propelled artillery battalions. However, the development of the equipment was slow and only one or two experimental vehicles were built by 1940, such as the promising S.A.U.40 built by S.O.M.U.A.

But while the development of self-propelled guns remained largely stagnant artillery did not, of course, remain unaffected by the progress of the automotive age. In addition to the mounting of guns on vehicles there was the other and in some ways quicker method : the use of motor vehicles for towing in place of the horse team.

An early and not too promising forerunner of this method was the British steam gun-tractor of the South African War of 1899 to 1902. The first motor-towed guns were tried in 1903 in Portugal and on the outbreak of the First World War the French Army could boast of the first motorised artillery unit—a battery of the 4th Heavy Artillery Regiment. During the war the use of lorries and tractors for towing guns became more common and it was gradually extended in the post-war period.

Apart from being faster than the horse traction previously

employed, the towing of guns by motor vehicles did not depart in principle from the methods consecrated by at least three centuries' usage—a fact which made it much more acceptable to the conservative-minded majority. The guns went into action in much the same way as before and while they were in position the towing vehicles were kept away. But because this method departed so little from earlier practice it suffered from the same disadvantages, the chief being that it still required considerable time and effort to go into action through the necessity of unlimbering and associated motions.

Where wheeled vehicles were used for towing strategic mobility was high but the tactical mobility poor. With tracked tractors the reverse was true and they were in no respect better than tracked self-propelled carriages. The real advantage of the towed over self-propelled guns was an economic one since reliable and commercially available vehicles could be used, while only minor modifications had to be made to the existing guns. This, however, was not always recognised and the economic advantage was lost when special tracked tractors were developed for gun towing.

Special tractors were a necessity if better cross-country performance were to be obtained without the crippling disadvantages of using slow-speed commercial tracked tractors. Prior to their development attempts were made to use a combination of commercial trucks and of small agricultural tractors : the truck carried or towed the gun, tractor and trailer for road transport and the tractor was used for hauling the gun across difficult terrain. This cumbersome and unsightly combination did not prove satisfactory, as might have been expected, and gave way to special artillery tractors. These varied considerably in appearance and performance and included such types as the half-track Citroën-Kegresse tractors of the French Army, the fully tracked Dragons and four wheeled Ant tractors of the British Army and the German half-track vehicles, the last two representing the farthest point reached in the development of mobility of the artillery before the outbreak of the Second World War.

In the meantime developments were taking place in other fields, notably that of tanks, which were soon to re-exert a strong influence on the evolution of artillery equipment. Considerable progress had taken place in the design of tanks and during the thirties the numbers of tanks in all the major armies began to increase steadily.

One immediate effect of this was a development of countermeasures, mainly in the form of anti-tank artillery. At the time this meant guns of 25 to 47 mm., miniature versions of the contemporary field guns used defensively. The Germans, who led in this development and who had 75 anti-tank guns per infantry division long before anyone else did, were not, however, long contented with a passive role for their 37 mm. *Pak*. To make better use of them they began to emphasise the mobility of the motorised anti-tank units and the importance of an aggressive, mobile employment. In keeping with this policy, anti-tank units were called *Panzerjäger*, or " tank hunters," and were also used offensively in support of the infantry. When the Second World War broke out the Germans moved a stage further and in 1940 introduced a few self-propelled anti-tank guns, starting with a Czech-made 47 mm. gun on a Pz.Kpfw.I light tank chassis. From this somewhat tentative beginning they moved on and introduced increasing numbers of self-propelled anti-tank guns, particularly in 1942 as a result of meeting the Soviet tank masses.

All the early self-propelled anti-tank guns were of an improvised nature but in spite of this they served the double purpose of increasing the mobility and hence the effectiveness of anti-tank artillery and of filling the gap until more powerful tanks became available. Typical of this class were the 7.5 cm. Pak 40 mounted atop Pz.Kpfw.II and 38t light tank chassis in a simple open-top superstructure but there were many others, ranging from the tapered bore 2.8 cm. S.Pz.B.41 on a light armoured car chassis, through guns mounted on captured French light tank chassis and half-tracks, to a 128 mm. gun on an experimental forerunner of the Tiger heavy tank.

Other armies followed the German lead, finding from their own experience the limitation of towed anti-tank guns. Until then towed anti-tank guns were acclaimed as the best means of defeating tanks but a defence system based on them lacked flexibility and being semi-static proved ineffectual once operations assumed a mobile character. In fact, its effectiveness depended largely on the chance of hostile tanks attacking just where adequate numbers of anti-tank guns had previously been emplaced. On the other hand, the same guns mounted on self-propelled carriages, or in tanks, could be used in a much more mobile and flexible manner and consequently could be much more effective.

Thus, after the first few days of the 1940 campaign, the French mounted their 47 mm. anti-tank guns on Laffly 6 x 6 chassis and issued a few of these *chasseurs de chars* to their 2nd and 4th Armoured Divisions which used them with success. The following year, 1941, saw the appearance of British 40 mm. 2-pounder guns mounted on light four wheeled trucks and other rather primitive forms of self-propelled anti-tank guns in Libya.

The United States Army began with similar improvisations, such as the 37 mm. Gun Motor Carriage M6 based on a standard 4 x 4 truck. Although the last to enter this field it developed the mobile offensive role of anti-tank artillery farthest by creating the Tank Destroyer Command whose units, in the words of the Tank Destroyer Field Manual, were " especially designed for offensive action against hostile armoured forces." Their equipment included such powerful and mobile weapons as the 75 mm. Gun Motor Carriage M3 based on the armoured half-track, the 3 in. M10 and the 90 mm. M36, and, finally, the 76 mm. M18. A common characteristic of the last 3 vehicles was that they had thinner armour and open top turrets but were otherwise very similar to contemporary tanks. The M10 and M36 were actually based on modifications of the M4 medium tank but the M18 was designed specifically as a highly mobile tank destroyer and was capable of a maximum speed of 55 m.p.h.

The desire to increase the mobility of anti-tank guns was not the only factor responsible for the development of self-propelled guns : another was a shortage of tanks with effective armour piercing weapons. Although as early as 1916 Colonel Swinton had stated that the best way of fighting a tank is with another tank, contrary views, that " tanks are not meant to fight tanks," all too often prevailed in the years that followed. In consequence, insufficient attention was frequently given to the problem of effective tank armament and when the need to fight hostile tanks arose improvisations or special vehicles had to be resorted to. When, finally, the importance of being able to combat hostile tanks was recognised and adequately armed tanks were introduced in number the need for special self-propelled anti-tank guns or tank destroyers disappeared. This was clearly shown after the Second World War when the American Tank Destroyer Command was abolished and the attached tank destroyer battalions of the American infantry division were replaced by organic tank battalions.

However, some of the wartime self-propelled anti-tank guns continued in service after the Second World War. For instance, the 90 mm. M36 has been used by Turkish and South Korean Armies and the 76 mm. 17-pounder Archer, based on the Valentine tank chassis, continued to be used for a time by the British Army until it was replaced by the Charioteer. The latter was an emergency design consisting of a Cromwell tank rearmed with a 83.9 mm. 20-pounder gun in a new turret and it resembled somewhat the American tank destroyer approach. Otherwise, self-propelled anti-tank guns introduced since the Second World War have been confined either to very light weapons, such as the American 105 and 106 mm. recoilless guns on 4 x 4 quarter-ton trucks, or to special applications, as in the case of the United States Marine Corps Ontos with six 106 mm. guns and the airborne 90 mm. M56 self-propelled anti-tank gun.

Apart from their influence on the development of self-propelled anti-tank guns, the other effect of the appearance of large numbers of tanks on all sides or, more precisely, of armoured formations was a partial mechanisation of field artillery. In the first permanent mechanised formation, such as the French Division Légère Mécanique of 1934 or the German Panzer Division of 1935, all artillery was towed and this was still true of all the armoured divisions during the first two years of the Second World War. Even in the German Army, which was leading at the time in the technique of armoured warfare, guns continued to be towed as of yore in spite of requests from some of the leading panzer commanders for self-propelled artillery. The lack of interest, if not actual opposition, on the part of the artillery combined with a shortage of suitable chassis after meeting other demands prevented anything being done about it for some time.

However, the use of towed artillery in support of tank units presented unquestionable difficulties. As a result, semi-improvised self-propelled howitzers, such as the 105 mm. " Wasp " and the 150 mm. " Bumble Bee " based on Pz.Kpfw.II and IV chassis respectively, appeared in 1943. Further development was, however, severely restricted by the more urgent calls for mobile anti-tank and close support guns. In consequence, not more than one battalion in a panzer division could usually be equipped with them and the others continued to use towed guns. At the same time, with the introduction of heavily armed tanks such as the Tigers and Panthers, many panzer commanders felt that the need for self-propelled guns was less urgent and there was already a tendency to go over to multiple rocket launchers for area bombardment.

Nevertheless, development of new types of self-propelled guns continued right up to the end of the war. The most interesting and promising were the *Waffenträger*, or Weapon Carriers, whose development began in 1942 in response to a military requirement for guns with all-round traverse which could be fired either from the vehicle or from the ground. The first was the Krupp-built *Heuschrecke*, or " Grasshopper," which consisted of a dismountable turret with a 105 mm. howitzer on a Pz.Kpfw.IV medium tank chassis. It provided an answer to the conservative minded gunners who objected for years to self-propelled guns because the guns could not be emplaced without their motor carriages but, for what it was worth, the *Heuschrecke* was too large, too heavy and too complicated.

Consequently, a new series of designs was started in 1943 out of which emerged two slightly different *Waffenträger*, or Weapon Carriers. Both were based on the Czech-built Pz.Kpfw.38t light tank chassis, widened, the principal difference between the two being that the lighter type had 4 bogie wheels per side whereas the heavier and longer version had 6. The light type was intended to carry an 88 mm. anti-tank gun or a dismountable 105 mm. howitzer, and the larger version the same weapons or a 128 mm. gun or 150 mm. howitzer, both with limited traverse. Production was intended to start in the spring of 1945 but in the event only a few prototypes were built : an Ardelt-built light *Waffenträger* was successfully tested in April 1944 and was remarkable for its day in that it mounted a gun as powerful as the 8.8 cm. Pak 43 with 360° traverse in a vehicle which weighed just over 14 tons. A somewhat similar 88 mm. gun *Waffenträger* was built by Krupp and Steyr but, unlike the Ardelt and Rheinmetall-Borsig/Ardelt prototypes based on the 38t chassis, this bore some resemblance to the *Raupenschlepper Ost* tracked truck.

Another series of self-propelled carriages called the *Grille*, for mounting guns of up to 170 mm., or a 210 mm. howitzer, was started by Krupp in 1942–43 but only the 17 cm.K got as far as the initial stages of prototype construction, using a lengthened Tiger II heavy tank chassis. Even heavier R 1 to R 14 self-propelled guns, ranging in calibre from 150 mm. to 380 mm., were sponsored by the German Navy for coast defence from 1943 onwards but for sheer size—and wasted effort—they were all easily surpassed by the *Karl* 600/540 mm. 123-ton self-propelled siege howitzer. Six specimens of this monstrous vehicle were built, the first, with 600 mm.

barrels, in 1942 and the rest, with interchangeable 540 mm. barrels, in mid-1944.

By the end of the Second World War the United States Army was also developing some large-calibre self-propelled guns but, unlike the German, it had at least first made sure of providing its field units with more urgently needed equipment. It was, in fact, the first to put the whole of its armoured divisions' artillery on self-propelled carriages, which is all the more remarkable for the fact that in 1940, after the *Blitzkrieg* in France, there were still some American artillery officers who claimed that horse-drawn 75s were all that were needed. By 1941, however, the majority held different views and the development of self-propelled guns began at a frantic rate.

One of the first to be standardised was the 105 mm. Howitzer Motor Carriage M7, conceived in June 1941 on the basis of the M3 medium tank chassis, which became standard artillery equipment of the American armoured divisions and also some British. It was first used by the latter at El Alamein, in October, 1942, and served as a model for the very similar British Sexton self-propelled 87.6 mm. 25-pounder, which succeeded the original, 1942, hasty installation of this gun on top of the Valentine tank chassis.

In relation to their armament, both the 105 mm. M7 and the 25-pounder Sexton were too heavy. The former weighed 22.6 and the latter 25.4 tons and the only justification for such extravagance was the availability of M3, M4 or Canadian Ram medium tank chassis on which they were based. The Americans recognised the inefficiency of the 105 mm. M7 at an early date and already in August 1942 started the development of the T16 4.5 in. gun and T64 155 mm. howitzer on the basis of the M5 light tank chassis. Before it was completed, however, the M5 was superseded by the M24 and the development of the lighter self-propelled guns was transferred on to the latter basis. In consequence, the second generation vehicles, such as the 105 mm. Howitzer M37 (T76) and the 155 mm. Howitzer M41 (T64E1), which were standardised shortly before the end of the Second World War or immediately afterwards, were based on the M24 light tank chassis.

The medium tank chassis were more appropriate to heavier guns, such as the 155 mm. M12 (T6) which was conceived at the same time as the 105 mm. M7 and which was used successfully in 1944 and 1945, when it was superseded by the more powerful 155 mm. M40 (T83), based on the M4 instead of M3 chassis. The mounting of even larger calibre weapons proved possible and the M4 medium tank chassis was also used as the basis of the 8 in. (203 mm.) Howitzer M43 (T89), designed before the end of the Second World War.

Still heavier guns required heavier tank chassis and the 240 mm. Howitzer T92 and the 8 in. Gun T93, whose design began in January 1945, were both based on the M26 heavy tank. They weighed 56 and 58.6 tons, respectively, and represented the peak of the American wartime self-propelled gun development. Neither, however, was standardised and after the war ideas changed, leading to a different type of carriage from that represented by the T92 and T93.

Until then American self-propelled guns had open-top crew compartments and, like others of their type, very limited traverse ; after the war complete crew protection and greater traverse were demanded. In consequence, a new design was evolved which incorporated a roomy limited-traverse turret at the rear of the vehicle. The armour of the turret is still relatively thin, like that of the earlier self-propelled carriages, but it affords all-round protection to the weapon and crew housed in it, including the driver who was previously at the front of the vehicle where the engine and transmission now are. Apart from the improved protection, the new carriages also offer greater, though still incomplete traverse, but they compare unfavourably with earlier designs on account of their higher silhouette caused by their large turrets. In calibre they cover the same range as the earlier standard vehicles and include the 105 mm. Howitzer M52 (T98), the 155 mm.

Howitzer T99, the 155 mm. Gun M53 (T97) and the 8 in. Howitzer M55 (T108), all introduced into service since 1954. They were preceded by the 155 mm. Howitzer M44, a hybrid which used the same type of chassis as the other post-war models but still had an open-top compartment like the wartime carriages.

Of the new self-propelled guns, the M52 and M44, which weigh 24.2 and 27.9 tons respectively, use mechanical components of the M41 light tank series and the heavier M53 and M55, of 40 and 42 tons, those of the M48 medium tank. The 105 mm. M52, 155 mm. M44 and 8 in. M55 are used by the artillery of the armoured divisions : the first replaces the earlier M7 and M37, the second replaces the M41 155 mm. self-propelled howitzers which were first incorporated in the armoured divisons after the Second World War and the 8 in. M55 replaces the M43 which was first added in 1957 as part of a composite artillery battalion. All 3 are also used by corps artillery, which also uses the 155 mm. M53 self-propelled guns in parallel with towed equipment of the same calibre. The latest 175 mm. gun, however, is to be used only in the self-propelled T235 form.

The latest and largest Soviet guns of about 300 mm. are also self-propelled. On the whole, however, the Soviet Army, in contrast to the United States, has shown little interest in what might be called conventional self-propelled guns. Instead it has concentrated on the development of another class of self-propelled equipment which was originated by the German *Sturmgeschütz*, or assault gun.

The origin of the *Sturmgeschütz* can be traced to the evolution of German infantry weapons. As a result of studies conducted after the First World War the Germans rightly concluded that neither rifles nor light machine-guns were sufficient in themselves for the needs of infantry combat and took the initiative in re-equipping the infantry with more powerful weapons. Thus, among others, they introduced regimental infantry gun companies of six 75 mm. and two 150 mm. howitzers, which were a logical outcome of earlier experiments with infantry-accompanying field guns and the sound German views that a gun on the spot is worth a whole battery later.

The infantry howitzers paid dividends in the field but they brought their own problems. The chief was that of mobility, particularly as they were used well forward. Improvised self-propelled 150 mm. infantry howitzers on Pz.Kpfw.I and, later, 38t chassis were tried but, because of their large silhouette and incomplete thin armour, did not prove successful. A more thoroughly designed type was required and the Germans, anticipating many of the later lessons, produced their first assault guns.

Since the replacement of the existing infantry guns was out of the question, assault guns were used to supplement them, particularly when the employment of the former was difficult, as in attacks on well defended positions. In keeping with this policy assault guns were grouped in independent battalions and later brigades and were allotted as required to infantry units. The first were tried in France, in May 1940, by which time only 6 had been produced but thereafter their numbers grew steadily, particularly as the Germans did not subscribe to any " infantry tank " ideas.

The original Sturmgeschütz III consisted of a turretless Pz.Kpfw.III light-medium tank chassis, more heavily armoured and with a low-velocity 75 mm. gun mounted in the front superstructure plate. The original gun was the same as that of the Pz.Kpfw.IV medium tank but in 1942 it was replaced by a higher-velocity Stu.K.L/43, which turned the Sturmgeschütz into an effective anti-tank as well as infantry support weapon. This, in turn, paved the way for a possible merger of the assault guns and self-propelled anti-tank guns into a single *Panzerjäger* class, although a small number of the assault guns continued to be armed with low-velocity weapons, such as the 105 mm. howitzer and the 150 mm. infantry howitzer.

The new class, which came into prominence during 1944–45, included such vehicles as the 88 mm. gun Jagdpanther, the 75 mm. Jagdpanzer IV and the light 16-ton Jagdpanzer 38t, as well as the heavy 70-ton 128 mm. gun Jagdtiger. In the last quarter of 1944 their production exceeded that of German tanks with a total of 2,866 for the three months, and in the production programme planned for 1945 as much as 61 per cent. of the total number of armoured fighting vehicles was to be made of the Jagdpanzer 38. As it was there were 54 Sturmgeschütz brigades by the end of the war and in January 1945 the German Army already had more assault gun type vehicles than tanks.

The popularity of the assault gun type vehicle was understandable. By virtue of its low silhouette and good, all-round protection it was superior to other types of self-propelled guns. At the same time, at the expense of traverse, it carried more powerful armament or better protection, and frequently both, than a corresponding weight tank ; moreover, it was somewhat easier to produce. In consequence, it provided an attractive supplement to tanks, or an alternative in all cases where manoeuvrability and consequently gun-traverse was not a primary consideration.

The German views came to be fully shared by the Russians who, from 1943 onwards, introduced a whole series of vehicles of the assault gun type. In fact, the Russians confined themselves almost entirely to this type of self-propelled gun. Among the few early exceptions was the SU 76, a 76 mm. anti-tank gun based on the T-70 light tank chassis which resembled the original semi-improvised German self-propelled guns and which was quickly relegated to a secondary role with infantry formations and then satellite troops in whose hands it turned up in Korea in 1950.

The other SUs were entirely different, completely and thickly armoured and based on T-34 medium tank or KV heavy tank chassis. To the former category belonged the SU 122 howitzer and the SU 85 anti-tank gun, which first appeared in the summer of 1943, and the SU 100, a 100 mm. gun on a similar, low-silhouette turretless version of the T-34 tank, which began to replace the SU 85 before the end of the Second World War. The second category comprised the SU 152, a 152 mm. gun-howitzer introduced in 1943 and the less common SU 122 gun on the same KV chassis, both later replaced by improved versions on the JS or Stalin tank chassis.

All these assault gun type SUs were intended for direct fire which the Russians employed extensively even with field artillery but which the SUs could perform much more effectively. At the same time, the SUs made it possible to increase the fire power of the armoured units, through the quicker mounting of heavier guns on existing tank chassis, and gunpower was the thing the Russians always regarded most important in their armoured equipment. In consequence, SUs were produced and used on a large scale and the SU 100 and JSU 152 have figured prominently in Soviet armoured formations since the Second World War.

In relation to tanks, the role of the SUs has been to provide a mobile base of fire on which the more manoeuvrable tanks can pivot and in some cases, towards the end of the Second World War, they were mixed right down to platoon level in the ratio of one SU 85 to two T-34. The combination is not surprising, however, since the Soviet SUs and the German assault guns were " turretless tanks " rather than self-propelled artillery in the sense commonly understood in the West, where the SU type has found little favour.

Both Britain and the United States produced only a few experimental vehicles of the assault gun type and only of very heavy weight. In 1941–42, for instance, twenty-four 3 in. Gun Carriers Mark I were built, consisting of a 3 in. anti-aircraft gun in a turretless Churchill infantry tank, but for some reason were never used ; at a later date six prototypes of the turretless Tortoise (A.39) 76–78 ton assault tank were also built, too late to be of any use. At about the same time, towards the end of the Second World War, a somewhat similar vehicle originally called the T95 Gun Motor Carriage and later the T28 heavy tank was also built in the United States. It was a formidable low-silhouette vehicle of 85 tons with a long 105 mm. gun and up to 12 inches of frontal armour, but again the development did not get beyond the prototype stage. Much more recently, in 1952, yet another experimental type appeared, this time in France : it resembled the German Jagd-panther but consisted of a 120 mm. gun on the AMX 50 ton experimental chassis.

Otherwise, Britain and later the United States got fairly close to the lighter assault howitzers by rearming some of their tanks with howitzers or mortars. The first such rearmed tank appeared in 1930, when a Vickers Medium Mark I was fitted with a 3.7 in. 15-pounder mortar in place of the standard 47 mm. 3-pounder tank gun. It was adopted, unfortunately, in preference to the contemporary self-propelled 18-pounder guns, which were much more versatile and effective, and became the first British " close support tank." Later close support tanks consisted of A.9 and A.10 cruisers rearmed with 3.7 in. mortars, Matilda infantry tanks and Covenanter and Crusader cruisers with 3 in. howitzers and Churchill infantry tanks and Centaur and Cromwell cruisers with 95 mm. howitzers, but the whole thing died a natural death when tanks were finally armed with large calibre guns capable of firing effective high-explosive shells.

However, toward the end of the Second World War, just when the British close support tanks were fading out, the United States Army began to use howitzer-armed tanks. Among the first vehicles of this type was the M8 75 mm. howitzer, which consisted of an M5 light tank with a special open-top turret. Later came M4 medium tanks with 105 mm. howitzers in place of the 75 or 76 mm. tank guns and just before the end of the Second World War the T26E2 heavy tank, which was essentially an M26 (T26E3) tank with a 105 mm. howitzer instead of the high-velocity 90 mm. gun. At one stage it was even proposed to build three 105 mm. howitzer versions to each 90 mm. gun tank, and although this dubious scheme came to nothing the T26E2 survived into the post-war period as the M45 medium tank.

The future value of such limited purpose tanks armed with howitzers not much different in calibre from the guns of other tanks is doubtful. There is much more to be said for the larger calibre assault gun-howitzers of the JSU 152 type, which may retain their value even longer than similar calibre guns on " conventional " self-propelled carriages. At any rate, the latter are more likely to be challenged by self-propelled rocket launchers of the type foreshadowed by the Soviet launcher mounted on an amphibious light tank chassis and the 2 larger missile launchers on JS heavy tank type chassis, which were paraded in Moscow in November 1957.

Earlier surface-to-surface missile launchers have resembled the earliest self-propelled guns in that they were mounted on ordinary trucks. Thus, the American 762 mm. Honest John rocket launcher has been mounted on a 5-ton 6 x 6 truck and the French SS-10, as well as the American Dart anti-tank guided missile, on quarter-ton light trucks, while the Corporal guided missile is carried on another, if special, truck. It is difficult to imagine such equipment taking the place of well-developed self-propelled guns but more advanced and properly designed self-propelled missile launchers may well, eventually, replace most guns.

In the meantime, self-propelled guns provide the most effective form of artillery equipment and make artillery capable of much more than the traditional role of a supporting arm. However true it may have been that the relatively immobile towed guns had to confine themselves to supporting roles, this is certainly not the case with self-propelled guns. Like tanks, self-propelled guns are capable of much more mobile and direct employment and, in general, they make artillery more versatile and effective.

28

Armoured Infantry Carriers

INFANTRY and its relationship to tanks has been one of the thorniest aspects of the evolution of mechanised forces. For years it has been argued that the principal function of tanks is to support the infantry and that they should, therefore, be subordinated to it. For almost as long a few have argued from the other side that tanks can virtually dispense with the infantry and, in general, assigned a subsidiary role to the latter. The former view still finds support in tradition-bound military doctrines but arguments and counter-arguments about the superiority of infantry over tanks, or vice versa, are essentially futile for the two arms are complementary and the real problem is not to decide between them but to effectively combine them together.

The core of the problem of an effective combination between infantry and tanks is the fact that infantry is less mobile, *per se*, than tanks. In consequence, as long as the infantry was not mechanised, it tended to be separated from tanks or else it has prevented tanks from making full use of their mobility. An extreme case of the latter was the complete subordination of tanks to the infantry and tying them down to the pace of the foot soldier. The other extreme, diametrically opposed but also generated by the inferior mobility of the infantry, as well as overestimates of what tanks could accomplish on their own, was the view that armoured forces should contain no infantry at all. This was subscribed to by several of the British tank pioneers who thought in terms of " landships " and tank " fleets " and who saw little use for infantry, even as " tank marines." General Fuller, the leading apostle of tank warfare, advocated armoured formations without organic infantry as late as 1943, and the development

385

of British armoured forces during the early thirties was almost entirely on an " all-tank " basis.

Experience has shown, however, the inadequacy of armoured formations based on tanks alone and the need to supplement tanks with riflemen. As early as 1917, the French found it necessary to attach a company of specially trained *infanterie d'accompagnement* to each *groupe* of 16 tanks. The task of these infantry units was to act as assault pioneers, to provide close-in protection, to clean up, with rifle and grenade, small nests of enemy resistance and, in general, to complement tanks.

In the following two decades of peacetime development, with its extremes of complete subordination of tanks to the infantry or of sweeping mechanised manoeuvres, this wartime tactical lesson was largely overlooked. However, the Germans rediscovered it and the need for a strong infantry component when they began to develop their first panzer divisions in the mid-thirties. To start with, they had 3 rifle battalions per division but peacetime experiments showed that even this was not enough and by 1939 each panzer division had 4 rifle battalions to 4 tank battalions.

The obvious success of the German tank–infantry combination led to it being copied elsewhere and from 1941 onwards practically all armoured formations have had a sizeable infantry component, approximately equal proportions of tank and infantry units being generally considered best. The recognition of the need to include a strong force of infantry in armoured formations was not, however, generally followed by the provision of means which would enable the infantry to participate in all phases of armoured operations. The lack of such means, in the form of suitable vehicles, deprived the infantry of the armoured divisions of much of their usefulness and has often prevented it from playing a fully effective role.

Yet the development of armoured personnel carriers goes back to the earliest days of tank development. The first was designed in Britain in September 1917, on the basis of the contemporary rhomboidal British heavy tank. Called the

Mark IX, it could carry 50 men in addition to a crew of four, or 10 tons of supplies when its laden weight reached 37 tons. Thirty-five were built in 1918 but the development of this type was brought to an end by the Armistice of the same year and the general lack of interest in the part to be played by mechanised infantry in future warfare.

What little attention was devoted in the early days to the role of the mechanised infantryman in future warfare was inclined toward the individual solution, that is providing each infantryman with his armoured vehicle or, in other words, replacing the infantryman on foot by a small one-man tank. Such ideas were already at the back of the French Renault F.T. light tank of the First World War and after the war they were pursued with some vigour in Britain. General Martel was responsible for much of the pioneer work which was ably carried on by Sir John Carden, who became famous through the Carden Loyd tankettes.

Actually, the Renault F.T. and all but the earliest Carden Loyds were two-man machines and the latter branched out into two distinct lines. One consisted of turreted vehicles, similar in principle to the Renault F.T., which produced the long series of Vickers Carden Loyd light tanks. The other line was that of the machine-gun carriers, best exemplified by the 1.5-ton low-silhouette Carden Loyd Mark VI of 1928–29. In 1935 the latter was succeeded by a larger three-man machine-gun carrier which evolved into the 3.8-ton Bren Gun Carrier. This began to be issued to British infantry, on the scale of ten per battalion, on the eve of the Second World War and it also became the first armoured personnel carrier in the British armoured divisions. Improved and modified versions of the carrier were developed later and altogether about 40,000 were built during the war.

Unfortunately, the Bren Gun Carrier was not an efficient armoured personnel carrier in view of its very limited carrying capacity of three to four men. However, this was in accord with the contemporary views on the limited role of infantry in armoured formations, namely that of a passive ground-holding element. Hence the accent on the automatic weapon and the development of the vehicle as a machine-gun carrier, or a scouting vehicle, rather than as a means of carrying riflemen for dismounted offensive action. This was underlined by the fact that for some time it was issued only to the scout platoons of the motor companies in British armoured formations while the remaining rifle platoons moved about in light trucks.

It was left to the Germans to make the first determined effort to provide the infantry of the armoured divisions with armoured cross-country personnel carriers. Interestingly enough, the origin of this type of vehicle may be traced as far back as the immediate post-First World War period.

Prohibited by the Allies from having tanks, the Germans were, however, allowed a small number of unarmed armoured cars for use as personnel or supply carriers in internal security duties. They were large and clumsy but by the mid-twenties Krupp evolved a much improved design with sloping armour and a few samples of this type were actually sold to the Netherlands East Indies. It was still a 4-wheeler with solid tyres but in the mid-thirties the Krupp-type hull appeared on half-track chassis. The latter were originally developed for artillery tractors but subsequently the German Army adapted half-track vehicles to a wide variety of roles, including that of the *Panzergrenadierwagen*, or armoured infantry carrier. There were two main types, the light Sd.Kfz.250 which could carry 6 men and weighed 5.7 tons and the Sd.Kfz.251 which could carry 12 men and weighed 8.5 tons.

A few of the German armoured half-tracks were used during the 1939 Polish campaign and they appeared in greater number during the 1940 French campaign. But it was only in 1942 that there was anything like one Panzer Grenadier battalion per division equipped with them and even by the end of the war only the most favoured panzer divisions, such as the *Panzer Lehr* and the *Grossdeutschland*, were better provided with armoured half-track carriers. To provide more was simply beyond the capabilities of the German industry in the latter part of the Second World War.

Thus, largely because of industrial limitations, the Germans were unable to provide the whole of the infantry in their armoured divisions with armoured carriers. This was done for the first time by the Americans, who had the obvious advantage of United States industrial resources and the added advantage of a relatively simple and inexpensive half-track armoured personnel carrier.

The origins of this last vehicle actually go back to France, which provided much of the impetus to the development of half-track vehicles. It was there that Adolphe Kegresse, after his return from Russia, developed the half-track vehicle with continuous rubber tracks. And it was there that the Citroën Company, which has never lacked courage to pioneer new automotive developments, first took up its manufacture.

Some of the potentialities of the Citroën-Kegresse half-tracks were demonstrated in 1923, when five of them made the first motor crossing of the Sahara desert. From then on the chassis was adopted as the basis of a number of French armoured cars and, also, of a weapon carrier for the *dragons portés* who formed the rifle component in the mechanised formations of the French cavalry. As a carrier the Citroën-Kegresse was not armoured although in Britain an armoured machine-gun carrier version, the Burford-Kegresse, was briefly experimented with in 1930.

The armoured personnel carrier version of the Kegresse half-track was largely an American development. The United States Army bought a sample vehicle from France in 1931 and from then on began its own development of half-track vehicles.

The first Half-Track Car T1 was built in 1931 by the Cunningham Company and was followed by several other experimental models. The majority of the early half-tracks were intended as artillery prime movers but in 1938 the half-track chassis was combined with the armoured body of the wheeled scout car, which had been developed as a reconnaissance vehicle for the United States Cavalry. The resulting Personnel Carrier T7 was the first American armoured half-track and was followed by the Half-Track Scout Car T14, whose development was authorised in 1939 and which was the prototype of the Second World War carriers.

The demand for armoured half-track carriers initiated by the mechanised elements of the United States Cavalry before the war was greatly strengthened by the 1940 Louisiana manoeuvres where, for the first time, motorised infantry was combined with armoured units of the 7th United States Cavalry Brigade. One of the lessons of the manoeuvres was the need for something better than trucks for the infantry of armoured formations and the half-track armoured personnel carrier was adopted as the solution, although it actually retained many commercial truck features.

The T14 was standardised as the M2 and was followed by the M3 Half-Track Personnel Carrier which was capable of carrying 14 men. Six hundred and forty-two half-tracks, including 145 M3 carriers, were included in the establishment of the first American armoured divisions which had 2 infantry battalions each. From then on the whole of the American armoured infantry was carried in these vehicles. In the latter part of the war, when American armoured divisions had 3 infantry battalions, each battalion was fully equipped with 62 half-track armoured personnel carriers. Armoured half-tracks were also used for many other purposes and to satisfy the various requirements 41,170 were produced in 1941 to 1945.

From about 1943 on, American-built half-track carriers were also supplied to British armoured divisions. There, however, they were only furnished to the motor battalions of the armoured brigades where they replaced the light truck of the rifle platoons. The rest of the divisional infantry continued to rely on trucks for their transport. The position was, therefore, similar to that in the German armoured divisions where, in general, only one out of the four infantry battalions was equipped with armoured carriers. The rest of the German Panzer Grenadiers, like the 3 battalions of the British lorried infantry brigade and the majority of infantry in other armoured formations, had to rely on trucks which were generally mere adaptations of commercial designs.

Equipped with such vehicles, the ability of the infantry to co-operate closely with tanks was obviously limited. It was particularly so under the difficult terrain conditions encountered on the Eastern Front, in Russia. These and the general shortage of motor transport forced the Russians to the expedient of carrying infantrymen into action on tanks. This was by no means a novel method, for it was used earlier during Soviet peacetime manoeuvres, nor was it confined to the Soviet Army. The latter was the only one, however, to use this method consistently and on a large scale and to adopt it as the method of transport for the organic infantry detachments of its armoured brigades. The troop-carrying capacity of each tank became part of its official characteristics—that of the T-34 being set at 12 men and of the KV at 15—and the Russians even introduced the designation of " tank landing troops " for those who rode into action on tanks.

Another expedient, though far less costly in terms of infantry casualties than the Soviet method, was tried in the closing stages of the Second World War by the Canadian and British forces. In fact, it was dictated by a desire to reduce infantry casualties as much as to increase infantry mobility. It consisted of converting tanks or self-propelled guns into heavily armoured personnel carriers, by removing turrets in the first case and the main armament in the latter. The vehicles actually used were American-built M7 105 mm. self-propelled howitzers or Priests, M4 or Sherman medium tanks and the similar Canadian-built Ram tanks and after conversion were given the generic name of Kangaroos. The first were used in Normandy in 1944 and in December of that year the Canadian and British Armies each formed a special armoured carrier regiment equipped with Kangaroos which were allotted as required to infantry units. By their make-shift nature the Kangaroos were inefficient as personnel carriers but they provided a degree of protection and cross-country mobility superior to that of other contemporary infantry carriers, including the American half-tracks which were the principal type in use.

Even without such unfavourable comparisons, dissatisfaction with the American half-track carriers was inevitable after a time in any case. They were largely a compromise solution which retained some of the shortcomings of both the truck and the tracked vehicle without having the full advantages of either. So much so that after the Second World War the United States Army decided to abandon them in favour of fully tracked carriers.

The first of the American fully tracked armoured personnel carriers, introduced soon after the Second World War, was of the Kangaroo type. Designated the M39, it consisted of the highly mobile 76 mm. gun M18 tank destroyer minus its turret and armament. It suffered from the same disadvantages as the Canadian and British Kangaroos and was still open-topped. However, it was followed fairly closely by the M44 which had armour protection all round and which was designed from the start as an armoured personnel carrier. As a carrier it was definitely much more efficient but because it was built to carry as many as 27 men it rivalled in size a large bus.

In view of the enormous target which it presented it is not surprising that only a few M44s were built and that this model was abandoned in 1950–51 in favour of its smaller edition, the M75. This has the same type of box-like superstructure with overhead protection but because it was only designed to carry 12 men, including the driver, its overall dimensions are much more reasonable.

A small number of M75s was tried in the closing stages of the Korean war, by which time this model was joined in service by the very similar M59. Externally the 18.7-ton M59 is almost identical with the 18.8-ton M75 but it makes use of components from civilian production to keep costs down and by clever detail design advantage has been taken of its relative bulk to provide it with limited amphibious characteristics, so that it can operate in relatively calm water without any preparation. Otherwise the mechanical characteristics of the M59, as of the M75, are similar to those of the M41 light tank and their performance comparable, in general, to that of tanks. They can, therefore, follow tanks over all types of terrain and make possible the formation of closely knit tank-infantry teams, right down to platoon level, which are a common feature of American armoured tactics.

The post-Second World War British Saracen 6 x 6 armoured personnel carrier is less suited to such methods. Because of its mobility it can be used to rush infantry detachments from one part of the battlefield to another but the differences between its characteristics and those of the Centurion tanks with which it would be expected to work are not conducive to effective close combination. Moreover, by comparison with tracked armoured personnel carriers, it suffers from the disadvantage of a higher silhouette caused by the drive to the 6 wheels which has to be accommodated under the floor of the crew compartment.

By 1951 the Russians also introduced a 6 wheeled armoured personnel carrier, the B.T.R. 152, and a smaller 4 wheeled B.T.R. 40. Like the pre-Second World War American scout cars, both Soviet vehicles follow conventional truck lines and are open-topped but the B.T.R. can carry 14 men and is, at least, a considerable improvement on conveying riflemen in ordinary unprotected trucks. More recently, in 1957, the Russians have demonstrated their first tracked armoured personnel carrier, based on the 76 mm. gun amphibious reconnaissance tank. It is rather of the Kangaroo type and the crew compartment is again open-topped. To that extent it is behind American, British and French carriers designed since the Second World War, all of which have overhead protection, but like the American M59 it is amphibious.

The earliest of the French carriers is the small Hotchkiss TT 6, a 6.4-ton tracked vehicle capable of carrying 7 men, including the driver, and only 6 ft. 1 in. high, which is more than 2 ft. lower than the American M59. A later and larger 12-man carrier is based on the AMX light tank chassis and another, the ETT, on the Panhard EBR 8-wheeled armoured car. Apart from the French Army, the Hotchkiss TT 6 has been adopted also by the German Army as its light carrier. The second and larger German armoured personnel carrier is of Hispano Suiza origin. Like the Hotchkiss, it has a low silhouette, which is most important because the vehicle offers a smaller target and is, therefore, less vulnerable. In consequence, it can accompany tanks more closely and makes possible closer co-operation between them and riflemen. At the same time the riflemen can stay mounted in the carrier longer which helps to maintain the mobile tempo of armoured operations.

The latest American M113 armoured personnel carrier further illustrates the efforts made to lower the silhouette of this type of vehicle, being 7 ft. 2 in. high compared with the 8 ft. 2 in. of the M59, and it weighs only 9.9 tons, thanks to the aluminium alloy armour used in it for the first time on a production basis. At the same time, the M113 can still carry 12 men and, like the M59, is capable of crossing inland waterways without any preparation.

In all respects the latest tracked armoured personnel carriers represent a considerable advance on the half-track carriers of the Second World War and significant progress in the development of more mobile mechanised infantry. The number of different carriers which has appeared is in marked contrast with the situation before the Second World War and a sign of the importance generally attached to the infantry component of mechanised forces. Regressive attempts to return to the " all-tank " principles have not been absent, as shown by the British experimental organisation of 1955 where there was only one infantry battalion to 4 armoured regiments, but in general they only serve to re-emphasise the need for a strong infantry component. Time and time again tanks and riflemen have proved mutually complementary and optimum results require their effective combination, which has been made possible by the development of armoured personnel carriers.

29

Anti-Aircraft Tanks

THE problem of anti-aircraft defence appeared at an early stage of the development of tanks and has existed ever since. More often than not, however, little attention has been given to it, although on occasions it assumed serious proportions and may do so again.

That relatively little attention was given to anti-aircraft defence in the early days of the tank is not surprising : when the standard armament of attacking aircraft consisted of rifle-calibre machine-guns and 20 or 30 lb. bombs the threat to tanks was negligible.

It is true that as a result of a few attacks by German planes against British tanks in the First World War some attention was given to the problem in the immediate post-war period. For instance, British tanks designed immediately after the war, such as the Vickers Medium, incorporated a ball-mounted Hotchkiss machine-gun in the turret roof, to be fired from within the tank at attacking aircraft. But the concern was based on a potential rather than actual air threat ; it was really premature and the measure adopted was more in the nature of a gesture than anything else.

A much more practical approach was adopted in the late twenties when the first anti-aircraft tank was built, again in Britain. It consisted of two .5 in. Vickers water-cooled machine-guns on a modified Light Tank Mark I (Carden Loyd Mark VIII). There was, however, still little incentive to develop this type of vehicle and attention was directed more towards the problem of anti-aircraft defence of various unarmoured vehicular columns associated with tank units rather than tank units themselves. Even in the first year of the Second World War General Guderian could still write suggesting that the tank was about the safest place on the battlefield so far as air attacks were concerned.

In the early stages of the Second World War the situation was beginning to change, however. The air threat to all motorised columns, which formed—and still do—the bulk of all mechanised formations, was already real and considerable. By the late thirties the technique of ground air attack had made considerable progress and led to the creation of a number of special air units, such as the " attack squadrons " of the United States Army Air Corps, the " assault squadrons " of the Italian *Regia Aeronautica*, the French *l'aviation d'assaut* and the *sturmkampflugzeuge* of the German *Luftwaffe*.

Some of the potentialities of these tactical air units were already demonstrated during the Spanish Civil War, notably in low-level attacks against motorised transport columns. German *Stuka*, Junkers Ju 87 dive-bombers, also made their debut in Spain, before becoming famous by their exploits in all the early *Blitzkrieg* campaigns of the Second World War. Their action too was mainly effective against transport columns and troop positions, one of the more significant examples of the former being the destruction of the fuel supply trains of the French 1st Armoured Division in May 1940, which contributed to the immobilisation and destruction of that formation. Material damage inflicted directly on tank units was generally small, although the moral effect was often considerable.

On the Allied side in the 1940 campaign, the French claimed successful employment of their 20 mm. cannon armed fighters against German armoured vehicles. But a year or so later, in the Libyan Desert, the Royal Air Force found that its Hawker Hurricane fighters, which had just been rearmed with 20 mm. cannon, were ineffective against tanks, though, once more, they were highly effective against all soft-skinned transport. Fighter-bombers, like dive-bombers, were also ineffective against individual armoured vehicles and were used chiefly against troop positions, concentrations and transport.

The first direct threat to tanks did not come until 1942, when heavier guns were mounted in aircraft, leading to such ground attack models as the British Hurricane IID with two 40 mm. guns, the German Henschel 129 with a long 30 mm. gun and the modified Ju 87 with two 37 mm. guns. The first scored a few successes in the closing stages of the war in North Africa; the others were more successful against Soviet tanks on the Eastern Front and the ace German pilot, Hans Rudel, flying Ju 87s, was credited with the destruction of 500 Soviet tanks between 1943 and 1945.

In general, however, this type of aircraft did not prove a success. One of the main reasons was that the requirement of a fairly heavy type of gun turned it into a limited-purpose aircraft which fell easy prey to hostile fighter planes. The heavy gun aircraft ultimately found better employment in naval operations, as shown by the British de Havilland Mosquito armed with a 57 mm. gun and the successes of the North American B-25 with a 75 mm. gun against Japanese shipping.

It was not until the introduction of rockets that a really effective airborne anti-tank weapon was found. The rocket provided the heavy and yet relatively accurate weapon with which aircraft could attack individual tanks, as well as other ground targets, with a reasonable chance of scoring a hit and without loss of their overall performance.

One of the first fighters to be equipped with rockets was the British Hawker Typhoon. Armed with 60 lb. semi armour-piercing rockets, it saw considerable service in Normandy and North West Europe and met with a good measure of success. However, the losses inflicted in what was at the time claimed to be the greatest success of the rocket-firing fighters—the destruction of German tanks in the final German counter-attack in Normandy, in the Mortain Pocket, in August 1944—proved to be, in after-battle analysis, due largely to ground fire.

Another form of air attack also proved effective against tank units in Normandy, having been first tried in Tunisia in 1943, namely the " carpet bombing " technique of Allied heavy bomber formations. By multiplying the number of bombs per acre, this method could not avoid scoring some direct hits as well as disrupting and stunning the units under attack. The fate of the German *Panzer Lehr* Division at St. Lo in July 1944, which had about 70 per cent. of its effectives knocked out in one such attack, has provided ample testimony of its effectiveness.

Since then this form of air attack has not been tried against armoured formations and probably will not be tried again in view of the altered conditions of aerial warfare. The place of mass bombing raids has been taken by the bomber with the nuclear bomb and nuclear missiles but the serious problems which these raise are outside the realm of anti-aircraft defence of individual tanks or small tank units.

Rockets, on the other hand, have been used against tanks since the Second World War—in Korea. Their precise effectiveness there has been difficult to assess, not only on account of disagreements as to the exact amount of damage inflicted but, even more, the initial absence of hostile anti-aircraft defences and the almost continuous absence of hostile fighters over the front line. On some occasions the success of rocket-firing fighters certainly has been exaggerated and there is no doubt that they have not spelt the doom of the tank any more that the much vaunted Bell P.39 Airacobra or the Soviet Stormovik, or any of the other so-called " tank busters " of the Second World War. Rocket armed fighters have shown, however, that aircraft are capable of inflicting serious casualties not only on unarmoured but also on armoured units, particularly in the absence of friendly air cover and effective anti-aircraft defences. Close defence of tank units is, therefore, something which cannot be ignored, especially in face of a potential enemy with strong tactical air forces.

The development of counter-measures to the growing threat of ground attack aircraft has been slow and erratic. On the eve of the Second World War anti-aircraft defence of armoured units was still almost entirely concerned with the protection of transport columns. For this attached towed anti-aircraft artillery units at divisional level were considered adequate, supplemented by a few self-propelled weapons, such as the German 20 mm. cannon mounted on half-tracks or the quadruple Soviet Maxim machine-guns on trucks. Here and there machine-guns were affixed to the outside of tank turrets, more for moral effect than anything else.

The first drastic change in this situation was brought about by the success of the German *Stuka* in the Polish and French campaigns of 1939 and 1940. Their considerable moral and material effect on all opposing arms and occasional hits on tanks revived in Britain the development of the anti-aircraft tank. The first of the series consisted of a special turret with four 7.92 mm. Besa machine-guns on the Light Tank Mark VI and this became the first anti-aircraft tank to be permanently incorporated within the framework of armoured units, 4 being allotted after 1941 to the headquarters squadron of each British armoured regiment, or battalion.

This first anti-aircraft model saw some service in the Western Desert in Africa and was followed by considerably improved types, such as the A.A. Tank Mark I with a single 40 mm. Bofors and the A.A. Mark II and III with twin 20 mm. Polsten cannon, all based on the Crusader cruiser tank chassis. In 1943 the last 2 became standard equipment in British armoured units, there being 6 or even 8 Mark II or III to each armoured regiment.

By then, however, the menace of the German dive-bombers was virtually over. With the passing of air superiority into Allied hands it was the turn of the Germans to be harassed from the air. They began to experience it on the Eastern Front and, in a much more intensive form, in Africa from the Royal Air Force's Hawker Hurricane and American-built Curtiss P.40 Kittyhawk fighter-bombers. It was now their turn to take up the development of anti-aircraft tanks, as well as increasing the number of various towed and self-propelled anti-aircraft guns, particularly multiple 20 mm., and armouring their half-track carriages.

The winter of 1943–44 saw the appearance of the first fully tracked *Flakpanzer* : the light *Flakpanzer* 38t based on the ubiquitous Czech-built 38t chassis, the *Wirbelwind* (Whirlwind) with quadruple 20 mm. cannon on the Pz.Kpfw.IV medium tank chassis and the *Mobelwagen* (Furniture Van) with a single 37 mm. gun on the same chassis. They were not before their time and within a short time the need for them became almost desperate, when Allied armies landed on the continent of Europe accompanied by massive air strikes and swarms of rocket firing fighters and fighter-bombers. How serious the effect of British and American fighter attacks was can best be gauged from the proposal made by the Inspector of Panzer Troops in France soon after D-Day that one out of 3 tank battalions in each Panzer division be made a *Flakpanzer* battalion.

As it was, the best that could be done under the pressure of various demands on German productive capacity was an anti-aircraft tank platoon with 3 to 8 A.A. tanks in the tank battalion and tank regiment headquarters companies.

Development of further and improved A.A. tanks was similarly hampered by inadequate industrial resources. In 1944, however, a new model was brought out, the *Kugelblitz* (Ball Lightning) with two 30 mm. cannon in a fully enclosed power operated turret mounted on the Pz.Kpfw.IV chassis. But this was only an interim design, pending the development of similar equipment on the lighter, diesel-powered Panzer-jäger 38d chassis. The latter was intended to be the standard light anti-aircraft tank and at the same time a heavy 88 mm. gun anti-aircraft model was being developed on the Panther medium tank chassis.

The Panther A.A. tank was a logical outcome of the widespread dual-purpose employment of 88 mm. guns by the German Army and was further necessitated by the medium and high level attacks by British and American bomber formations, which were outside the range of the lighter anti-aircraft weapons and which could roam about unopposed in the absence of any serious *Luftwaffe* fighter opposition over the battlefield. A somewhat similar heavy self-propelled anti-aircraft gun had actually been built earlier by the Canadians, using a 3.7 in. gun on the Ram medium tank chassis. Earlier still came the British 83.8 mm. 18-pounder on the Vickers Medium type chassis. This remarkable vehicle of the mid-twenties, capable of anti-aircraft as well as field artillery employment, would have bestowed a considerable advantage on British armoured forces in the early stages of the Second World War had its development not been unwisely abandoned.

Since the Second World War the need for the heavy self-propelled anti-aircraft gun has disappeared, as defence against medium and high level bombers not dealt with by friendly fighters is being taken over by ground-to-air guided missiles.

In contrast to the German problems, when the Allied forces landed on the continent of Europe in 1944, and Anglo-American armoured forces went into action on a large scale, hostile bomber forces were virtually non-existent and the problem of Allied anti-aircraft defence reduced itself largely to that of occasional attacks by fighter-bombers.

In American armoured formations, then as more recently, anti-aircraft weapons were handled by Antiaircraft Artillery Automatic Weapons Battalions at divisional level. Unlike the British and German, American tank units have had no anti-aircraft tanks but, instead, single .5 in. machine-guns mounted on tank turrets—a method of anti-aircraft defence of questionable efficiency which has found little favour elsewhere.

The only fully tracked American self-propelled anti-aircraft weapon to appear in action before the end of the Second World War was the twin 40 mm. gun M19 on the M24 light tank chassis. This type, like the Bofors-designed 40 mm. gun itself, originated in Sweden in the late thirties in the shape of a 40 mm. gun on a Landsverk light tank chassis which was followed later by the twin 40 mm. gun Lvkv fm /43.

A number of experimental anti-aircraft tanks was built in the United States in the early forties, including the twin .5 in. machine-gun on the M3 light tank chassis, the single 40 mm. T36 and T52 on the M4 medium tank chassis and the sextuple .5 in. T77 on the M24 light tank chassis. The Canadians also built a few specimens of the Skink anti-aircraft tank on the M4 medium tank chassis, replacing the normal turret by a special one with four 20 mm. Polsten cannon. However, apart from the M19 and the more recent twin 40 mm. gun M42, the only anti-aircraft armoured vehicles in regular service were the half-track multiple gun carriages, such as the M15 and M16. Their design dates from 1941 and their origin can be traced back even farther, for they were preceded by a French twin 13.2 mm. heavy machine-gun on the Citroën-Kegresse half-track of the mid-twenties and the German multiple 20 mm. cannon half-track installations.

The limited progress in the direction of anti-aircraft tanks in the United States must be ascribed to a lack of incentive in the shape of a strong and effective hostile tactical air force at the time when the American armoured forces were in action. The war in Korea provided even less experience or incentive than the closing stages of the Second World War, for the United States Air Force ruled the skies over the battlefield. Such a happy state of affairs may not, however, always apply and it would be unwise to take the quantitative and qualitative superiority of friendly air forces for granted and hope that they will be able to give ample protection at all times.

Moreover, considerable progress has taken place in the development of air to ground weapons and in particular of rockets with shaped charge heads. This is partly offset by the trend to supersonic speeds in fighter design, which renders the average interceptor type less capable of attacking relatively small ground targets. Slower ground attack aircraft continue to be developed, however, and there are also helicopters armed with anti-tank guided missiles. The last form of aerial attack was introduced by the French Sud So 1221 Djinn and SE

3130 Alouette helicopters carrying S.S.10 missiles and, were it ignored, could represent a serious threat to tanks.

As it is, neither American nor British armoured forces have experienced anything approaching the full weight of tactical air attack. The Germans, on the other hand, did in 1944–45 and learnt from bitter experience how damaging it could be. Their reaction is, therefore, worth considering and it was quite unequivocal: effective organic means of anti-aircraft defence.

This meant the provision of an adequate number of properly designed anti-aircraft tanks, at least down to the level of the tank battalion, tanks which could inflict heavy punishment on low-flying aircraft and make it very unprofitable for them to try to attack individual targets or vehicles. The Germans were rather slow to realise this and had to pay for their inability to provide an adequate number of anti-aircraft vehicles with heavy tank losses and a loss of freedom to manoeuvre. But in the few cases where they managed to assemble an adequate number of anti-aircraft weapons they made it impossible for Allied fighter-bombers to attack except at the cost of heavy losses.

The same need for organic anti-aircraft tanks was realised earlier in the British Army, under the threat of *Luftwaffe* attacks, although the actual need passed before they were ready. It was realised in the Japanese Army, which developed the *Taha* twin 37 mm. gun anti-aircraft tank by the end of the Second World War. It was also realised by the Soviet Army, which, towards the end of the Second World War, introduced a 37 mm. anti-aircraft gun on the T-70 light tank chassis and similar to the early German *Flakpanzer*, but twelve years later came out with a much superior anti-aircraft tank mounting two 57 mm. guns on a T-54 medium tank type chassis.

Granted the need, the actual form of the anti-aircraft tank has varied considerably. The main variable and the principal feature has been the armament and this frequently has followed that of fighter aircraft. During the greater part of the Second World War the latter consisted of .5 in. machine-guns in the United States and 20 mm. cannon in Britain and Germany. As early as 1942, however, the Germans, who led in this field, came to consider 20 mm. as the minimum useful calibre for air combat. This operations research conclusion accelerated the development of 30 mm. cannon and led to the Rheinmetall 30 mm. MK-108 mounted in the very first operational turbo-jet fighters, the Messerschmitt Me 262 of 1944, the MK-103 of the Kugelblitz A.A. tank and, finally, to the remarkable Mauser MG-213C 30 mm. revolver cannon.

After the Second World War several other countries followed the German example and adopted 30 mm. cannon as standard fighter armament. Thus, by the mid-fifties fighter aircraft were being armed with 30 mm. guns such as the British Aden, French D.E.F.A. and Swiss Oerlikon 302 RK—all, like the contemporary American 20 mm. M39, based on the Mauser MG-213C. At about the same time 30 mm. guns were also reapplied to anti-aircraft tanks, the earliest example consisting of two 30 mm. Hispano guns on a Hispano Suiza HS 30 chassis, which was introduced in pro-totype form in 1955.

Before the end of the Second World War the Germans evolved even larger calibre aircraft guns—of 55 mm. calibre—for air to air combat. But these were abandoned in favour of the 55 mm. R4M rocket, which achieved brief though remarkable success against American B-17 Flying Fortresses in the final stages of the war and which was developed after the war in the United States into the 2.75 in. Mighty Mouse unguided rocket. Nevertheless, though they did not find favour as fighter armament, automatic guns of similar calibre have been adopted for anti-aircraft use, as shown by the Soviet twin 57 mm. anti-aircraft tank.

The larger calibre guns possess the advantage of more powerful projectiles but they are heavier and need heavier vehicles to carry them. Moreover, the more powerful they are the more questionable is their further development in the light of progress in surface-to-air guided missiles. Conversely, guns of about 30 mm. calibre are less likely to be challenged by guided missiles and can be mounted in lighter, more versatile vehicles. Suitably designed 30 mm. gun tanks could, in fact, be used not only as specialised anti-aircraft vehicles but also as general-purpose automatic weapon vehicles. As such, they could well supplement the fire power of the more powerful gun tanks and relieve the latter of part of the difficult task of dealing with hostile infantry and its anti-tank weapons.

The effectiveness of automatic anti-aircraft weapons against infantry was amply demonstrated towards the end of the Second World War in Europe and in the Pacific and subsequently in Korea and by neutralising hostile infantry positions with a blanket of automatic weapons fire anti-aircraft tanks could provide valuable support to other tanks and armoured vehicles. In addition, light anti-aircraft tanks can be usefully employed for various security and policing duties—in fact for all the many tasks where the more powerful gun tanks are unnecessary and where it is patently uneconomical to employ the latter.

In all, there are several useful applications for suitably designed anti-aircraft tanks, in addition to their primary role of protecting armoured units against ground attack aircraft, whose threat remains as serious as ever.

30

Amphibious Vehicles

THE idea of applying armoured vehicles to the problems of forcing water obstacles and of landing from the sea on hostile shores is almost as old as the vehicles themselves. Tanks were hardly introduced into service on land when thoughts turned towards their possible use in assault landing operations and towards making them capable of swimming across rivers.

Thus, soon after the first British tanks were used in France in 1916, a scheme was advanced for their use in a landing operation on the Belgian coast, between Nieuport and Ostend, then in German hands. The tanks were to be landed from very large pontoons and experimental work, in preparation for the landing, was carried out by the Tank Corps in France between May and July 1917. Considering the limitations of the contemporary Mark IV tanks the project was too ambitious, however, and it is perhaps as well that it was never put to test, because of the failure of the land offensive with which the landing was to coincide.

The first attempts at making tanks float, which followed in 1918 and which were partly prompted by the prospect of having to cross the Rhine in the final Allied offensive, were much more to the point. The necessary buoyancy was not difficult to achieve with the relatively bulky British tanks of the period and just before the end of the First World War, in October 1918, the first tank successfully crossed a stretch of water, at the Brent Reservoir in London. The vehicle was a Mark IX, a large 27-ton supply tank or carrier which could carry 54 men, including a crew of 4 ; it was suitably waterproofed and had two " Camel " caissons attached, one to each side, which provided additional buoyancy but which were to be detached on reaching the far bank.

407

The caisson flotation method was not put to use in the field but interest in tanks which could float continued in Britain after the war. Their development was instigated by Colonel J. F. C. Fuller, who was in charge of tank affairs at the War Office immediately after the First World War and who stipulated that the tanks then being designed should be able to float. The requirement was based on the need which Colonel Fuller foresaw for amphibious tanks in British overseas expeditions and in a lecture given in February 1920 at the Royal United Service Institution he even envisaged submarine tank carriers for bringing tanks up for landing operations.

As a result, a prototype of the Medium D tank, which was the first to be completed after the First World War, was modified to make it amphibious ; the modification was carried out at the Engineering Establishment at Christchurch and the first successful water trials took place there in 1921. During subsequent trials in the Thames, near the Woolwich Arsenal in London, the tank developed a leak and sank but it was salvaged and the development continued. A similar but lighter amphibious tank, known as the Light Infantry Tank, was also designed and two prototypes were built in 1922. This vehicle, which weighed about 7 tons against the Medium D's 14, could propel itself in water at $1\frac{1}{2}$ m.p.h. and on land it exceeded the latter's maximum speed of 20 m.p.h. by attaining no less than 30 m.p.h.

The performance of the Medium D and, even more, of the Light Infantry Tank was remarkable for their day and, in spite of some troublesome mechanical features, they deserved further development. As it was, instead of their potentialities being emphasised, the inevitable development troubles of such advanced designs were seized upon to condemn them and in 1923, in a wave of financial stringency, they were both abandoned. At the same time the government Tank Design Department, which had been established under Lt.-Colonel Philip Johnson at Charlton and which was responsible for the work, was closed down and with it died the first attempt at a truly amphibious tank.

However, the idea did not die out. Even before the British Medium D and the Light Infantry Tank were abandoned, work had begun in the United States, where the former considerably influenced the design of the first post-war American tank, the Medium A. Neither the Medium A nor its subsequent developments were amphibious but in 1920, as part of the development of a light reconnaissance tractor for the United States Ordnance, the second modification of the Peoria built model was made amphibious. Five other versions were built between 1920 and 1922 but the development got no further.

Once more, however, the development of amphibious vehicles was taken up elsewhere. This time it was by J. Walter Christie, who shortly after the First World War designed a number of self-propelled guns for the United States Ordnance and who in 1922 came out with his first amphibian.

The Christie amphibian has usually been described as a tank but more correctly it was an open-top amphibious self-propelled 75 mm. gun. One of its salient points was the convertible feature associated with Christie designs, which enabled it to travel on tracks or on wheels when the tracks were removed. Another feature of it was that, unlike the Medium D and other British tanks, it was propelled in water by means of 2 screws instead of tracks. It was rebuilt twice, the second version being longer than the first and the third having 4 bogie wheels per side instead of 3, and being covered in.

United States Army and Marine Corps both tested it and during the trials and demonstrations it swam across the Hudson and the Potomac and in 1923, at Culebra, off Puerto Rico, it gave the first practical demonstration of a mechanised ship-to-shore movement when it swam ashore from the *U.S.S. Wisconsin*. Six vehicles of the second type were ordered by the Marine Corps and are believed to have been used by it in China in 1927. At this, however, further official interest stopped and Christie turned his attention once more to ground vehicles. His loss to the amphibious field was certainly a gain to land warfare, for his next and last series of designs established new standards in high speed tank suspensions and tank speeds in general, exceeding by a handsome margin the record previously established by the Light Infantry Tank.

By an odd turn of events, while the tank speed record passed from Britain to the United States, the lead in the development of amphibious vehicles passed back from the United States to Britain. The new amphibious vehicle which regained the lead for Britain was a light tank introduced in 1931 by Vickers-Armstrongs. It formed part of the A.4 series of Vickers Carden Loyd light tanks which was being developed for the British Army and two experimental models were actually built, designated the A.4 E.11 and A.4 E.12. It weighed 3.35 tons with a crew of 2 and an armament of a single .303 in. Vickers machine-gun mounted in the turret ; on land it had a maximum speed of 20 m.p.h. and in water it could propel itself at up to 3.7 m.p.h. by means of a single screw.

The potentialities of tanks as lightly armed as the Vickers amphibian were limited although, in all fairness, they were in keeping with the contemporary trend toward relatively large numbers of small tanks rather than smaller numbers of more powerfully armed models. Moreover, their amphibious capabilities were limited and they could only operate in calm water. Mechanically, however, they were successful and they attracted a good deal of attention at the time, even though the British Army did not adopt them. Soviet Russia, for instance, bought eight samples when this vehicle became available commercially and subsequently went into quantity production with a very similar model designated the T-37. A few more of the Vickers amphibians were purchased by China and the Netherlands East Indies.

As far as the Russians were concerned they regarded their light amphibious tanks principally as reconnaissance vehicles, a role in which their light armour and armament were less of a handicap and where river crossing capabilities were particularly valuable. Apart from the T-37 the Russians also built a small number of a large 6-wheeled amphibious armoured car and later a somewhat improved version of the T-37, the T-38 amphibious tank. The latter, apart from being one of the few amphibious vehicles in service, also had the distinction of being the first tank carried by air, during peacetime Soviet manoeuvres in the mid-thirties, slung under the bellies of ANT-6 transport-bombers.

Soviet interest in amphibious tanks continued into the early stages of the Second World War, when almost simultaneously with the introduction of the T-34 medium and KV heavy tanks they brought out the T-40 amphibious light tank, another 2-man model armed with coaxial 12.7 amd 7.62 mm. machine-guns. The T-40 did not, however, show up particularly well in the early Soviet-German campaigns thus justifying in part the attitude of other armies which generally showed little interest in this type of vehicle, partly on account of the limitations of the amphibious tanks which had been built and partly because they did not foresee a real need for them. What little effort was devoted to amphibious tanks was half-hearted and did not proceed beyond the experimental stage.

In 1935, for instance, the French built an experimental light amphibious reconnaissance tank for their cavalry, the DP2. It came to an early end, however, when it was damaged and sank during its first amphibious trials. In Britain, in 1939, Vickers-Armstrongs built one more experimental amphibious tank based on the contemporary Mark VI light tank. The Czechs built one also, the F4HE, which it was generally assumed the Germans would take over with the rest of the Czech tanks after the occupation of Czechoslovakia in 1939. As a result, the F4HE appeared in all the 1940–41 British and American intelligence manuals on German Army equipment together with a good deal of other inaccurate information. In fact, the Germans showed as little interest in this type of vehicle as most others and did not continue its development.

The only people, apart from the Russians, to show consistent interest in amphibious tanks before the Second World War were the Japanese. Even when the Russians temporarily dropped the development at the T-40, when this tank failed to stand up to the combat conditions of the Eastern Front, the Japanese persevered and continued their development right up to the end of the Second World War.

The Japanese had already shown considerable interest in Christie's original amphibian and in the Vickers-Armstrongs model of 1931 and in the early thirties began to develop and build amphibious armoured vehicles of their own. Two lines of development were actually pursued, one by the Japanese Army and the other by the Imperial Navy. The latter was generally more successful and produced the best known Japanese amphibian, the Type 2 *Kamisha* light tank of the Second World War.

Kamisha was a 10.9-ton vehicle with a crew of 3 and an armament of one 37 mm. gun and 2 machine-guns. As a design it belonged to much the same category as the 1931 Vickers-Armstrongs amphibious light tanks and like them was propelled in water by means of screws but in this case two instead of one. It incorporated, however, one novel feature in the shape of 2 very neatly designed detachable floats—one at the front and one at the rear. These provided the necessary buoyancy and stability in water but, being detachable, did not impair permanently the vehicle's performance on land.

The detachable float feature was tried on several other vehicles, including the Navy's *Kachisha* 26-ton heavy amphibious tank. The Navy also had under development a large amphibious carrier, the *Katsusha*, while the Army experimented with several light tanks, including the *A-Igo* which was water-jet propelled.

All the effort and ingenuity did not, however, bring the Japanese much profit. None of the Japanese amphibians was produced in any quantity, as fighting vehicles they were inadequately armed and the faulty tactical employment in insignificant driblets condemned them to failure.

In the meantime, well before the Japanese entered the struggle for the Pacific, the problem of amphibious operations arose on the other side of the globe. In 1940, after their victory in France, the German forces found themselves faced with Operation Sea Lion, the projected invasion of the British Isles. One aspect of their problem was that of landing tanks, which had played such a prominent part in the earlier German campaigns in Poland and France, and the Germans struck upon the idea of a submerged approach as a means of getting tanks ashore during an amphibious assault landing.

The new German method was based on submersible tanks which could be launched from landing barges standing some distance off-shore, in relatively shallow water, and which could then move underwater, along the sea bed, until they emerged on the hostile shore. Submersible tanks themselves consisted of standard models, such as Pz.Kpfw. III, suitably sealed and provided with flexible air and exhaust tubes connected to a buoy which floated on the surface of the water while the tank moved along the bottom.

The development of submersible tanks proceeded rapidly and by June 26, 1940, it had already advanced to the stage of a demonstration before various government and military officials. Troop trials began in July, the majority of the submersible tanks being at Putlos, near Kiel, on the Baltic coast, and 4 battalions of submersible tanks were ready for use in September. The 4 battalions contained some 250 submersible medium tanks and they were to be landed with the leading echelons of 6 infantry divisions within the first 2 hours of the German amphibious landing on the south-east coast of England. Operation Sea Lion, the German invasion of England, never materialised, however, and the submersible tanks were never put to test in amphibious operations. But they were used with success during the crossing of the river Bug in Poland on the first day of the German campaign against Russia in June 1941.

Provision for submerged operation, or deep wading, with the use of snorkel-type breathing tubes was subsequently incorporated in the design of the Tiger I heavy tank, but it does not appear to have ever been used and it did not reappear on later German tanks, such as the Panther and Tiger II. The only tracked amphibious vehicle used by the Germans was what might best be described as a " tracked tug, " a piece of engineering equipment used chiefly for bridging operations.

When the tide of war turned it was the turn of the British Army to face the problem of landing tanks on hostile shores, the German-held shores of the continent of Europe.

Soon after the evacuation of British troops from the Continent, in July 1940, the Ministry of Supply, urged by the Prime Minister, Winston Churchill, began the development of tank landing craft. The first of the Landing Craft, Tank, or L.C.T., was completed in October 1940 and two years later they were first put to use during the amphibious raid on Dieppe in August 1942, to carry 30 Churchill infantry tanks prepared for wading up to their turret tops. However, for the main invasion of Normandy in 1944 an entirely novel contrivance for landing tanks was developed in Britain, called the D.D., or Duplex Drive, device.

The D.D. tank device was the invention of Nicholas Straussler, a Hungarian-born British engineer, who had previously worked on armoured vehicles and bridging equipment, and it was, in essence, a logical derivative of his collapsible canvas-hulled assault boat. Thus, the D.D. tank was a standard tank suitably water-proofed fitted with a collapsible canvas hull. When fully extended this hull enabled the tank to float, though unfortunately the tank was well below the water line and unable to use its armament until it reached firm ground, when the hull could be collapsed.

The D.D. device was also rather vulnerable to rough seas and enemy fire and the Admiralty strongly opposed its development. The Army, however, eventually decided to use it. It was first tried in June 1941, fitted to a Tetrarch light tank, at the Hendon Reservoir in London, and in the following year orders were given for the conversion of some 650 Valentine infantry tanks into D.D. tanks.

The Valentine D.D. tanks were used extensively for training but by 1944, when the Allied armies actually landed in Europe, they had become obsolete and it had already been decided to turn to American-built M4 medium tanks with which British, as well as American, armoured units were then largely equipped. In consequence, several hundred M4s were converted in Britain into D.D. amphibious tanks and five months before D-Day, on the personal intervention of the Allied Supreme Commander, General Eisenhower, the United States Army and industry joined in to produce more D.D. tanks.

By D-Day, June 6, 1944, there were 5 British, 2 Canadian and 3 American tank battalions trained and equipped with D.D. M4 medium tanks. In the British landing zones they were used with some success, although on account of the rough weather many could not be launched in the water and had to be put ashore by tank landing craft, like the great majority of the British tanks used in the assault landing. In general, the large-scale employment of tanks delivered by landing craft proved far more important than the D.D. tanks and it was the former which was mainly responsible for the success of the British assault landings and for saving many casualties. Altogether, the tanks landed with the assault waves in the 3 British and Canadian sectors—Sword, Juno and Gold—amounted to 3 armoured brigades and several special units of mine-sweeping flail tanks and assault tanks of the Royal Engineers.

Compared with the British, the use of tanks in the 2 American sectors—Omaha and Utah—was very limited and the losses among the assaulting troops correspondingly greater. Of the 3 American D.D. tank battalions one was used at Utah and of the 32 tanks launched 2 miles out 28 swam ashore, which compared with the British performance in the Sword sector where 33 out of 40 D.D. tanks reached the shore. At Omaha, however, where the remaining two

American battalions were deployed, only one battalion was launched as intended because of rough seas and only 2 out of the 29 tanks reached the shore, justifying some of the Admiralty's worst fears about the D.D. device. The second of the 2 D.D. battalions at Omaha, like the British D.D. tanks in the Gold sector, was put ashore by landing craft.

Prior to the adoption of the British D.D. device, the effort of the United States Army in the field of amphibious tracked vehicles was largely concentrated on the light M29 Weasel tractor which was amphibious but which was intended originally for over-snow operation. It was only in the latter part of the Second World War that the Ordnance Corps built the T86 and T87 amphibious self-propelled guns based on the 76 mm. gun M18 tank destroyer and embarked upon the development of tank flotation methods based on large detachable steel floats.

This last method was similar in principle to that used on the *Kamisha* and other Japanese amphibious tanks and had the great advantage over the British D.D. approach in that it was less vulnerable and enabled the main armament to be used while in water. Its great disadvantage compared with the D.D. device was the size of the floats and the consequent demand on shipboard space. For instance, the M19 swimming device developed for the M4 medium tank increased its length from 19 to 47 feet and its width from $8\frac{1}{2}$ to 11 feet.

Work on the swimming devices was actually begun in 1943 but by the end of the Second World War it had not progressed far enough for them to be used in action. The same applied to the T86 and T87 amphibious self-propelled guns. Work on swimming devices was subsequently transferred to the M26 and then M46 medium tanks, but in the meantime the United States Army followed the example of the Marine Corps and adopted the tracked landing vehicle, or LVT, as the most suitable vehicle for landing operations, in spite of the fact that in 1942 the Armoured Board rejected the LVT as too vulnerable.

The development of the LVT began in the mid-thirties with an amphibious tracked vehicle evolved by Donald Roebling for rescue work in the swamp areas of Florida. The first Roebling amphibian was working by 1937 and during the following two years the United States Marine Corps became interested in it in view of its potential value for amphibious operations. At the beginning of 1940 the Marine Corps ordered from Roebling the first model, redesigned to make it more suitable for military use, which was completed by the end of October 1940, at the cost of 16,000 dollars, and within days of its receipt placed an order for a production batch of 100 LVT1.

The faith of the Marine Corps in the Roebling amphibian, or Alligator as it was called, proved fully justified and the LVT advanced considerably the technique of amphibious assault landings. Its use mechanised the critical ship-to-shore approach phase of an assault landing and, what is more, made possible an uninterrupted movement from ships to positions well inland which increased the overall tempo of amphibious operations and eliminated the vulnerable debarkation on the shore line. Thus, the LVT helped to re-establish amphibious operations as a respected form of warfare, which up to the early stages of the Second World War the Marine Corps almost alone believed possible and continued to develop. Most others were still thinking of the heavy losses in men and ships suffered in the abortive British landings at Gallipoli in 1915 and virtually dismissed the possibility of major assault landings on defended shores. The successful large-scale landings in the latter part of the Second World War were all the more remarkable in view of the position a decade earlier when amphibious operations were still in the primitive stage of landing from open boats, with muffled oars, in the dead of night.

The first production LVT1 was completed in July 1941, by the Food Machinery Corporation. Like the original Roebling Alligator, the LVT1 was a large 7.8-ton unarmoured amphibious tractor built out of sheet metal which could

27

propel itself in water, as well as on land, by means of tracks with specially shaped shoes at up to 7 m.p.h. It could carry up to 25 men but it was originally intended chiefly for carrying supplies and it was in this role that the 1st Amphibious Tractor Battalion, created by the Marine Corps in December 1941, was first employed in the landings at Guadalcanal in August 1942.

The rest of the Solomons campaign followed the pattern of Guadalcanal and the LVT continued to be used to provide logistical support. The change to an assault role did not come until the landing on Tarawa, in the Gilbert Islands in November 1943, and was prompted by the fact that Tarawa, like other central Pacific islands, was coral fringed and its shores consequently inaccessible to landing boats. Without the LVT1 of the 2nd Amphibious Tractor Battalion, which carried part of the assaulting troops across the reef-fringed beaches, the costly landing on Tarawa might well have failed altogether.

To adapt the LVT to the role of an amphibious assault troop carrier armour protection was improvised by the use of boiler plate and after Tarawa all LVT were fitted with some form of armour. Later improved models were built out of light armour plate instead of sheet steel but the term " armoured " was never applied to the cargo or troop-carrying LVT, except for the LVTA2, an armour plate version of the sheet metal LVT2, built at the request of the United States Army. All other armoured LVT, or LVTA, were turreted amphibians conceived as amphibious tanks which would open the way for other troop-carrying LVT.

The first turreted LVTA1 was used in the Marshall Islands operations in February 1944 and consisted of a cargo LVT hull with a 37 mm. gun mounted in the turret of the contemporary M3 light tank. It proved useful but a larger-calibre gun was considered desirable and, in consequence, the next LVTA4 was fitted with the open-top turret of the 75 mm. howitzer motor carriage M8. Organised into armoured amphibian battalions, the 37 mm. gun LVTA1 and the 75 mm. howitzer LVTA4 were used extensively in the Marianas as tanks but, because of their large silhouette and relatively thin armour, they came to be considered more as amphibious self-propelled artillery and it was largely in this supporting role that the armoured amphibian battalions were used in the last major amphibious operation of the Second World War on Okinawa.

In addition to the turreted LVTA, other types of LVT were also developed. After the LVT2, which was an improved version of the original LVT1, came the LVT4, first used on Saipan, in the Marianas Islands, in June 1944. This had the Continental radial engine mounted at the front instead of the rear, where a ramp had been added, thus making it unnecessary for troops to dismount by jumping over the high sides and greatly facilitating the loading and unloading of cargo. On Okinawa an improved rear ramp model was introduced, the LVT3 which had 2 Cadillac engines and transmissions neatly fitted into its sides.

Altogether, 18,620 LVT were built up to the end of the Second World War and their use was being continually extended. The employment of a reinforced amphibian tractor battalion at Tarawa was followed by the use of 2 tractor and 1 armoured battalions at Roi-Namur in February 1944, and 6 tractor and 2 armoured amphibian battalions on Saipan, half of them Marine and half Army, which called its LVTA units amphibian tank battalions. By the end of the war the Marine Corps alone had 9 LVT and 3 LVTA battalions, all in the Pacific theatre of operations.

Towards the end of 1944, LVT were also made available in Europe and at the crossing of the Rhine, in March 1945, there were 4 British armoured regiments (battalions) equipped with them, as well as 2 regiments with about 120 D.D. M4 medium tanks. When the war in Europe ended a special LVT assault brigade of the Royal Marines was being formed for service in the Far East and deliveries begun of the British-built version of the LVT, the Neptune, designed and built by the Nuffield Organisation.

After the war the United States Marine Corps retained the LVT3 and LVTA5, an improved version of the LVTA4 with a gyro-stabilised 75 mm. howitzer which was developed too late for use in action, while the United States Army retained the LVT4 and the LVTA5, as well as LVTA4. Almost immediately, however, as a result of the appearance of nuclear wepons, doubts arose about the further application of the amphibious methods so successfully evolved during the Second World War. Operation Crossroads in 1946, at Bikini in the western Marshalls, which involved the explosion of two nuclear bombs amidst a fleet of obsolescent warships, demonstrated clearly that large naval concentrations of the kind seen off Normandy in 1944, or off Iwo Jima in 1945, were unthinkable in face of nuclear weapons. But the Marine Corps did not despair of the amphibious mission officially assigned to it : instead, it took the lead, once more, in the development of new amphibious tactics and, in particular, new methods of landing assault troops from widely dispersed ships by means of helicopters. Nor did it lose its faith in amphibians which, if anything, acquired even greater value in the light of the possible tactical employment of nuclear weapons.

The first step in the continued post-Second World War development of amphibious vehicles sponsored by the Marine Corps was the provision of overhead protection. Hitherto the personnel or cargo compartments of the amphibious vehicles were all open-topped and to make them less vulnerable to heavy seas and high surf, as well as air-burst fire and, later, the threat of nuclear explosions, the existing LVT3 were fitted with armoured covers in 1949. A little later overhead protection was similarly fitted to the open-top turrets of the LVTA5.

Modified LVT3c were used in the early stages of the Korean conflict, not only in the successful Inchon landing in September 1950, which outflanked the North Korean invaders, but also as armoured personnel carriers in the subsequent drive on Seoul and the crossing of the Han river.

Unmodified Second World War LVT were also used by French forces in the later stages of the war in Indochina and by hastily reorganised British LVT units in the fruitless Anglo-French landing at Port Said, Egypt, in November 1956.

In the meantime, much more advanced amphibious vehicles had been developed in the United States as a result of a new programme initiated after the outbreak of the Korean war. The first was an armoured amphibious assault personnel and cargo carrier, the LVTP5. By comparison with the LVT3c, which it supersedes, the LVTP5 is a somewhat heavier and larger vehicle completely covered in from the start and it is provided with a front ramp, in contrast to the rear ramp LVT3 and LVT4. Fully equipped it weighs about 31 tons and it can carry $5\frac{1}{2}$ tons of cargo or 34 men ; it is 29 ft. long, 11.75 ft. wide and 9 ft. high. On land the LVTP5 has a maximum speed of 27 m.p.h. and in water its tracks can propel it at up to 7 m.p.h. which its fuel tanks allow it to do for about seven hours.

The basic LVTP5 hull has also been adapted to a number of special purpose vehicles, such as the LVTR1 amphibious recovery vehicle, the LVTAAX1 anti-aircraft artillery weapon carrier with twin 40 mm. guns, the LVTEX1 assault engineer vehicle and the LVTH6, an armoured amphibious vehicle with a turret mounted 105 mm. howitzer which supersedes the earlier, 75 mm. howitzer LVTA5. A second series of smaller amphibious personnel and weapon carriers has also been developed in prototype form. The basic vehicle is the LVTP6 which is related to the M59 armoured personnel carrier produced for the United States Army but which is somewhat larger to provide additional buoyancy and make it capable of operating in heavy seas and surf. It weighs 18.3 tons fully equipped and is less expensive and more manoeuvrable, as well as being considerably lighter, than the LVTP5.

The M59 armoured personnel carrier to which the LVTP6 is related is also amphibious but only in the limited sense of being able to cross calm inland waters. It represents, never-theless, a significant contribution towards eliminating the problem of rivers as obstacles to mechanised forces. With tanks the problem is more difficult than with the relatively bulky armoured personnel carriers but work has continued since the Second World War on various tank flotation devices and the D.D. method has been successfully re-applied in Britain to the Centurion tank. The latter, like the earlier M4 D.D. tanks, is fitted with a collapsible canvas hull and propelled in water by means of two propellers driven from the final drives to the sprockets. The Russians, on the other hand, have revived the development of amphibious recon-naissance tanks and introduced a 76 mm. gun tank of this type whose chassis is also used for an armoured personnel carrier and a self-propelled missile launcher, both first displayed at a Moscow parade in November 1957.

In general, more attention has been devoted since the Second World War to the need for amphibious vehicles in land operations and to making more armoured vehicles capable of operating in water, as well as on land, so that they can cross rivers and other water obstacles swiftly and without aid. In the field of amphibious operations, on the other hand, where the advantages of using armoured vehicles and of being able to land them directly from ships were so clearly demonstrated during the war, more attention has been given to extending the operation of amphibious assault vehicles well inland. So far, the requirements of land and landing operations have tended to produce two separate categories of amphibious vehicles but the more recent trends point to a common goal of more versatile vehicles and in both cases they offer the same advantage of increased overall mobility, which amply justifies continued development of amphibious armoured vehicles.

31

Armoured Cars

ARMOURED cars provide a fitting subject for a concluding chapter. Being the first of the kind, they take the story of armoured vehicles right round to the very beginning. At the same time they also carry it forward since wheeled armoured vehicles continue to fulfil several important functions.

The development of armoured cars may be traced to the de Dion-Bouton powered quadricycle which F. R. Simms fitted with a Maxim machine-gun and shield in 1899, in Britain, and the 3-wheeled car mounting a Colt machine-gun behind a shield built at about the same time in the United States for Major R. P. Davidson. In 1902, at the Crystal Palace in London, Simms exhibited another and much more substantial vehicle : this was a 4-wheeler with an armoured boat-shaped hull which resembled drawings of an armoured vehicle proposed in 1896 by E. J. Pennington but, contrary to several statements, never actually built. A more practical semi-armoured model was exhibited in 1902 in France, at the Paris Salon de l'Automobile, by the Société Charron-Girardot et Voigt and its reception encouraged its builders to proceed with the development of a much improved model with a fully armoured body surmounted by a turret with all-round traverse. The second model was completed by the beginning of 1906 and 10 cars of this type were subsequently ordered by the Russian Army.

In the meantime, in 1904–05, in Austria, the Austro-Daimler company built another turreted armoured car which, for the first time, had all 4 of its wheels driven. Two years later, in Germany, Ehrhardt built an anti-balloon armoured car with a 50 mm. gun. In 1912 came the first Italian armoured car, built at the Turin arsenal on a Fiat truck chassis, and this, together with a Bianchi armoured car, saw limited service in Libya following the Italo-Turkish war.

Further experiments with unarmoured machine-gun cars were also continued, notably by Major Davidson in the United States and by Captain Genty in France. As a further result of the former's pioneering efforts, General N. A. Miles, Commanding General of the United States Army, recommended in 1903 that 5 American cavalry regiments be converted from horses to cars but this remarkable proposal proved too far in advance of its day.

In August 1914, when the First World War broke out, there was still only a handful of armoured, or even armed, cars in existence. However, once the war began, the opening fluid stages provided favourable opportunities for the use of motor-cars for reconnaissance and raids and this greatly accelerated the development of armoured cars. Within weeks the Belgians were using armoured cars improvised on Minerva touring car chassis and in September the French started issuing similar improvised armoured cars, of which they ordered 136, to their cavalry formations. By the end of 1914 and the beginning of 1915, the improvised open-top Minervas, Peugeots and Renaults, which mounted their machine-guns or short 37 mm. guns behind simple shields, began to be succeeded by greatly improved models, fully armoured and mounting their armament in revolving turrets.

The most notable of the second generation of wartime armoured cars was the British Rolls-Royce, the first of which was built in December 1914. It was based on the Rolls-Royce Silver Ghost car chassis which carried an armoured body surmounted by a bevelled turret with a single Maxim machine-gun; with a crew of 3 it weighed 3.5 tons and had a maximum speed of 60 m.p.h.

The Rolls-Royce and similar Lanchester, Wolseley and other armoured cars were originally built for the Royal Naval Air Service, which took up armoured vehicles to supplement and support its reconnaissance aircraft sent to operate in France. Some of the naval armoured cars were used in the

battle of Ypres in May 1915, but, just as their numbers began
to multiply, the Western Front settled down to trench warfare and opportunities for their use in France virtually disappeared. In consequence, the Armoured Car Division of
the Royal Naval Air Service had to look for opportunities
elsewhere, where the ground was more suitable or where
fluid conditions allowed operation along roads, or else to
devise ways of using armoured vehicles across broken ground.
Both alternatives were tried and the latter was largely responsible for the development of the first British tank.

The other alternative led to the transfer of the naval
armoured car squadrons to the Middle East and other
theatres of operations. One went to Russia, where the Belgian armoured cars had already been sent for similar reasons.
It enjoyed a somewhat adventurous career but its military
value proved small. Before it arrived, in 1915, the Russian
Army had already began to use armoured cars of its own,
mainly for mobile fire support and on occasions with dash
but without major consequences. The principal type were
Austins imported from Britain which had 2 machine-gun
turrets arranged side by side—a clumsy arrangement which,
oddly enough, reappeared many years later on the Vickers-
Armstrongs Six Ton Tank, its Soviet T-26 copies and American
light tanks of the thirties. Later various imported truck
chassis were armoured in Russia, including the American
Garford which was armed with a 76.2 mm. gun, as well as
three machine-guns, and remained for several years the most
heavily armed armoured car.

In the Middle East, where the conditions were much more
favourable, the armoured cars of the Royal Naval Air Service
were much more successful, their first successes being scored
in 1916 against the Senussi in Cyrenaica. By this time, however, they had passed from naval to army control, for in
September 1915 the R.N.A.S. armoured car squadrons were
either disbanded or transformed into armoured motor batteries
of the Army which, thanks to naval initiative, thus acquired
its first armoured units.

Following their Cyrenaican debut, armoured motor batteries equipped with Rolls-Royce armoured cars were employed
during the operations in Palestine in 1917 and 1918, in support
of cavalry units, to which they were usually attached, in
reconnaissance, in raids and, with particular success, in the
final pursuit of the Turkish forces into Syria in October 1918.
By the end of 1917 a force of six Light Armoured Motor
Batteries, or Lambs, equipped with Rolls-Royce armoured
cars, was also assembled in Iraq. After some piecemeal
employment in support of cavalry and truck-borne infantry
and in guarding lines of communication, the Lambs were
combined into a Light Armoured Motor Brigade and the
armoured cars used more effectively in larger bodies, supported by specially organised motorised infantry detachments,
in the van of the British advance beyond Baghdad. Another
armoured motor brigade, with Austin twin-turret armoured
cars, was organised in Iraq in 1918, for operations into northern Persia, as part of what was known as the Dunsterforce.
Politically the venture proved abortive but the armoured cars
of the Dunsterforce put up a very creditable performance
overcoming the difficulties of mountainous terrain.

In the meantime, while the British armoured cars were
winning for themselves respect in the Middle East, they also
experienced a revival of interest on the Western Front in
Europe. As a result of the last German offensive in March
1918, one newly formed battalion of the Tank Corps, the 17th,
was hastily equipped with Austin twin-turret armoured cars
destined for the eastern theatres of operations. The emergency
passed before the battalion was ready but it was later used
with some success in exploiting the tank break-through at
Amiens in August 1918, and harassing German rearguards in
the closing stages of the war, when many more armoured cars
could have been used to advantage.

The French Army, in contrast to the British, maintained
armoured cars at the Western Front throughout the conflict
and they proved their worth in delaying actions during the
1918 German offensive. The experience gained encouraged

the production of more armoured cars and during the last 6 months of the war the French produced some 200 of a new type, based on the American White truck chassis, which mounted a 37 mm. gun and a Hotchkiss machine-gun at opposite ends of its turret. The Italians also built a sizeable force of 120 Lancia I.Z. armoured cars and used them effectively in covering their retreat after the battle of Caporetto in 1917 and in the final advance from the Piave in 1918.

After the Armistice in the West armoured cars saw further action in eastern Europe, in the fighting between Poland and Soviet Russia. The fluid conditions of the Polish-Soviet front again favoured their employment and on two occasions it took the novel form of spearheading strategic raids by Polish motorised forces, such as that against the railway junction of Kowel in 1920, where light armoured cars based on the famous Ford Model T chassis were particularly effective.

When the fighting on the various fronts stopped the use of armoured cars continued. They had emerged out of the First World War and its aftermath with an established reputation in several fields and clear cut limitations in one or two others. The principal limitation of the models used was their inability to operate off the roads, except under very favourable conditions such as those which existed in parts of the Middle East. Elsewhere they were usually tied to the roads and at times their movements were as inflexible and vulnerable as those of armoured trains. In consequence, whenever fighting fronts stabilised and the roads were cut, as happened in France in 1915, the contemporary armoured cars could no longer be used. Inevitably, this lead to attempts at making armoured cars capable of operating over soft, uneven ground but the immediate result was an entirely different armoured vehicle, the tank.

On the other hand, what it lacked in cross-country performance the armoured car made up by other attributes. It was relatively reliable, economical to operate and mobile over hard surfaces; during periods of mobile operations it proved useful for long-distance road reconnaissance and for

fire support of cavalry and motorised infantry units and, off
the battlefield, it proved very suitable for security and police
duties. As a result, armoured cars continued to be in demand
throughout the twenties.

The use of armoured cars for security and police duties
began as early as 1915, in India, where, after the recall of
many British units to Europe and the Middle East, a number
of armoured cars was improvised to strengthen the depleted
garrisons. After the First World War even greater need
arose for armoured cars to strengthen the newly established
British garrisons in Palestine and Iraq, as well as in Egypt
and Ireland, and for service with the Army of Occupation in
Germany. To fill the need on a permanent basis, twelve
armoured car companies were formed in 1920 and 1921 as
part of the post-war Tank Corps. They absorbed the light
armoured motor batteries, which had formed part of the
Machine Gun Corps and which were still scattered about the
Middle East, and what remained of the 17th (Armoured Car)
Battalion and for a time the twelve companies represented
one half of the total strength of the Royal Tank Corps.

A different pattern in the employment and organisation
of armoured cars was set by the French Army. In 1916
armoured cars were permanently assigned to the cavalry for
the support of mounted units and for reconnaissance, and in
1917 the establishment of French cavalry divisions was augmented by the addition of 18 armoured cars. After the First
World War this figure was doubled and by 1932 the armoured
car strength of the cavalry division was expanded into a
regiment of eighty. During the same period the reconnaissance and combat functions of armoured cars were differentiated and in 1931 the French General Staff established 3
distinct categories. They were the *auto-mitrailleuse de découverte*, or A.M.D., for fast, long-range road reconnaissance, the
auto-mitrailleuse de reconnaissance, or A.M.R., a light vehicle
for close tactical reconnaissance, and the *auto-mitrailleuse de
combat*, A.M.C., more powerful than the others and capable
of fighting hostile armoured vehicles. Specifications for new

vehicles, which were laid down at the same time, very sensibly made no attempt to predetermine the issue but allowed for tracked or wheeled vehicles in each of the three categories and the A.M.R. and the A.M.C. which were eventually accepted in 1933 and 1934 were fully tracked. They were tanks, in fact, but they retained their *auto-mitrailleuse* designation because tanks were still supposed to be a prerogative of the French infantry.

The French example of assigning armoured cars to the cavalry was followed by several other armies and by the early thirties they too began to replace their armoured cars with tracked vehicles. In Britain, for instance, in 1920, 8 cavalry regiments of the Territorial Army were converted into a like number of armoured car companies and in 1929 the first 2 regular cavalry regiments exchanged their horses for armoured cars. In 1933, however, 2 of the armoured car companies of the Royal Tank Corps were converted into light tank companies and gradually light tanks displaced armoured cars in other tank and mechanised cavalry units. Two armoured car companies still formed part of the reconnaissance group of the first British Experimental Mechanised Force of 1927 but the later tank brigade experiments and the first British armoured division of the late thirties made no use of armoured cars.

In the United States the use of armoured cars by the cavalry had barely begun when their role was largely taken over by tracked vehicles. In spite of Major Davidson's leadership and the use of a few armoured cars on the Mexican border in 1916, it was only in 1927 that the United States Cavalry took up armoured cars. Moreover, the contemporary T1 model was still of a very primitive type, nothing more, in fact, than an open-top Pontiac touring car fitted with a shield and a machine-gun. Better armoured cars were built later and the T4 of 1931 was standardised as the M1, but in 1937 further development of armoured cars was abandoned. The only wheeled armoured vehicle retained by the United States Army was the scout car, an open-top 4-wheeler suitable mainly for the role of a light personnel carrier.

The principal reason for the decline in the use of armoured cars during the thirties was their continued inability to operate off the roads, which confined their usefulness to favourable circumstances, and the contemporary progress in tank design. Tanks had become much faster and their tracks more durable than they were during or immediately after the First World War, so that they could compete with armoured cars in road operation and this, combined with their off the road performance, enabled them to take over some of the duties hitherto performed by armoured cars.

The design and performance of armoured cars had, of course, also improved during the twenties and early thirties, but not as much as that of tanks. The two major developments of the period were the replacement of the 2 driven rear wheels by short rubber tracks and the introduction of a second driven rear axle. The first scheme was devised by Adolphe Kégresse, a Frenchman employed in Russia as director of the Tsar's garage, and was applied in 1917 to some of the Austin armoured cars used by the Russian Army. After the Russian revolution Kégresse returned to his native land where his ideas were taken up by the Citroën Company and where the resulting Citroën-Kégresse half-track vehicle was used as the basis for several armoured cars. The first 16 Citroën-Kégresse-Schneider half-track armoured cars were ordered by the French Army in 1923, at about the same time as 5 Citroën-Kégresse vehicles performed the first motor crossing of the Sahara desert. Improved models followed and by 1930 one hundred new half-track armoured cars based on the Citroën-Kégresse chassis were delivered. Designated the Schneider P16 armoured cars, they represented a significant step in the re-equipment of the French cavalry which until then was still relying on White armoured cars of 1918 vintage.

The first successful application of a second driven rear axle to armoured car design was to a 9-ton Guy model ordered for British forces in India and delivered in 1928. Another

6-wheeled armoured car with 4 driven rear wheels was built by Crossley and in 1929 an even better 6-wheeled 4-wheel-drive, or 6 x 4, armoured car was designed by the Lanchester company. The Lanchester armoured car weighed 7.3 tons with a crew of 4 and was capable of a maximum speed of 45 m.p.h. Its Mark I version had a single Vickers machine-gun in the turret and another beside the driver but the Mark Ia and the Mark II had a second turret machine-gun, one being a .303 in. and the other .5 in.

Armoured cars such as the French Schneider P16 half-track and the British 6 x 4 Lanchester were a considerable improvement on the 4 x 2 armoured cars built during the First World War, or immediately afterwards. But, in essence, they were still only adaptations of commercial vehicles designed for road operation and off the road their performance left a good deal to be desired. Like other contemporary armoured cars based on truck chassis, they still had no front wheel drive, despite the encouraging example of the 1904 Austro-Daimler ; their silhouettes were high and yet their ground clearance was inadequately low and the beam axle suspensions with hard springing could not cope with movement over broken ground. On the credit side, they were still relatively simple and cheap to build, which gave them a considerable economic advantage over tanks and which meant that they could be produced quickly in an emergency. In fact, the simplest types of such truck-based armoured cars required no more for their construction than a sufficiently strong commercial chassis, some steel plate and the facilities of a small workshop. This is why the first armoured cars of the First World War could be so quickly built and this is how armoured cars have been improvised several times since. Given favourable conditions such car or truck-based armoured cars have proved capable of effective employment but, in general, they remain heavily handicapped by the limitations of their chassis.

To make a really significant advance on the armoured cars of the First World War and to meet competition from light tanks much more was required than adaptations of commercial vehicle practice, even if they were as good as the French half-tracks or the British and other 6 x 4 armoured cars. They had to become much more versatile and, above all, better suited to operating off the road, which could only be achieved by building armoured cars from scratch, instead of by armouring car or truck chassis.

An early pointer to the attainable improvement in the cross-country performance of wheeled armoured vehicles was provided by the Italian Pavesi experimental armoured vehicle of the mid-twenties, which had an articulated chassis, all wheel drive and very large diameter wheels. Another noteworthy 4 x 4 armoured vehicle of the mid-twenties was the Czech PA-2, although its virtue was not off the road performance but the good arrangement of its armour, which amply justified the nickname of " Tortoise." Like a few armoured cars of the First World War and a number of later large armoured cars, the PA-2 also had double controls, so that it could be driven equally well in either direction and which got over the problem of turning it round quickly.

Further progress during the thirties was indicated by three Austro-Daimler armoured cars of the 1934–38 period : the 11.7-ton 8 x 8 ADGZ which was large but performed well off the road thanks to its multiwheel drive ; the 6 x 6 ADKZ whose rear-engined layout resembled that of a tank and a small low-silhouette 4 x 4 turretless model which foreshadowed the British Daimler scout cars of the Second World War. Another 6-wheeled rear-engined armoured car was the 1938 D.A.F. built in Holland by the Van Doorne Company ; it had a type of hull with well sloped armour all round which was much admired when it was introduced later on the Soviet T-34 medium tank. In France the Panhard company produced a very good type 178 4 x 4 7.8-ton rear-engined armoured car which was accepted in 1935 as the standard *auto-mitrailleuse de découverte*. At about the same time another very promising armoured car appeared in France, the Gendron-Poniatowski later known as the Gendron-Somua.

This was a small 6.5-ton 2-man turreted armoured car with 6 wheels, the middle pair being retractable for normal road operation. Its performance proved superior to that of the competitive fully tracked Renault A.M.R. but unfortunately production orders for the latter had already been given.

The new armoured cars, specifically designed as such, represented a major advance on the various adaptations of car and truck chassis. They differed from the latter in such features as all wheel drive, independent suspensions, greater ground clearances, rear engine location, and their performance set them a class apart. They were too few, however, and lacked opportunities to reverse the adverse trend, produced by the shortcomings of the majority of armoured cars based on commercial chassis, which relegated wheeled armoured vehicles into the background by the outbreak of the Second World War.

How limited the interest had become in some cases is shown by the fact that the pre-war British plans envisaged only a single armoured car regiment with an establishment of 38 cars and this represented all the British armoured cars used in the 1940 campaign in France. Neither the one armoured division nor the seven mechanised cavalry regiments which formed part of the British Expeditionary Force contained any armoured cars. A year later, when the Russian campaign began, the Soviet Army had considerable numbers of armoured cars but they were of obsolete types based on truck chassis and when the majority was lost no serious effort was made to replace them. The Germans did not even deign to include the lighter 4 x 2 BA 20 in their 1941 anti-tank instructions and the only point worth noting about the heavier 6 x 4 BA 10 was its main armament of a 45 mm. gun, which made it the most powerfully armed armoured car from the mid-thirties until 1941.

In the 1940 campaign, however, the French Army employed about 350 Panhard type 178 in the reconnaissance units of the *Divisions Légères Mécaniques* and others, and the Germans made good use of some 600 armoured cars within the reconnaissance battalions of the panzer and motorised divisions. The development of German armoured cars had continued on a small scale since the First World War and they were the only armoured vehicles allowed to Germany under the terms imposed by the Western Allies but it was only after the creation of the *Panzerwaffe* in 1935 that they were produced in quantity. There were 2 main types : a light 4.6-ton 4 x 4 with a crew of 2 or 3 and an open-top turret with a coaxial 20 mm. gun and machine-gun or a machine-gun only, and a heavy 6-ton 6 x 4, which still had its engine at the front but which was superseded in 1940 by a larger rear-engined 8.15-ton 8 x 8 model. Both heavy models had 4-man crews, duplicate controls for driving in either direction and fully enclosed turrets with coaxial 20 mm. gun and machine-gun. Six heavy and 18 light cars made an armoured car company and two such mixed companies formed the basis of the reconnaissance battalions of the panzer divisions.

As a result of the 1940 campaign there was a revival of interest in armoured cars, particularly in Britain, and they were brought right back into prominence by the subsequent operations in Africa. The only new armoured car issued to British units by the outbreak of the Second World War was the Morris Light Armoured Reconnaissance Car, a mediocre type based on the Morris 15-cwt 4 x 2 light truck. A better armoured car had, however, been designed and some of it were issued in 1940. This was the Guy I, a 4 x 4 short-wheelbase rear-engined car which was at first illogically designated Light Tank, Wheeled. It weighed 5.75 tons with a crew of 3 and was armed with coaxial .5 in. and .303 in. Vickers machine-guns. A far more advanced Daimler scout car was also designed before the war, and the first built in December 1939. This was a low, rear-engined 4 x 4 turretless vehicle with a crew of 2 which weighed only 3.15 tons ; unlike the Guy I and all earlier British armoured cars it had independent suspension all round and the drive to the 4 wheels was from a single central differential through side shafts, which allowed the engine and the driver to be located much lower in the hull, between the shafts.

Originally the Daimler scout cars were intended for liaison within the tank regiments of the armoured divisions, each regiment having an intercommunication troop of 12 scout cars, but after the 1940 campaign their use was extended, as was that of armoured cars. In the reorganisation which followed, each armoured division was given a reconnaissance regiment equipped with 60 armoured cars and 54 scout cars and in total the 1941 division possessed no less than 187 scout cars. The armoured cars at this time were mainly Humbers, Humber I being almost identical with Guy Ia and like the latter armed with coaxial 15 mm. and 7.92 mm. Besa machine-guns ; Humber II and III were similar but the latter had a 4-man crew.

Apart from the armoured cars and scout cars, a whole host of other wheeled armoured vehicles was also built after the debacle in France to meet the threat of the German invasion of Britain. They ranged from light reconnaissance cars, such as the Standard Beaverette, of which 2,800 were produced, to flamethrower armoured cars and heavy " mobile pill boxes " ; there were also heavy 8-wheeled trucks turned into self-propelled carriages for 4 in. naval guns. Some two dozen different types were built and they helped to fill the gap until properly designed armoured vehicles could be produced in greater quantity. Some displayed considerable ingenuity in adapting civilian vehicles to military purposes and one or two of the most successful types were kept in production even after the emergency passed. Such were the Humber Light Reconnaissance Cars, built on the Humber Snipe car chassis, which continued to be produced for the reconnaissance battalions of the infantry divisions and for the R.A.F. Regiment for airfield defence. The others continued to be used by the Home Guard or were broken up and it is probably just as well that some never went into action—particularly the " mobile pill boxes."

At about the same time an urgent demand for armoured cars developed in the Middle East. When hostilities between British and Italian forces began in 1940, the few obsolete armoured cars which were available gave a good account of themselves in raids across the Egyptian-Libyan frontier and the successful British offensive in Cyrenaica in the winter of 1940–41 brought out clearly the need for many more armoured cars. In East Africa semi-improvised armoured cars played an even more important role spearheading the advance of British and South African forces into Italian Somaliland and southern Ethiopia in 1941.

The armoured cars in use in the Middle East when the hostilities began were still Rolls-Royce Mark I and II, of 1920 and 1924 vintage and little different from the original 1914 model built for the Royal Naval Air Service. Some of these belonged to the R.A.F., which used them before the war for policing Iraq and Jordan. The Army also had some Morris Light Armoured Reconnaissance Cars of more recent make but hardly an improvement on the veteran Rolls-Royce. In 1941 Humber armoured cars began to arrive from Britain and Marmon-Herringtons from South Africa. The latter were built in the Union using Ford engines and Marmon-Herrington chassis components imported from the United States and their first three Marks, of which 3,630 were built, were widely used in the desert campaigns, in spite of their obsolescent design. They had 4-wheel drive but their engines were still located at the front, their silhouettes were high and they only had small turrets with a single machine-gun. A more powerful Marmon-Herrington Mark IV was developed only toward the end of the war in Africa : it had a larger turret with a 40 mm. 2-pounder gun and the engine transferred to the rear. By this time a far superior Daimler armoured car began to arrive in Africa from Britain. Like the earlier Guys and Humbers, the Daimler was a manoeuvrable short-wheelbase 4 x 4 vehicle but it had an independent suspension, a much lower silhouette and its turret mounted a coaxial 2-pounder gun and machine-gun. Its mechanical design was actually based on that of the earlier Daimler scout car but it weighed 7.5 tons and carried a crew of 3.

The principal use of armoured cars during the $2\frac{1}{2}$ years of the war in the desert was the same as in mobile operations elsewhere, that is for medium-distance reconnaissance. But they were also very successfully used to maintain counter-reconnaissance screens against hostile units, to patrol gaps between dispersed major units, to screen open flanks and to raid supply dumps and transport columns behind enemy lines. By the end of 1941, in Operation Crusader, there were already 5 armoured car regiments in the British 8th Army and armoured cars continued to be used on a large scale to the end of the desert campaigns, when they led the pursuit after the battle of El Alamein. The German Afrika Korps also made good use of the armoured cars of its reconnaissance battalions and the Italians had introduced a good 4 x 4 *Autoblinda 41* with a transmission layout somewhat similar to that of the British Daimlers.

The operations in Africa also revived the development of armoured cars in the United States. None had been built there since the M2 (T11E2) of 1934 and the only wheeled armoured vehicle produced in 1941 was still the 4 x 4 open-top M3A1 Scout Car. However, contemporary reports from Africa stressed the need for armoured cars and their design was belatedly undertaken. The first 191 were produced in 1942 and by the end of the Second World War the total had risen to 16,438.

First of the new generation of American armoured cars was actually a private venture, misnamed the Trackless Tank. This was a large rear-engined 8 x 6 vehicle which in 1942 became the T13 armoured car ; in the latter guise it weighed 11.2 tons, carried a crew of 4 and mounted a coaxial 37 mm. gun and machine-gun in the turret and a second machine-gun in the front glacis plate. Two other experimental 8-wheeled armoured cars appeared in 1942, both designed to British requirements. One was the Marmon-Herrington VI, which had a crew of 4 and mounted a coaxial 2-pounder gun and machine-gun in an open-top turret ; the other was the even larger 23.6-ton T18, or Boarhound, which had a crew of 5 and mounted a 37 mm. gun and coaxial machine-gun in a cast turret and a second machine-gun beside the driver, while on the later T18E2 the main armament was changed to a 57 mm. 6-pounder gun. Both the Marmon-Herrington VI and the Boarhound had 8-wheel drive but they were clumsy and large, the T18E2 being no less than 8 ft. 7 in. high and 20 ft. 6 in. long. Whether either would have proved satisfactory in the desert operations for which it was intended is doubtful but neither was ever put to test as the war in Africa came to an end before they were ready and neither got beyond experimental models.

A much more successful design of the same period, also to British requirements, was the 12-ton 4 x 4 T17E1, which had a 5-man crew and the same armament as the T18. It was adopted by the British Army as the Staghound I armoured car and used during the operations in Italy and north-west Europe in 1944 and 1945. It was not, however, adopted by the United States Army and neither was the lighter and very promising 6 x 6 T19, designed to American requirements. The choice eventually fell on a vehicle designed initially as a light, mobile and easy-to-produce self-propelled carriage for the 37 mm. anti-tank gun, the T22. This became the M8 armoured car, a 7.4-ton rear-engined 6 x 6 with an open-top turret, which was used from 1943 onwards by the reconnaissance battalions of the American armoured divisions and the reconnaissance troops of the infantry divisions. Up to the end of the war 8,523 M8 were produced and this, together with 3,791 of its turretless companion vehicle, the M20 armoured utility car, and 3,844 Staghounds, accounted for practically the whole of the American armoured car production.

Concurrently with the American-designed Marmon-Herrington VI, Boarhound and Staghound, a heavy armoured car inspired by desert warfare was also developed in Britain by the Associated Equipment Company. The original 11-ton A.E.C.I consisted of a Valentine tank turret with 2-pounder gun and coaxial machine-gun on a 4 x 4 armoured chassis which used many components of the A.E.C. Matador gun tractor. Some were used in North Africa towards the end of 1942 and two other versions were later brought out, the A.E.C.II with a larger turret and 57 mm. 6-pounder gun and a similar 12.7-ton A.E.C.III rearmed with a medium velocity 75 mm. gun. A much better 75 mm. gun armoured car with a lower silhouette and independent suspension was developed later by the makers of the Humber armoured cars. Called the Coventry II, it was a 4 x 4 11.5 tonner with a crew of 3 ; its earlier, 1944 version, the Coventry I, was still armed with a 2-pounder gun but, in contrast to the 520 A.E.C., only a few of either version of the Coventry armoured car were produced up to the end of the Second World War.

In the meantime, in 1943 and 1944, the fortunes of armoured cars declined. The favourable conditions of the African deserts gave way to the mountainous terrain of Italy and the close country of north-west Europe. Moreover, the tempo of operations slowed down and the fighting fronts were continuous and more strongly held, all of which reduced opportunities for the employment of armoured cars. So much so that in 1943, in preparation for operations in Europe, the British Army eliminated the armoured car regiments from its armoured divisions and replaced them with armoured regiments equipped with fast Cromwell medium tanks. Virtually the only wheeled armoured vehicles to be retained within armoured divisions were the scout cars—a troop of 9 per regiment—for close reconnaissance and liaison. They were either Daimlers or Humbers, the latter being similar but larger 4 x 4 turretless cars less advanced than the Daimlers and introduced largely because the more complicated Daimlers were not being produced in sufficient quantity.

At the time the Russians made even less use of armoured cars. Virtually the only Soviet armoured car in the latter part of the Second World War was the BA 64, a small, front-engined 4 x 4 2-tonner with a crew of 2 and one machine-gun in a small open-top turret, whose capabilities were very limited. The United States Army continued to use M8 armoured cars throughout the 1944–45 campaigns in Europe but set small store by them. In the German Army armoured cars also decreased in number, the place of the lighter models being taken over by half-track reconnaissance vehicles, but the production and employment of improved 8 x 8 armoured cars continued. There were three versions of the improved 10–12-ton Sd.Kfz.234 : one with an open-top turret and 20 mm. main armament, another with a larger closed-top turret and 50 mm. gun, and the third turretless but mounting either a short or a long 75 mm. gun. They had proved themselves capable of operating under some of the worst muddy conditions of the Russian front and they were included in the German production programmes right up to the end of the Second World War.

The British Army had no intention of abandoning armoured cars either. In the advance across France and into Germany, when operations resumed a mobile character, opportunities for armoured cars returned and armoured car regiments rejoined the armoured divisions. At this stage each regiment consisted of 4 squadrons and had a total of 72 armoured cars, including 5 anti-aircraft, and 65 scout cars.

After the war the best of the wartime vehicles, which were the Daimler scout and armoured cars and of which 6,626 and 2,694 respectively had been produced, were retained and further development continued. Its outcome, by the early fifties, were 3 new vehicles : the Ferret scout car, the Saracen armoured personnel carrier and the Saladin armoured car, the first built by Daimler and the other two by the Alvis company. The Ferret is a 4 x 4 4.1-ton vehicle similar to the earlier Daimler scout cars but longer and in its Ferret II form provided with a small machine-gun turret. The Saracen is a much larger 6 x 6 10-tonner capable of carrying 12 men. The 10.5-ton Saladin is based on the same 6 x 6 chassis as the Saracen but has the engine at the rear and mounts a medium-velocity 76.2 mm. gun and coaxial machine-gun in a turret. It has a crew of 3 and is intended as a replacement for the Daimler armoured car and the A.E.C.III, which had been retained to support the lighter Daimlers on a scale of 2 per squadron.

The French Army too resumed the development of armoured cars and by 1950 the Panhard company produced a new 13.5-ton 8 x 8 armoured car derived from the AM 201 experimental design of 1940. Its 4 centre wheels are retractable for road operation and it can be driven in either direction, the crew of 4 including 2 drivers; its main armament consists of a medium-velocity 75 mm. gun in an FL 11 oscillating turret but a later version carries the more powerful gun and FL 10 turret of the AMX light tank. In addition to the armoured car, designated the *Engin Blindé de Reconnaissance*, or E.B.R., there is also an E.T.T. armoured personnel carrier based on the same 8 x 8 chassis.

By the early fifties the Soviet Army had also introduced 2 new wheeled armoured personnel carriers, although neither as advanced as the British Saracen or the French E.T.T. One is the 5.3-ton open-top 4 x 4 BTR 40, somewhat similar to the earlier American M3A1 Scout Car; the other is the larger 6 x 6 BTR 152, capable of carrying 14 men.

In contrast, shortly after the Second World War, the United States Army once more abandoned the development of armoured cars, although it continued to use the existing M8 into the early fifties. The functions performed elsewhere by armoured cars have been taken over by a combination of light tanks and unarmoured quarter-ton 4 x 4 light trucks, which act as scout carriers and in many other capacities, including that of a carriage for recoilless 105 and 106 mm. guns. This and the extensive use of similar light trucks by other armies indicates a continued need for a mobile wheeled vehicle as a light general-purpose personnel and weapon carrier. Light trucks meet this requirement to a limited extent only, for their occupants are exposed to every stray bullet or shell splinter and vulnerable even to a well-aimed brick. In consequence, in many circumstances, they cannot move as freely as can light armoured cars and their overall mobility is lower.

It is to overcome the obvious handicap under which unarmoured cars labour that, time and time again, armour protection has been improvised for them and that the development of armoured cars was started in the first instance. In general, the effort put into the latter has been amply justified and armoured cars have proved greatly superior to unarmoured vehicles, especially when designed as such and not based on adaptations of vehicles built for other purposes.

The development of armoured cars has not been uniformly successful however. It has gone astray at times, particularly when it was tried to match tanks in gun power and armour protection. The tendency to acquire more powerful guns and greater protection is natural but it has led to large and clumsy vehicles, such as the Boarhound, which forfeited much of the armoured cars' advantage of mobility and were inferior, in general, to tracked vehicles of comparable power. Earlier, a few armoured cars just about managed to catch up with medium tanks in armament. The Soviet BA 10 and the British Daimler I did this, for instance, but it was a losing game and one which the armoured cars could not play once tank armament moved beyond medium-velocity 75 mm. guns. Even the latter were a problem, as they called for vehicles of 10 tons, or more. Successful vehicles of up to 12 or 14 tons have been built, of course, as shown by the German 8 x 8 Sd.Kfz. 231 and 234 and the French Panhard E.B.R., which have proved as good as contemporary tanks over some of the worst muddy ground and much more mobile under other conditions. But such multi-wheel drive vehicles are, unfortunately, rather complex and it is in the lighter categories that wheeled armoured vehicles are most attractive and most competitive with tracked vehicles.

In general, from the point of view of relative performance, overall mobility and mechanical simplicity, the smaller and lighter the armoured car can be the better and this is no longer incompatible with the provision of adequate armament. The latter has been a major obstacle to the construction of light, mobile armoured cars but largely it has ceased to be a problem with the introduction of recoilless guns and anti-tank guided missiles which can be mounted in relatively light vehicles and provide them with powerful armament. Given a proportion of cars with such armament, armoured car units need not lack weapon power while retaining their other advantages of speed, range and limited maintenance requirements.

The efficiency and reliability of armoured cars have been amply demonstrated by such instances as the trouble-free march of an Indian cavalry unit equipped with Stag-hounds (T17E1) from Iraq to Egypt at the beginning of 1944, a long-distance move which no tracked vehicle unit could accomplish without considerable maintenance effort. Similar Staghound armoured cars have seen extensive service since the Second World War in Italy, Switzerland, Israel and Lebanon. Other armoured cars have given a good account of themselves elsewhere. For instance, the French E.B.R. have proved their value fighting Algerian guerrillas and the Soviet wheeled armoured carriers proved effective in support of tanks in the streets of Budapest during the Hungarian rising of 1956; American-built M8 armoured cars of a Yugoslav reconnaissance unit and British-built Ferrets of a Canadian unit formed a very useful component of the United Nations police force in the Gaza area in 1957, while other Ferrets more than proved themselves patrolling the troubled Aden-Yemen border.

In addition to all this recent experience in the successful use of wheeled armoured cars, further incentive to the continued development of armoured cars is provided by the latest tactical concepts of dispersed operation in mobile battle groups. In the light of these, there is a clear requirement for highly mobile light armoured units capable of sustained operation over wide areas, for reconnaissance over wide fronts, to screen the flanks and gaps between major units and to combat light hostile forces, as there is for security and policing duties. For such units suitably designed armoured cars and other light wheeled armoured personnel and weapon carriers offer the most promising solution.

Appendix

The Ancestry of the Tank

IN search of parallel and example, or merely for the sake of picturesque background, it is common to turn to the pages of history and compare the tank with various early methods and devices. The list of such similes is quite extensive, ranging as it does from medieval battle-wagons and mail-clad horsemen to ancient battering rams, elephants and war chariots.

Of these and many other methods and devices, recalled with varying degrees of aptness and described in terms ranging from archaeological fact to fanciful tale, one certainly deserves serious consideration, namely the chariot. It does so for being the first combat vehicle ever used and because its introduction, many centuries ago, represented the first advance on the primitive and still predominant method of fighting on foot. Chariot troops, or chariotry, were, in fact, the first mobile troops to appear in warfare and may be regarded as the lineal ancestor of the mobile armoured forces of today—the grandparent so to speak, the in-between generation being represented by cavalry.

The chariot first gained prominence as an implement of war in the Middle East at the beginning of the second millennium B.C. However, even then, it already had a considerable background of earlier developments. Wheeled vehicles, drawn by oxen, were used soon after 3500 B.C. by the Sumerians, the ancient inhabitants of lower Mesopotamia—the fertile delta of Tigris-Euphrates in what is now Iraq. And by about 3000 B.C. 4- and 2-wheeled vehicles drawn by onagers, or wild asses, were being used in war.

Of the 2 vehicle types, the 2-wheeled chariot gradually ousted the less manoeuvrable 4-wheelers and in the latter part of the third millennium the Sumerian onager-chariot is thought to have attained a position of considerable importance. It was, however, still a cumbersome vehicle, with relatively small, heavy, solid disc-wheels, and slow even when drawn by 4 onagers. Its effectiveness was probably greater as a transport vehicle, in bringing warriors more quickly to battle, rather than as a vehicle from which to fight in battle.

Soon after 2000 B.C., however, two events occurred which revolutionised the use of chariots and warfare itself. The solid disc-wheel, usually made of 3 wooden planks suitably carved, was replaced by the much lighter spoked wheel and horses were introduced as draught animals, probably from the Iranian plateau.

445

The simultaneous appearance of the chariot-horse and of the spoked wheel greatly increased the mobility of chariots and this, in turn, revolutionised the pace of warfare. Their appearance coincided also with a wave of tribal migration which swept across south-west Asia, and in the hands of the Indo-European Kassites, who conquered Mesopotamia, the Hittites, who established themselves in Asia Minor, and the Semitic Hyksos, who conquered Egypt, chariotry became the decisive mobile arm.

The Hyksos invasion of Egypt around 1680 B.C. is the best-known exploit in the early use of chariots. So effective were they, in combination with missile weapons, or bows, that the Egyptians spoke of their land as having been conquered " without a battle "—which to them, hitherto, meant a pitched fight at close quarters. Then, after a century or so of domination, during which the Egyptians learnt to copy the methods of the invaders, the Hyksos were driven out and the Egyptians, in turn, used chariots to carry their arms into Syria and to the Euphrates.

Horse-drawn chariots came into large-scale use in Egypt at the beginning of the eighteenth dynasty, which ruled between 1587 and 1375 B.C. and which completed the expulsion of the Hyksos. During this period the Egyptians mastered the art of chariot-making and their army, composed of a large proportion of chariotry, became the dominant element within the state and the basis of its importance to the world at large.

The Egyptian chariots were very light 2-wheeled vehicles each drawn by 2 horses. They were light enough to be lifted by one man and their light-weight construction can be studied in detail from the marvellously preserved specimens found in Egyptian tombs. Probably the best known is that from a fifteenth-century tomb at Thebes, which is now at the Museo Archeologico in Florence, Italy; others, notably from the tomb of Tutankhamun, are at the Cairo Museum in Egypt.

The framework of an Egyptian chariot was of light wood, heat-bent where necessary, the body being filled in with canvas or leather. In the case of the chariots of Tutankhamun, for instance, the floor was made of interlaced leather strips. The light leather-tyred wheels had 4 or 6 spokes and were set well back; they were of relatively large diameter and with a wide track—the former giving low rolling resistance and the latter stability when manoeuvred at speed.

The normal crew of an Egyptian chariot consisted of 2 men : a driver and a weapon bearer. The principal weapon of the latter was the bow, and the chariot was essentially a highly mobile platform from which to shoot arrows. Its effectiveness, in other words, was based on a combination of mobility with missile power and it carried no armour.

The battle tactics of the Egyptian chariotry were in keeping with their vehicles and weapons. They would charge shooting arrows and, if the enemy stood firm and could not be ridden down, wheel round for another missile attack. Or they would sweep round the hostile force showering it with missiles, one of the advantages of the chariot being that it could carry a good supply of arrows.

Such, in essence, were the tactics at the battle of Kadesh, on the Orontes in Syria, in 1286 B.C., the first battle in history of which detailed record has survived. The battle was brought about by Egyptian attempts to maintain their position in Syria against the Hittites who in the latter part of the second millennium established themselves as the leading power in south-west Asia and were pushing southward from their Anatolian base.

The power of the Hittites was based on their chariotry, which resembled the Egyptian but used somewhat heavier vehicles carrying 3 men, the third man being a shield bearer. At the approaches to Kadesh a large force of such chariotry surprised an Egyptian expeditionary force led by Pharaoh Ramses II, advancing north in a strung-out column of 4 divisions. The surprise flank attack of the Hittite chariotry overwhelmed the second Egyptian division but the personal example of the Pharaoh, who led repeated charges of his bodyguard chariotry, and disorganisation among the Hittites, who stopped to plunder an Egyptian camp, saved the Egyptian army from disaster. Both sides suffered heavy losses and the battered Egyptian forces drew off to the south.

The strength of each of the opposing armies, in what was one of the biggest battles of antiquity, has been estimated at about 20,000 men. What proportion of the Egyptian army was made up of chariotry is not clear but it is known that the Egyptian chariotry of the period was organised into squadrons of 25 chariots. On the Hittite side the forces engaged consisted entirely of chariotry and the Egyptian account of the battle speaks of a main body of 2,500 Hittite chariots and a reserve force of 1,000. Two centuries earlier Thutmoses III recorded the capture of 924 chariots after the fall of Megiddo, a figure which is a further illustration of the numbers used and an indirect reminder of the massed employment of chariots which contributed to their importance and success in battle.

Kadesh was the last major battle between the Hittites and the Egyptians. It was, in a way, the high-water mark of the offensive power of both empires which thereafter passed on to the defensive and begun to decline. Within a century of the battle of Kadesh the Hittite empire perished in another wave of tribal migration. The Egyptian, more fortunate in its geographical position, lasted several centuries longer but eventually, having lost its earlier spirit and military proficiency, it too succumbed—to Assyria.

The Assyrians, who took the place of the Hittites as the leading nation of south-west Asia, began with an army similar to that of the earlier states, that is composed of chariotry and infantry. The Assyrian chariots, however, were heavier than the Egyptian and they grew larger and heavier still ; they carried three or even four men, those additional to the driver and the bowman bearing shields. The greater carrying capacity and the heavier build inevitably made them less mobile and the terrain over which the Assyrian armies operated was also more difficult at times. For instance, the records of Tiglath-Pileser I, the first Assyrian conqueror-king of about 1115 to 1102 B.C., several times speak of difficult country where " chariots could not pass." Moreover, the Assyrians frequently were faced not with battles in the field but with siege operations, at which they came to excel and for which they gained a reputation equal almost to that for their cruelty. All these factors—the heavier vehicles, the terrain and the frequent sieges— must have had an adverse effect on Assyrian chariotry but it continued to occupy an important position, as an élite corps, right up to the end of the Assyrian empire at the close of the seventh century B.C.

The importance of chariots during the period of Assyrian domination is reflected in the Hebrew scriptures and in particular in the often quoted passage from the Book of Judges, Chapter I, verse 19:

" And the Lord was with Judah and he drove out the inhabitants of the mountains, but he could not drive out the inhabitants of the valley because they had chariots of iron."

This shows clearly the importance attached to chariots by the Hebrew scripture-writers. It also indicates the technological revolution which took place during the period of Assyrian domination when iron begun to replace bronze as the principal working metal. As a result, bronze chariot parts were superseded by others made in iron but there is no reason to believe, as some modern writers have done, that the chariots referred to in the Book of Judges went beyond this and departed from the established wooden construction, or that they were actually protected with iron.

A further factor which affected the position of chariots in the Assyrian army was the appearance of a new mobile arm, the cavalry. It supplemented and eventually, in the armies of another power, took the place of chariotry. This power was Persia, which succeeded Assyria after an interlude of Neo-Babylonian or Chaldean domination and whose armies dispensed almost entirely with chariots.

The art of fighting on horseback was only evolved around 1000 B.C. In Assyria mounted troops first appear during the reign of Ashur-nasir-pal II, which lasted from 883 to 859 B.C., and were probably the result of contacts with the horse-riding peoples of the Central Asian steppes. A century later, under Sargon II (722 to 705 B.C.) when Assyria reached the height of its power, cavalry was a well-established element of the army and being more adaptable was used by Sargon as the mobile arm in circumstances where chariots could not operate.

Assyrian cavalry, which was the first regular cavalry in the world, consisted of 2 types : archers and lancers. Of the 2, the former appear to be the earlier and they fought dismounted, as well as mounted. The latter were armed with a light lance and they wore pointed conical helmets and armour of small metal plates sewn on to linen or leather. In a way, Assyrian lancers were the forerunners of the heavy cavalry of the following 2,000 years and especially of the Parthian and Sassanid *cataphracts* and the mailed knights of medieval Europe.

The Persians, who took the place of the Assyrians as the masters of western Asia, exploited further the advantages of cavalry. Indeed, at first Persian armies consisted largely of cavalry and they owed much of their success to the consequent ease and rapidity of their movement. With the appearance of the Persians the chariotry, which hitherto had been the dominant mobile arm but which was less adaptable and flexible than cavalry, was inexorably displaced. What little chariotry was retained by the Persians degenerated into a kind of ponderous super-heavy cavalry. It was employed sporadically and not too successfully, in spite of the formidable appearance of their chariots which were now fitted with scythe blades at the wheels or at the end of the draught pole.

Xenophon, the Athenian general and historian of the early fourth century B.C., credits Cyrus the Great, the founder of the Persian empire, with the successful use of 300 scythe-bearing, or *drephanephoros*, chariots at the battle of Thymbra in 546 B.C. However, the description of this battle between the Persians and the Lydians of Asia Minor in Xenophon's *Cyropaedia* is open to doubt. What is far more important in Xenophon's writings is his eye-witness account of the use of scythed chariots at the battle of Cunaxa in 401 B.C. This battle ended the attempt by Cyrus the Younger to wrest the Persian throne from his brother Artaxerxes and was the starting point of the famous retreat to the Black Sea of Cyrus' Greek mercenaries, the Ten Thousand, which Xenophon led and subsequently described in the *Anabasis*. As for the scythed chariots, of which 150 were used by Artaxerxes, they proved ineffective against the Greeks who opened their ranks and let such of the unhandy vehicles as reached them pass through while others, out of control, did more damage to their own troops.

Scythed chariots were used again at the battle of Gaugamela, or Arbela, in 331 B.C., where Alexander the Great dealt the final blow to the Persian empire. The Persian army, a large motley collection which bore little resemblance to its predecessor of two centuries earlier, possessed 200 scythed chariots which were made to charge Alexander's troops over specially levelled ground. But, showered with arrows and javelins by Alexander's light infantry, they accomplished little beyond their own destruction.

Scythed chariots were used yet again at the battle of Magnesia, in Asia Minor in 190 B.C., where the Romans and their allies fought Antiochus IV, ruler of the Seleucid kingdom carved out by one of Alexander's generals from the Asiatic portion of the latter's empire. Antiochus' chariots were, however, quickly disposed of in a preliminary encounter by the slingers of

29

the opposing forces. Antiochus also used elephants, with disastrous results for his own infantry, and Magnesia proved to be their last really serious appearance in European warfare. The first was in Alexander's battle on the Hydaspes against the Indian king Porus in 326 B.C.

The last of the infrequent major engagements of scythed chariots was at the twin battles of Chaeroneia and Orchomenus in Greece in 86 B.C., where a Roman army defeated the forces of Mithridates Eupator, King of Pontus and Crimea. In neither battle were the Pontic scythed chariots successful and in the second they recoiled upon their own line, throwing it into confusion and presenting the Romans with an opportunity for a decisive cavalry charge.

After the battle of Orchomenus the Asiatic scythed chariots finally disappeared from the armament of the major powers. But on the fringes of the civilised world other chariots continued to be used, notably among the Celtic tribes of western Europe.

The Celts were among the last to adopt the horse-drawn war chariot which was evolved in western Asia and which slowly spread from there to other parts of the world. At about the time the Egyptians adopted it from the Hyksos the chariot also began to appear in south-east Europe, probably as a result of contacts with the Hittites of Asia Minor. At any rate, by about 1500 B.C. chariots were used on the mainland of Greece and by 1000 B.C. they reached northern Italy and Sweden. The use of chariots also spread in the opposite direction, that is eastward. Thus, by about 1300 B.C., the middle of the Shang period, horse-drawn chariots were also being used in China.

Among the Celts of western Europe the use of chariots began around 500 B.C. and it was subsequently extended by them to the British Isles. The Celtic adoption of chariots was probably the result of contacts with the Etruscans, who dominated the northern part of the Italian peninsula and whose chariots were modelled on those of Greece. In all 3 cases the chariots usually carried two men and were drawn by 2 horses, although 3-horse teams were used by the Etruscans and in some cases the Greeks even used 4-horse teams. However, by the time the Celts adopted chariots the Greeks themselves had already abandoned them as an implement of war. Their place was taken by horse riding but the Greeks produced virtually no cavalry of note and relied almost entirely on their infantry. It was the Macedonians of the fourth century B.C. who were the first in Europe to make really effective use of cavalry and Alexander the Great owed as much to his Companion cavalry as to his Macedonian infantry phalanx. Cavalry was, in fact, Alexander's main striking force. A little earlier, in the fifth century B.C., cavalry also appeared for the first time in China, in the northern state of Chao (modern Shansi) as a result of contacts with the ·neighbouring Turko-Mongol tribes.

Like the use of chariots, the method of fighting on horseback also spread westward across Europe and gradually displaced the former. For instance, when the Romans first gained prominence in the fifth century B.C. war chariots had already gone out of fashion in Italy. Thus, contrary to widespread belief, the Romans did not use chariots in war but only for ceremonial purposes and for racing. At the same time, however, the Romans, like the Greeks, remained well behind western Asia in the use of the new mobile arm, the cavalry. What cavalry they had was usually supplied by their various allies.

Eventually even among the Celts horse riding displaced chariots. In the third century B.C. the Celts of France, or Gauls, were using chariots on a large scale and at the battle of Sentinum in 295 B.C. the initial onrush of the Gallic chariots almost overwhelmed the Romans. But they recovered and, significantly, carried the day with a cavalry charge. Two centuries later, at the time of Caesar's conquest of Gaul, the Gauls too had gone over to cavalry as the mobile arm.

But the Celts of Britain were still using chariots and Caesar met them in numbers during his 2 forays into south-east England, in 55 and 54 B.C., and described them in *De Bello Gallico*. Chariots were still in use in Britain a hundred years later and the Romans met them again after their landing in A.D. 43, when they were conquering southern England. Romance and modern artists have endowed the chariots of the British Queen Boudicca, or Boadicea, who led the revolt of her tribe against Roman rule in East Anglia in A.D. 61, with scythe blades but there is no evidence to support this.

According to Tacitus, the Roman historian of the first century A.D., chariots were also used by the Caledonian tribes when Agricola, extending Roman rule over Britain, defeated them at the Grampian Hills in Scotland in A.D. 83. In this case Roman auxiliary cavalry had no difficulty in disposing of the Caledonian chariots and, in general, Tacitus in his *Agricola*, written soon after the latter's campaigns, attaches little importance to British chariotry, clearly placing British strength in infantry.

After the Roman conquest of Britain only a few war-chariots remained in Europe. They lingered on among the lesser Celtic tribes, on the fringes of the Roman world, into the third century A.D.

The British use of chariots against Caesar was typical of their use in Europe in general. Except for occasional javelin throwing, particularly in a surprise swoop, fighting was seldom carried on from chariots. For serious fighting the warrior dismounted and fought on foot while the chariot and its driver stood by ready to carry him away if things went wrong. This was the method practised by Homeric heroes and most European chariot users after them. It was probably also the way the Sumerians used the original onager-chariots in war and it differed radically from the methods evolved in the hey-day of the chariots in the Middle East and particularly in Egypt.

To the Egyptians the chariot was a fighting vehicle in the full sense of the word—a vehicle from which they fought in battle. In Europe, on the other hand, the chariot was usually only a means of bringing the warrior to battle, or, in modern military parlance, a personnel carrier. The operational mobility which the chariot bestowed upon its European users was a great asset and the harrying hit-and-run tactics of the British chariotry gave Caesar's troops considerable trouble during the campaign of 54 B.C. Nevertheless, the use of chariots in Europe represented a less advanced level of development than that reached earlier in the Middle East.

The explanation of this phenomenon must be sought in a combination of circumstances. The manufacturing resources were considerably smaller in Europe than in the older states of the Middle East and at first chariots were few in number and merely the conveyance of princes, whose armies marched and fought on foot. On the whole the terrain was also less favourable, though this did not prevent the Gauls from eventually using chariots in large numbers. But the principal reason why European chariots were never as effective as the Egyptian, for instance, appears to lie in the failure to combine their use with that of missile armament.

The Egyptian chariot owed its effectiveness to being, in essence, a highly mobile missile platform—a swift vehicle from which to shoot arrows. But Europe was slow to make full use of the bow and for a long time despised the use of archery in warfare. None other than Homer, in the *Iliad*, illustrates the preference for the sword and spear over the bow and the cult of the *arme blanche* was still strong a generation ago. For centuries, somehow, Europeans preferred to hack each other at close quarters and leave the more subtle ways of mobile fighting with bows to the " crafty " Asiatics. And as long as the methods of fighting at close quarters prevailed the European chariot could be little more than a transport vehicle.

Other and later war vehicles, which span the centuries between the chariots and the first automotive fighting vehicles, may be divided into 2 broad categories of defensive wagons and siege or assault vehicles.

Of the 2 categories, the first is probably best exemplified by the Hussite battle-wagons of the fifteenth century, commonly associated with John Ziska, the Czech war leader of the period, who used them successfully in several battles. However, successful as it was, the use of wagons by Ziska was only a fragment of a long story of the use of wagons in battle.

The use of wagons in battle arose naturally from the habit of the nomadic tribes of using wagons to carry their women, children and belongings when they migrated from place to place. The wagons formed the basis of their encampments and the wagon camps were inevitably the focus of their defence. It was natural, in consequence, that when threatened by attack they would form the wagons in a way which would facilitate defence—a practice which developed well before our era and which lasted into the second half of the nineteenth century, when American settlers were trekking westward and fighting off Indian attacks and when the Boers were penetrating into the interior of South Africa.

The first evidence of the trekking wagon-folk comes from the reign of Pharaoh Ramses III (1195 to 1164 B.C.), who managed to arrest the southward progress of the nomadic tribes which swept across south-west Asia at the end of the second millennium. But the battle scenes depicted on the walls of the temple of Amon in Medinet Habu near Thebes, from which this evidence comes, do not indicate any tactical use yet being made by the nomads of their ponderous ox-drawn wagons.

Several centuries later, however, Caesar described the Helvetii, whom he met in the early stages of his conquest of Gaul, defending themselves in a wagon-laager after an unsuccessful battle with the Romans. Three years later, in 55 B.C., a migrating German tribe attacked by Caesar also attempted to defend itself in its wagon-laager. But it was only in the fourth century that the wagon-laager first gained real prominence when at Adrianople, in A.D. 378, another Germanic tribe—the Goths—inflicted a crushing defeat upon the Roman army. The role of the wagon-laager in this battle was to provide a firm defensive position for the Gothic foot until the arrival of the Gothic horse, which actually decided the issue.

The battle of Adrianople also marked the final ruin of the Roman military system based on the infantry legions and accelerated the return of cavalry to the decisive role it played during the Persian and Hellenistic periods. As a result, the next decisive battle, fought at Chalons in 451 between the combined forces of Rome and the Visigoths and the Huns of Attila, was largely a cavalry action. And again the wagon-laager played a prominent part by affording refuge to the defeated Huns.

The use of the wagon-laagers by the migrating tribes of the Dark Ages was followed, during the Middle Ages, by their adoption by regular forces, first of the Eastern Roman Empire and then of western Europe. Thus, according to the *Tactica* attributed to Emperor Leo VI (886-911), which describes Byzantine methods between the sixth and tenth centuries, Byzantine troops made frequent use of their supply wagons in combination with a ditch to protect their camps.

In the medieval order of things in western Europe each " lance," consisting of the knight and his retinue, was usually accompanied by at least one wagon carrying equipment and supplies. In consequence, large wagon trains formed an inseparable part of the later medieval armies. Among the better led the wagons were formed into protective encampments and the fortified wagon-camp gave rise to the often quoted—and misquoted—German term *wagenburg*, or literally " wagon-stronghold."

The tactical use of the medieval wagon-laager was generally limited to being a last resort for the losing side. This was the case, for instance, at the battle of Grunwald, or Tannenberg, in 1410, where the Order of Teutonic Knights, one of the most highly developed medieval military organisations, was defeated by the combined forces of Poland and Lithuania and where Ziska was said to have taken part. At this battle the remnant of the Knights tried to defend themselves in the wagon-laager which was formed in the normal way behind the battle line. The defence of the wagon-laager was unsuccessful and the presence of Ziska on the Polish side has never been verified but, nevertheless, Grunwald emphasises the use of wagon-laagers before the Hussite wars.

Where the Hussite forces under Ziska and his successor Prokop differed from the established methods was in a much more deliberate and consistent use of the wagon-laager. In fact, they based their battle tactics on it, usually assuming the defensive within the wagon-laager and, when the enemy spent himself attacking it, sallying out to effect his defeat.

To a large extent the wagon tactics were forced upon the Hussites by circumstances. Mainly Czech peasants and townsfolk, they were faced with the chivalry of Bohemia, Hungary and later Germany. Thus, having little cavalry themselves, they were faced by well-equipped mounted forces and it was to overcome this disadvantage that Ziska turned to the peasant wagons of his followers. From these he improvised defences behind which his foot troops could withstand heavy cavalry and thus meet the principal threat which faced them. Ziska's methods proved remarkably successful and enabled the Hussites to win their first battle, against greatly superior forces, at Sudomer, in 1420, and to remain unbeaten for the following 13 years.

During this period the wagons which formed the outside of the Hussite battle-array or wagon-laager were considerably improved and the original peasant type, hastily fitted with wooden boards to protect the sides, were replaced by more substantially built vehicles manned by men armed with cross-bows and hand-guns. When formed into a laager the wagons were chained together and the defences were often augmented by a trench dug round the outside.

With practice the Hussites learnt to form the wagon-laager quickly, to reproduce it fairly rapidly even from column of march, and as they gained confidence they passed from the defensive on to the offensive. However, the wagon-forces could only act offensively in the strategic sense. Offensive tactics were inconceivable with the heavy horse-drawn wagons and by its very nature the wagon-laager was compelled to adhere to defensive tactics. The nearest the Hussite wagons could come to offence was to move in such a way as to openly invite attack—if encouragement was needed—but such baited defence was still far removed from attacking with wagons which, in ignorance of the subject, some have ascribed to the Hussites.

The successful methods of the Hussites were undoubtedly helped by their opponents who, in the usual way of the medieval chivalry, suffered from an excess of offensive zeal and among whom discipline and effective tactical leadership were conspicuous by their absence. They learnt nothing and spent themselves in disastrous charges, in much the same way as they did earlier against Swiss pikemen and English archers. Whether the Hussites would have been as consistently successful against enemies who were more intelligent and less accommodating is open to doubt. As it was, they were not exposed to such trial and were eventually ruined by dissension in their own ranks which culminated in the fratricidal battle of Lipany, in 1434, where Ziska's successor Prokop and most of his army perished. It is noteworthy that in this battle where two similar armies met, each with its own defensive wagon-laager, the issue was decided in the open by troops fighting outside the laagers.

Different conditions and the rapid changes brought about by the spreading use of firearms resulted in the Hussite methods having negligible influence on the art of war in western Europe. In fact, the only evidence of their influence amounts to some German engravings of the late fifteenth and early sixteenth centuries, which depict armed horse-drawn wagons, and a mention of " war-carts " in the Acts of James II and James III of Scotland.

In contrast, in eastern Europe the Hussite methods were followed for a time and met with some success. In particular, in the sixteenth century Polish forces made deliberate use of wagon-laagers and in 1531, at Obertyn, won through it a notable victory over superior forces of Moldavia—the northeastern part of modern Roumania.

In the seventeenth century the place of the wagon-laager in Polish forces was taken by entrenchments but the use of the wagon-laager continued in the hands of the Cossacks who, about the middle of the century, rebelled against Polish rule in the Ukraine. However, the Cossack use of the wagon-laager was not due to Hussite influence but arose naturally from the large wagon train which accompanied the semi-nomad Cossack host. The wagons usually formed protective encampments but on one occasion at least they were used to form mobile defensive lines. This was at the battle of Beresteczko, in south-eastern Poland, in 1651, where the Cossack foot troops approached Polish positions in a long column protected on either side by a line of wagons, and after the defeat of the combined Tatar-Cossack army the Cossacks managed to form a laager and defended themselves for a time in it.

After the Polish-Cossack wars of the seventeenth century the wagon-laager disappeared from major military engagements and it did not return into prominence until the nineteenth century, when it was used against the primitive enemies of the white settlers of the American West and of South Africa, who carried their households in wagons and used the wagons to form defensive perimeters.

Of these and all the earlier instances of the use of wagon-laagers none can quite compare with the 13-year period of the Hussite wars, in which wagons played such a successful part, and the historical prominence of the Hussite wagons has led a number of modern writers to compare them with tanks. However, it is obvious from a close examination of the facts that to trace the ancestry of the tank to the Hussite wagons is completely erroneous. The Hussite wagons were clearly a mobile implement of defence and their use in battle was essentially static; they were not and could not be used in battle as mobile fighting vehicles.

If comparisons must be made between the Hussite wars and modern mechanised warfare, then the closest comparison with the horse-drawn wagons of Ziska is offered by towed anti-tank guns which, like the former, are movable but essentially static implements of defence.

The remaining category of vehicles used in war prior to the introduction of automotive fighting vehicles consists largely of those used in siege operations.

The origin of siege vehicles, as that of many other devices, is obscure. The first pictorial record of their employment is Assyrian, from the reign of Ashur-nasir-pal II (883-859 B.C.), on a bas-relief in the Nimrud Gallery of the British Museum. It shows a 6-wheeled platform carrying a protective wicker-work body surmounted by a high turret which, like the front of the vehicle, appears to be covered with hide. The turret is manned by an archer and attendant shield bearer while from the body of the vehicle protrudes the massive beam of a ram which hammers at the wall of the besieged town.

Thus, this earliest recorded Assyrian siege vehicle combines in one both principal features of the ancient siege vehicles. One was the high movable turret, or tower, which could bring attacking archers forward at the level of the battlements of the besieged town. The other was movable protection for the battering ram, a long heavy beam with a metal head which was swung to and fro from within the protective structure and which was the principal means of breaching the walls of hostile towns.

Some of the later Assyrian vehicles, such as those used at the siege of Lachish in Israel in 701 B.C., had no turrets but still carried archers, standing in the body of the vehicle, and a ram as before. Another type carried no archers but two rams, its role thus being solely to provide mobile protection for the men swinging the rams. Without the turret these vehicles were perhaps lighter, although they present a more solid appearance than the earlier wicker-bodied type, and they were mounted on four wheels only.

Yet another and rather odd assault vehicle appears on the bronze gates from the palace of King Shalmaneser III (859-824 B.C.), now in the Nineveh Gallery of the British Museum. It is a 6-wheeled ram-vehicle with a low solid-looking body but, in contrast to the others, the ram is not a beam worked from within the vehicle but forms an integral part of it, its prow in fact. As the vehicle is shown aimed at the gate of an enemy town it was probably pushed from behind and made to ram the gate. But if so the archers standing in it are difficult to understand, unless they jumped off before the ram-vehicle was sent crashing into the gate.

The last type of vehicle must have been abandoned as unsuccessful, for it did not reappear elsewhere, but the others were copied from the Assyrians and their use, in different forms, continued well into the Middle Ages.

Among those who found by bitter experience the effectiveness of the Assyrian siege vehicles were the cities of Syria and from them the knowledge passed on to the Greeks. It was only in the fourth century B.C. that the Greeks took up the use of vehicles in siege operations but by the time of Alexander the Great both movable siege towers and ram carrying vehicles were in use and they reached their highest level of development during the following Hellenistic period.

As before, the function of the latter type of vehicle was to provide mobile protection for the battering ram and the men swinging it ; the principal role of the towers was to bring in archers and catapults at the level of the hostile battlements and to clear them of the defenders. But one of Alexander's engineers, Diades, is supposed to have extended their use by adding a boarding bridge. Thus, when this bridge was let down on to the hostile wall, troops in the tower could get a footing on it. The towers were often built several storeys high and required many men—pushing and pulling—to move them forward ; to add to their already considerable weight during the Hellenistic period the original hide protection was occasionally replaced by iron plates.

The Romans made no advance on the Greco-Macedonian siege vehicles. However, the Roman *testudo,* or " tortoise," illustrates how siege vehicles may have originated. In its simplest form the *testudo* was no more than the interlocked shields of a legionary storming party, held by the legionaries over their heads to enable them to approach a hostile wall. In a more elaborate form it was a simple wheeled chassis with a strong roof which could withstand the arrows and stones likely to be hurled on it from above—an oversize overhead shield on wheels one might say. It is almost as if the siege vehicle was an outgrowth of the large man-high wicker shields which the Assyrian archers used in sieges, one man shooting and the other carrying the shield. At any rate, the principal role of the Roman *testudo* was to provide movable protection for the attackers and was not necessarily limited to the battering ram, although in its wheeled form it usually carried one.

The two types of vehicles, the ram carrying penthouse on wheels and the movable tower, continued in use in Europe during the Middle Ages, although the latter fell into temporary disuse after the sixth century and did not come into prominence again until the eleventh century. The Crusades of the twelfth century saw the final high level of employment of siege towers, which usually performed the double role of clearing hostile ramparts by missile action and of entering storming parties over the boarding bridge with which they were fitted. In the thirteenth century the tower was displaced by mining as the favourite method of attacking town walls and in the following century both types of vehicles were finally displaced by siege guns.

But the idea of a protected assault vehicle was kept alive by writers and others who, moreover, transformed its role and suggested constructional improvements.

The change which took place on paper transferred the application of assault vehicles from siege operations to battles in the open and altered the task from assaulting town walls to that of breaking enemy ranks in battle. This went hand in hand with ideas for improving the propulsion of the vehicles, which was an essential prerequisite to the new role.

In siege operations the degree of mobility required, and achieved, by assault vehicles was negligible. In the field, on the other hand, much more was required and as the use of the normal horse traction was out of the question inventive thought turned to alternative methods. In the main, three alternative solutions were proposed: one placed the horses inside the vehicle, another had it propelled from the inside by men turning cranks and the third had the propulsive effort supplied by windmills mounted on the vehicle!

The earliest presentation of the new type of vehicle, both in its crank and windmill form, appears to have been made by Guido da Vigevano, an Italian physician at the French Court, in a treatise on military engineering written in 1335. Next came a German, Konrad Kyeser who in the *Bellifortis*, the first illustrated handbook on military engineering, which he completed in 1405, described several siege vehicles. Roberto Valturio, an Italian military engineer, illustrated another windmill driven vehicle in his *De Re Militari* first published in Verona in 1472 and Leonardo da Vinci, who is often erroneously credited with the " invention " of the assault vehicle, drew a vehicle of the crank-operated type around 1500. Other vehicles include that represented on the 1558 German engraving by Holzschuher and the amphibious crank-operated assault vehicle with paddle wheels illustrated by Agostino Ramelli, an engineer to Henry III of France, in a book on engineering *Le diverse et artificiose machine* published in Paris in 1588. Further examples are provided by the Scottish mathematician John Napier, who proposed an assault vehicle in 1596, and the half-serious proposals of the French writer Voltaire who apparently managed to evoke some interest in France around 1757 and then at the Russian Court of Catherine the Great in 1769.

None of these schemes was translated into practice for the obvious reason that none incorporated a workable way of moving the vehicle in battle. But although they fell short of practical realisation they kept alive the idea of a protected assault vehicle and in relation to the ancestry of the tank they deserve a place together with the actual siege vehicles used in earlier times. In spite of differences in role and construction, both the siege vehicles and the proposed battle vehicles had the same basic characteristics of offering a degree of mobile, or movable protection and of being intended for a specialised assault role.

As such they bear comparison with the original tanks of the First World War. Moreover, the role of the original tanks was to break through lines of trenches which might be specifically compared with the wall-breaching role of the ram vehicles. The similarity between the siege vehicles and the beginnings of the tank is even closer because some of the earliest British experiments consisted of mobile shields for the infantry and the first French steps in the development of the tank were in the form of a tractor for cutting through barbed wire entanglements.

However, these comparisons with the ancient siege vehicles do not apply beyond the immediate introduction of the tank, which took place under the siege-like conditions of the First World War. Since then the tank has proved to be much more than a specialised assault vehicle and it has shown that protection is not its only or even main attribute. Consequently, if the ancient siege vehicles are to be given a place in the genealogy of the tank an even more important place must be accorded to others, for the tactical ancestors of the modern tank are most clearly the cavalryman and the chariot in its role of a highly mobile missile platform.

Selected Bibliography

ANON. *A Short History of the Royal Tank Corps.* 6th ed. Gale & Polden, Aldershot, 1945.
Armoured Fighting Vehicles. Vickers-Armstrongs, Chertsey, *c.* 1945.
War-time Tank Production. H.M.S.O., London, 1946.
Tank Museum Guide. Parts 1–5, Royal Armoured Corps Centre, Bovington, *c.* 1948–57.
Illustrated Record of German Army Equipment. Vol. III: 'Armoured Fighting Vehicles', War Office, London, 1947.
Sowiecka Bron Pancerna. 2 Warszawska Dywizja Pancerna, Italy, 1945.
Polskie Sily Zbrojne w Drugiej Wojnie Swiatowej. Vol. 1, Part 1, Sikorski Historical Institute, London, 1951.
The German Campaign in Russia: Planning and Operations (1940–1942). Department of the Army Pamphlet No. 20-261, Department of the Army, Washington, 1955.
British War Production 1939–1945. The Times, London, 1945.
Sketchbook. Ordnance Research and Development Centre, Aberdeen Proving Ground, Maryland, *c.* 1945.
Tank Data. U.S. Army Ordnance School, Aberdeen Proving Ground, Maryland, 1958.
ANDRONIKOW, I. G., and MOSTOWENKO, W. D. *Die Roten Panzer*, Lehmanns Verlag, Munich, 1963.
ANTONOV, A., ARTAMONOV, B., KOROBKOV, B., and MAGNIDOVICH, E. *Tank.* Ministerstva Oboroni Soyuza SSR, Moscow, 1954.
BACON, R., FULLER, J. F. C., PLAYFAIR, P. (eds.) *Warfare Today.* Odhams Press, London, 1944.
BARNES, G. M. *Weapons of World War II.* Van Nostrand, New York, 1947.
BEKKER, M. G. *Theory of Land Locomotion.* University of Michigan Press, Ann Arbor, 1956
Off-the-Road Locomotion. University of Michigan Press, Ann Arbor, 1960.
Introduction to Terrain-Vehicle Systems. University of Michigan Press, Ann Arbor, 1969.
BOURGET, P. A. *Le Général Estienne.* Berger-Levrault, Paris, 1956.
CHAMBERLAIN, P., and ELLIS, C. *British and German Tanks of World War I.* Arms and Armour Press, London, 1969, and Arco, New York, 1969.
British and American Tanks of World War II. Arms and Armour Press, London, 1969, and Arco, New York, 1969.
CHODKIEWICZ, L. *Bron Przeciwpancerna Piechoty.* Wydawnictwo Ministerstwa Obrony Narodowej, Warsaw, 1959.
CHURCHILL, Winston S. *The World Crisis 1911–1918.* Thornton Butterworth, London, 1932.
DEYGAS, F. J. *Les Chars d'Assaut.* Charles-Lavauzelle, Paris, 1937.
➤DISNEY. P. A. *Tactical Problems for Armor Units.* Military Service Publishing Co., Harrisburg, 1952.
DUTIL, L. *Les Chars d'Assaut.* Berger-Levrault, Paris, 1919.
DUVIGNAC, A. *Histoire de l'Armée Motorisée.* Imprimerie Nationale, Paris, 1948.
EIMANNSBERGER, L. von. *La Guerre des Chars.* (Der Kampfwagenkrieg). Berger-Levrault, Paris, 1936.
FERRE, G. *Le Défaut de l'Armure.* Charles-Lavauzelle, Paris, 1948.
FULLER, J. F. C. *Tanks in the Great War 1914–1918.* John Murray, London, 1920.
Memoirs of an Unconventional Soldier. Nicholson and Watson, London, 1936.

461

FULLER, (contd.) *Machine Warfare*. Hutchinson, London, 1942.
Armoured Warfare. Eyre and Spottiswoode, London, 1943.
GAULLE, C. de. *The Army of the Future*. Hutchinson, London, 1940.
GILLIE, M. H. *Forging the Thunderbolt*. Military Service Publishing Co., Harrisburg, 1947.
GUDERIAN, H. *Die Panzertruppen und ihr Zusammenwirken mit der anderen Waffen*. Mittler und Sohn, Berlin, 1940.
Panzer Leader. Michael Joseph, London, 1952.
HACKER, O. H., ICKS, R. J., MERKER, O., and ZEZSCHWITZ, G. P. von. *Heigls Taschenbuch der Tanks*. Parts I and II, Lehmanns Verlag, Munich, 1935.
HARA, T., and TAKEUCHI, A. *Japanese Tanks and Fighting Vehicles*. Shuppan Kyodo, Tokyo, 1961.
—EIMORI, D. *Japanese Tanks and Armoured Vehicles*. Shuppan Kyodo, Tokyo, 1961.
HEIGL, F. *Taschenbuch der Tanks*. Lehmanns Verlag, Munich, 1926 and 1927.
ICKS, R. J. *Tanks and Armoured Vehicles*. Duell, Sloan and Pearce, New York, 1945.
INOMA, S. *Sensha*. Sankai-do, Tokyo, 1941.
ISELY, J. and COWL, P. A. *The U.S. Marines and Amphibious War*. Princeton University Press, Princeton, 1951.
JACOMET, R. *L'Armement de la France (1936–1939)*. Lajeunesse, Paris, 1945.
JANICKI, D. *Czolg na Wspólczesnym Polu Walki*. Wydawnictwo Ministerstwa Obrony Narodowej, Warsaw, 1963.
JONES, R. E., RAREY, G. H., and ICKS, R. J. *The Fighting Tanks since 1916*. National Service Publishing Co., Washington, 1933.
KENNEDY, R. M. *The German Campaign in Poland (1939)*. Department of the Army, Washington, 1956.
KRUGER, R. *Tanks*. Richard Carl Schmidt, Berlin, 1921.
KUTZ, C. R. *War on Wheels*. Scientific Book Club, London, 1942.
LAFITTE, R. *L'Artillerie d'Assaut de 1916 à 1918*. Charles-Lavauzelle, Paris, 1921.
LESTER, J. R. *Tank Warfare*. Allen & Unwin, London, 1943.
LIDDELL HART, B. H. *When Britain Goes to War*. Faber & Faber, London, 1936.
The Other Side of the Hill. Cassell, London, 1951.
The Tanks: The History of the Royal Tank Regiment. Cassell, London, 1959.
The Rommel Papers. Collins, London, 1953.
The Soviet Army. Weidenfeld and Nicolson, London, 1956.
MAGNUSKI. J. *Wozy Bojowe 1914–1964*. Wydawnictwo Ministerstwa Obrony Narodowej, Warsaw, 1964.
MARTEL, G. le Q. *In the Wake of the Tank*. Sifton Praed, London, 1931.
Our Armoured Forces. Faber & Faber, London, 1945.
An Outspoken Soldier. Sifton Praed, London, 1949.
MELLENTHIN, F. W. von. *Panzer Battles 1939–1945*. Cassell, London, 1955.
MUNZEL, O. *Heinz Guderian—Panzer Marsch*. Schild Verlag, Munich, 1955.
MURLAND, J. R. W. *The Royal Armoured Corps*. Methuen, London, 1943.
MURRAY WILSON, G. (ed.) *Fighting Tanks*. Seeley Service, London, 1929.
OGORKIEWICZ, R. M. *Armour*. Stevens, London, 1960, and Frederick Praeger, New York, 1960.
I Corazzati. Istituto per la Divulgazione della Storia Militare, Rome, 1964.
Design and Development of Fighting Vehicles. Macdonald, London, 1968, and Doubleday, New York, 1968.
PAFI, B., FALESI, C. and FIORE, G. *Corazzati Italiani 1939–45*. D'Anna Editor, Rome, 1968.
PERRE, J. *Les Chars de Combat: Essai de Classification Positive*. Berger-Levrault, Paris, 1937.
Batailles et Combat des Chars Français. Charles-Lavauzelle, Paris, 1937 and 1940.

POSTAN, M. M. *British War Production.* H.M.S.O. and Longmans, London, 1952.

—— HAY, D., and SCOTT, J. D. *Design and Development of Weapons.* H.M.S.O. and Longmans, London, 1964.

→ PUGH, S. *Fighting Vehicles and Weapons of the Modern British Army.* Macdonald, London, 1962.

(ed.) *Armour in Profile.* Profile Publications, Leatherhead, 1968.

PUGNANI. A. *Storia della Motorizzatione Militare Italiana.* Roggero & Tortia, Turin, 1951.

SCHULTZE-DEYCKE, G. *Das Panzer Merkbuch.* Verlag Offene Worte, Berlin, c. 1937.

SENGER UND ETTERLIN, F. M. von. *Taschenbuch der Panzer 1943–1957.* Lehmanns Verlag, Munich, 1957.

Die Panzergrenadiere. Lehmanns Verlag, Munich, 1961.

The World's Armoured Fighting Vehicles. Macdonald, London, 1962.

Das Kleine Panzerbuch. Lehmanns Verlag, Munich, 1964.

Die Deutschen Panzer 1926–1945. Lehmanns Verlag, Munich, 1965.

Die Kampfpanzer von 1916–1966. Lehmanns Verlag, Munich, 1966.

German Tanks of World War II. Arms and Armour Press, London, 1969.

Taschenbuch der Panzer 1969. Lehmanns Verlag, Munich, 1969.

Der sowjetische mittlere Kampfpanzer der Baureihe T–34 bis T–62. Lehmanns Verlag, Munich, 1970.

SEYMOUR, W. J. *An Account of Our Stewardship.* Vauxhall Motors, Luton, 1946.

SHEPPARD, E. W. *Tanks in the Next War.* Geoffrey Bles, London, 1938.

SIMON, L. E. *German Research in World War II.* John Wiley, New York, 1947.

STERN, A. G. *Tanks 1914–1918: The Log-Book of a Pioneer.* Hodder and Stoughton, London, 1919.

STOUT, W. W. *Tanks are Mighty Fine Things.* Chrysler Corporation, Detroit, 1946.

SUETER, M. *The Evolution of the Tank.* Hutchinson, London, 1937.

SWINTON, E. D. *Eyewitness.* Hodder and Stoughton, London, 1932.

VERNEY, G. L. *The Desert Rats.* Hutchinson, London, 1954.

WARNICK, W. L., COOK, J. G., and BAKER, R. A. *The Tank Commander's Guide.* Stackpole, Harrisburg, 1963.

WHITE. B. T. *British Tanks and Fighting Vehicles 1941–1945.* Ian Allan, London, 1970.

WILLIAMS-ELLIS, C., and WILLIAMS-ELLIS, A. *The Tanks Corps.* Country Life, London, 1919.

→ WORLEY, M. L. *New Developments in Army Weapons, Tactics, Organization and Equipment.* Military Service Publishing Co., Harrisburg, 1958.

ZEZSCHWITZ, G. P. von. *Heigl's Taschenbuch der Tanks.* Part III, Lehmanns Verlag, Munich, 1938.

ZYRKIEWICZ, L. *Samochody Pancerne.* Główna Ksiegarnia Wojskowa, Warsaw, 1928.

Index

H.A.